Secondary Certificate Mathematics

SECONDARY CERTIFICATE SERIES

General Editor:
K. W. WATKINS, B.Sc.(Econ), Ph.D.

FACING LIFE'S CHALLENGE
A Study of St Mark's Gospel for Today
J. HILLS COTTERILL, B.A., Dip.Th.

SECONDARY CERTIFICATE MATHEMATICS
D. T. DANIEL, B.A.

SECONDARY CERTIFICATE ENGLISH
P. S MORRELL, B.A.

COMMERCE AND LIFE
K. LAMBERT, M.A.(Ed.), B.Sc.(Econ.), A.M.B.I.M.

HOUSECRAFT TODAY
G. M. SUTTON

RURAL SCIENCE COURSE
J. A. SHORNEY, M.I.Biol., Dip.R.Ed.

PHYSICS
I. M. L. JENKINS, B.Sc.
E. J. HANMORE, B.Sc.

BIOLOGY
H. T. PASCOE, B.Sc.

CHEMISTRY
E. J. HANMORE, B.Sc.

LIFE IN OUR SOCIETY
K. LAMBERT, M.A.(Ed.), B.Sc.(Econ.), A.M.B.I.M.

THE WORKING WORLD OF PHYSICS
I. M. L. JENKINS, B.Sc.

Secondary Certificate Mathematics

Second edition
Revised and metricated

D. T. DANIEL, B.A., Dip. Ed.
Head of Mathematics Dept., Lancastrian Boys' School
Formerly Head of Mathematics, The Weald School

NELSON

THOMAS NELSON AND SONS LTD.
36 Park Street London W1Y 4DE
P.O. Box 18123 Nairobi Kenya

THOMAS NELSON (AUSTRALIA) LTD.
597 Little Collins Street Melbourne Victoria 3000

THOMAS NELSON AND SONS (CANADA) LTD.
81 Curlew Drive Don Mills Ontario

THOMAS NELSON (NIGERIA) LTD.
P.O. Box 336 Apapa Lagos

First published 1964
Reprinted 1965 (twice), 1967, 1968
Second edition, revised and metricated, 1970
Sixth impression 1974

ISBN 0 17 431003 X

Made and printed by offset in Great Britain by
William Clowes & Sons, Limited, London, Beccles and Colchester

Introduction

This book is an attempt to meet the needs of those pupils who will be taking Mathematics in the Certificate of Secondary Education. It is the product of two decades of teaching at this age and ability level, reinforced by innumerable discussions with fellow mathematicians working in the same field.

There is the firm conviction that a text-book is a working tool in the hands of the individual teacher who alone can best know how to use and adapt it to the requirements of each specific teaching situation. Every effort has been made to avoid coming between the teacher and the class and of laying down and imposing a rigid course from outside. Hence, the introduction of artificially constructed 'real life' situations has been avoided in the certainty that the teacher can best interweave more formal instruction with the known interests, abilities, experiences, limitations, and background of his or her particular class.

There is a very wide range of ability among those who are staying on for the fifth, extra, year in order to sit C.S.E. Hence, an ample allowance of revision material from earlier years has been included. It is hoped that this will be found especially useful in those cases where classes will be working on an individual or group basis. The structure of the book is also geared to this concept. The subject matter has been presented under the main headings of Arithmetic, Algebra, Geometry, etc. This in no way denies the desirability of and necessity for a unified treatment of mathematics but has been done for the sake of ease of reference. It is essential that these students should be able, especially when working on their own, to find their way about a book with confidence.

A feature of the book is the large number of illustrations and graded exercises. The latter have been included on such a large scale because nothing more destroys a feeling for the subject or creates unnecessary frustration than an inability to perform the final mechanical solution of a problem when its fundamental nature has been grasped. In order to help this process a generous number of worked examples have been included that use individual techniques which the author has found to be successful in the form room.

As with any text-book, the author is deeply indebted to a number of people to whom he would like to express his thanks. Mr. L. G. Watson, for reading the first draft of the book, and making a number of valuable suggestions. Mr. A. Walker, M.A. (Cantab), of Dover College, who read the first draft, and was generous enough to place much of his time at my disposal and made innumerable valuable suggestions for the final draft. I would also like to thank my typist Mrs. A. Hance for her meticulous work and ready acceptance of an erratic schedule. Finally, I should like to thank Dr. K. W. Watkins, my general editor, who first suggested the book to me and whose constant enthusiasm and encouragement from the first suggestion to completed volume have sustained my endeavours.

D. T. D.

Note to the Second Edition

The advent of decimal coinage and the adoption of a rationalised system of metric weights and measures has occasioned this complete revision of the text. Greatly encouraged by its reception I have left the main format and method of presentation unchanged. The opportunity has been taken, however, to introduce certain additional topics suggested by teachers and students using the book.

D. T. D.

Contents

Contents

PART FOUR—GEOMETRY

1 The Four Rules

In our everyday life we are constantly concerned with such questions as, 'How much?', 'How far?', 'How many?', 'How heavy?' In order to be able to ask and answer these questions we have to use numbers and quantities. We have, in fact, to use mathematics, especially that branch of mathematics that is concerned particularly with number and quantities, that is to say, Arithmetic. Except in the most primitive societies the ability to measure, count, and perform various calculations is important, and as we become more civilised so the need for this ability becomes greater. Imagine a farmer who could not work out how much fodder his cattle needed, or a housewife unable to manage her household accounts, a shopkeeper or bank clerk who could not do simple 'money sums', a dressmaker or carpenter unable to measure accurately.

The exercise below is designed to revise these basic everyday skills.

Exercise 1

(1) Add:

	(a)	(b)	(c)
	63	672	198
	121	17	6
	247	365	3,416

(2) Add:

	(a)	(b)	(c)
	6,534	302	39
	79	73	2,471
	3,210	1,368	16
		7	394

(3) Add:
  (a) $691 + 13 + 7,432 + 76$
  (b) $4,814 + 512 + 45 + 309$
  (c) $65,382 + 367 + 3,190 + 9$
  (d) $614 + 8,652 + 17 + 9,070$

(4) Subtract:

	(a)	(b)	(c)
	478	867	375
	-325	-539	-326

(5) Subtract:　(*a*)　706　(*b*)　7,006　(*c*)　9,124
　　　　　　　　　− 479　　　− 6,534　　　− 6,377

(6) Subtract:　(*a*) 824 − 367　　(*c*) 7,306 − 6,908
　　　　　　　(*b*) 2,973 − 1,894　(*d*) 9,392 − 6,986

(7) Multiply:
　　(*a*) 284 × 4　(*c*) 457 × 27　(*e*) 629 × 351
　　(*b*) 476 × 9　(*d*) 329 × 38　(*f*) 680 × 608

(8) Multiply:
　　(*a*) 73 × 16 × 9　　(*c*) 56 × 28 × 49
　　(*b*) 38 × 27 × 42　(*d*) 126 × 13 × 274

(9) Divide:
　　(*a*) 872 ÷ 4　　(*e*) 561 ÷ 32　　(*i*) 1,328 ÷ 258
　　(*b*) 315 ÷ 9　　(*f*) 3,482 ÷ 18　(*j*) 56,246 ÷ 324
　　(*c*) 432 ÷ 14　(*g*) 6,384 ÷ 121　(*k*) 4,477 ÷ 407
　　(*d*) 8,808 ÷ 24　(*h*) 2,070 ÷ 28　(*l*) 57,879 ÷ 109

(10) Calculate:
　　(*a*) $\dfrac{117 \times 8}{13}$　(*c*) $\dfrac{33 \times 60 \times 60}{1000 \times 3}$

　　(*b*) $\dfrac{46 \times 12}{54 \times 18}$　(*d*) $\dfrac{126 \times 13 \times 274}{548 \times 9}$

(11) Find the sum of:
　　(*a*) 126 + 17 − 38 + 62 − 9
　　(*b*) 43 − 79 + 17 + 38
　　(*c*) − 36 + 17 − 49 + 72
　　(*d*) 246 + 673 − 1046 + 348

(12) Calculate:
　　(*a*) $\dfrac{26 + 9 + 17}{39 - 26}$　(*c*) $\dfrac{246 - 342 + 462}{118 + 44 - 70}$

　　(*b*) $\dfrac{57 + 63 - 36}{6 \times 7}$　(*d*) $\dfrac{317 + 159 - 102}{412 - 216 - 179}$

Numbers to any base

Think of a number, say 35. What do we mean by 35? Usually we mean $(3 \times 10) + 5$ or

10s	1s
3	5

In everyday use we normally count in tens when we are handling numbers, that is to say we count to base 10. Numbers to the base 10 are numbers in the decimal system, sometimes called denary numbers.

Often we need to use a base other than 10 and, if we do, we must make it quite clear what base we are using. Thus 35 in ordinary arithmetic (i.e. decimal) could be written as 35_{10} if we need to make it quite clear that we mean $(3 \times 10) + 5$. Similarly 35_8 explains that in this case we are using base 8 so, 35_8 means $(3 \times 8) + 5$.

A suffix (the 8 in 35_8 or the 10 in 35_{10}) is used to make clear what base is being used.

Thus:

$$13_4 \text{ means } (1 \times 4) + 3$$
$$24_6 \text{ means } (2 \times 6) + 4$$
$$247_8 \text{ means } (2 \times 8^2 \text{ i.e. } 8 \times 8) + (4 \times 8) + 7$$

Look at the last example again. Remember 247_{10} an ordinary decimal number means:

10^2 (i.e. 10×10) = 100s	10s	1s
2	4	7

So 247_8 means

8^2 (i.e. 8×8) = 64s	8s	1s
2	4	7

Example 1. Convert 247_8 into decimal.

$$247_8 = (2 \times 8^2) + (4 \times 8) + 7$$
$$= (2 \times 64) + 32 + 7$$
$$= 128 + 32 + 7$$
$$= 167_{10}$$

Example 2. Convert 463_7 into decimal.

$$463_7 = (4 \times 7^2) + (6 \times 7) + 3$$
$$= 196 + 42 + 3$$
$$= 241_{10}$$

Example 3. Convert 126_{10} into base 8.

$$\begin{array}{r|l}
8 & 126 \\
\hline
8 & 15 \quad \text{rem. 6} \quad (\text{A remainder of } 6 \times 1) \\
\hline
8 & 1 \quad \text{rem. 7} \quad (\text{A remainder of } 7 \times 8) \\
\hline
& 0 \quad \text{rem. 1} \quad (\text{A remainder of } 1 \times 8^2)
\end{array}$$

So $$126_{10} = 176_8$$

Basic calculations using numbers to any base are quite easy if you firmly fix in your mind the base used and make sure that all numbers are to the same base.

Example 4. Find the value of $23_6 + 55_6 + 143_6$

Remember all numbers are to base 6.
Add the right hand column: $3 + 5 + 3 = 15_6$

$\begin{array}{l} 23_6 \\ 55_6 \\ 143_6 \\ \hline 305_6 \\ \hline 21 \end{array}$ $\begin{array}{l} (3 + 5 + 3 = 11_{10} \text{ that is } (1 \times 6) + 5 = 15_6) \\ \text{Write down 5 carry 1, i.e. } (1 \times 6) \\ \text{Add next column: } 4 + 5 + 2 + 1 \text{ (carried)} = 20_6 \\ (4 + 5 + 2 + 1 = 12_{10} \text{ that is } (2 \times 6) + 0 = 20_6) \\ \text{Write down 0 carry 2, } 1 + 2 = 3 \end{array}$

Thus $$23_6 + 55_6 + 143_6 = 305_6$$

Example 5. From 742_8 take 637_8

Remember we are using base 8. Subtract right hand column.
$\begin{array}{l} 742_8 \\ 637_8 \\ \hline 103_8 \end{array}$ $2 - 7$—cannot be done, so we borrow one from the next column. The one we borrow is (1×8), so that, after borrowing, our subtraction for the right hand column becomes $12_8 - 7_8 = 3_8 (12_8 = (1 \times 8) + 2)$. Write 3 and continue in the usual way by paying back the one, and go on to complete the subtraction.

Thus $$742_8 - 637_8 = 103_8$$

Example 6. Find the products of:

(a) $3_5 \times 4_5$ (b) $43_5 \times 2_5$ (c) $43_5 \times 24_5$

Remember that *all* the rules of multiplication still apply, and that we are using base 5.

(a) $\begin{array}{r} 3_5 \\ \times \ 4_5 \\ \hline 22_5 \end{array}$ Check by using base 10
$3_{10} \times 4_{10} = 12_{10} = (2 \times 5) + 2 = 22_5$

(b)
$$43_5$$
$$\times\ 2_5$$
$$\overline{141_5}$$
$$\overline{1}$$

$3_5 \times 2_5 = 11_5$
Write 1 and carry 1
$4_5 \times 2_5 = 13_5$
Add the 1 carried $= 14_5$

$\left.\right\rbrace$ Check by decimal

(c)
$$43_5$$
$$\times\ 24_5$$
$$\overline{332}$$
$$1410$$
$$\overline{2242_5}$$

$3_5 \times 4_5 = 22_5$
$4_5 \times 4_5 = 31_5$
$2_5 \times 3_5 = 11_5$
$4_5 \times 2_5 = 13_5$

Division of numbers to any base is done in the usual way. The difficulty that arises is that while we know the multiplication tables to base 10 we do not know them to other bases. Here are two examples of division with bases other than 10. Try working through them for yourself, bearing in mind the base being used.

Example 7.

(a) $324_5 \div 4_5$

$$
\begin{array}{r}
42_5 \text{ rem. } 1 \\
4_5\overline{)324_5} \\
31 \\
\overline{14} \\
13 \\
\overline{1}
\end{array}
$$

(b) $731_8 \div 26_8$

$$
\begin{array}{r}
25_8 \text{ rem. } 13 \\
26_8\overline{)731_8} \\
54 \\
\overline{171} \\
156 \\
\overline{13}
\end{array}
$$

Numbers to base 12

Numbers to base 12 are called *duodecimal* numbers. Just as 'decimal' is another way of saying 10, so 'duodecimal' is another way of saying 12. In some ways 12 is more convenient than 10 as a base for a number system. For example, it is divisible by 2, 3, 4, and 6 (besides 1 and 12) while 10 is divisible only by 2 and 5 (besides 1 and 10). Many people have argued for a duodecimal as opposed to a decimal number system— the French did, at one time, seriously consider what advantages a monetary system based on 12 would have over their present decimal system. You may already have had some experience of working with a duodecimal system. For instance, any calculations involving feet and inches would be worked to base 12 since 1 foot = 12 inches.

5

Before we attempt any duodecimal calculations consider the following table:

Number Symbols

Decimal	Duodecimal
0	0
1	1
2	2
3	3
4	4
5	5
6	6
7	7
8	8
9	9
10	?
11	?
12	10

It appears that we are short of two number symbols between 9_{12} and 10_{12}. If you think about it you will see that this must be so, because when working with base 10 we use ten symbols i.e. 0, 1, 2, 3, 4, 5, 6, 7, 8, 9; with base 12 we need twelve symbols. Therefore we must 'invent' two new symbols. This is quite easy and can be done in a number of ways, of which the simplest is to use the letters T and E to stand for ten and eleven in our duodecimal number symbol system. So our number symbols are:

$$0, 1, 2, 3, 4, 5, 6, 7, 8, 9, T, E$$

Example 8. Change $3T5_{12}$ to decimal.

Remember:

$12^2 = 144s$	12s	1s
3	T	5

So

$$3T5_{12} = (3 \times 144) + (10 \text{ (i.e. T)} \times 12) + 5$$
$$= 432 + 120 + 5$$
$$= 557_{10}$$

Check this by reversing the process, i.e. change 557_{10} to base 12.

$$
\begin{array}{r|l}
12 & 557 \\
\hline
12 & 46 \text{ rem. } 5 \\
\hline
12 & 3 \text{ rem. } 10 \quad \text{(which is T in duodecimal symbols)} \\
\hline
& 0 \text{ rem. } 3
\end{array}
$$

So
$$557_{10} = 3T5_{12}$$

6

Example 9.

(a) Add $25_{12} + E7_{12} + 36T_{12}$ (b) From $53E_{12}$ take $2T7_{12}$

Remember that we are using base 12, so that all carrying and borrowing is done with 12, *not* 10.

(a)

$$
\begin{array}{r}
25_{12} \\
E7_{12} \\
36T_{12} \\
\hline
48T_{12} \\
11
\end{array}
$$

$5 + 7 + T = 1T$ (Write T and carry 1)
$2 + E + 6 + 1 = 18$ (Write 8 and carry 1)
$3 + 1 = 4$ (Write 4)

(b)

$$
\begin{array}{r}
53E_{12} \\
-2T7_{12} \\
\hline
254_{12}
\end{array}
$$

$E - 7 = 4$
$3 - T$ (Not possible; borrow 1)
So $13 - T = 5$
$5 - (2 + 1) = 2$

Multiplication and division using duodecimal numbers present no new problems. The main difficulty is that we are not very well acquainted with multiplication tables to base 12. This can be overcome with a little extra care and by always remembering that we are working with base 12. Work through the following examples checking the calculation.

Example 10.

(a) $735_{12} \times 4E_{12}$

$$
\begin{array}{r}
735_{12} \\
\times \quad 4E_{12} \\
\hline
6817 \\
25180 \\
\hline
2E997_{12}
\end{array}
$$

$5 \times E = 47_{12}$
$3 \times E = 29_{12}$ $(29 + 4 = 31_{12})$
$7 \times E = 65_{12}$ $(65 + 3 = 68_{12})$
$5 \times 4 = 18_{12}$
$3 \times 4 = 10_{12}$ $(10 + 1 = 11_{12})$
$\quad\quad\quad (11_{12} = 13_{10}$ *not* E)
$7 \times 4 = 24_{12}$ $(24 + 1 = 25_{12})$

(b) $446T_{12} \div 1E_{12}$

$$
\begin{array}{r}
235_{12} \text{ rem. } 3_{12} \\
1E_{12} \overline{)446T_{12}} \\
3T \\
\hline
66 \\
59 \\
\hline
9T \\
97 \\
\hline
3
\end{array}
$$

Work through each stage of this calculation to gain experience.

7

Binary Numbers

We have seen that it is possible to use any convenient number as a base for a number system. The simplest number system is that which uses base 2, called a *binary* system. A decimal number system requires 10 number symbols, a duodecimal system needs 12 symbols, a binary system works with only two symbols, 0 and 1.

Because of their simplicity, binary systems have been used by many primitive peoples. In the seventeenth century Leibniz, the German mathematician, did a great deal of work with a binary system. However, binary numbers suffer from the disadvantage of being unwieldy and have been rather neglected until modern times.

The revival in the use of the binary number system has been brought about by the development of the electronic computer. The modern computer has a phenomenal memory, is never bored by monotonous tasks, and is incredibly fast when doing calculations, yet its basic function is simply to add and subtract. It multiplies by repeated addition and divides by repeated subtraction. Problems presented to it must be so arranged that a solution can be obtained by using the computer's ability to add and subtract.

Electronic digital computers operate by means of a number of small electric circuits, and the supply of current to each of these circuits is controlled by a switch that can be either 'on' or 'off'. By using a number system that needs only two symbols, 0 and 1, and representing 0 as 'off' and 1 as 'on', we have a form of arithmetic that can be used by a digital computer.

Since Binary Arithmetic can be used by computers and we are, at the present moment, well into the Computer Age, it is clear that the simplest form of number system has come into its own and has taken on a new and important role.

Binary Arithmetic

Remember that binary numbers are to base 2 and only the symbols 0 and 1 are used. Take the number 101110_2. Written out with headings it becomes:

$2^5 = 32s$	$2^4 = 16s$	$2^3 = 8s$	$2^2 = 4s$	2s	1s
1	0	1	1	1	0

To convert to decimal:

$$101110_2 = (1 \times 32) + (0 \times 16) + (1 \times 8) + (1 \times 4) + (1 \times 2) + (0 \times 1)$$
$$= 32 + 0 + 8 + 4 + 2 + 0$$
$$= 46_{10}$$

To convert from decimal to binary numbers is simply a question of dividing by 2.

Convert 143_{10} to binary notation.

$$\begin{array}{r|l}
2 & 143 \\
\hline
2 & 71 \text{ rem. } 1 \\
\hline
2 & 35 \text{ rem. } 1 \\
\hline
2 & 17 \text{ rem. } 1 \\
\hline
2 & 8 \text{ rem. } 1 \\
\hline
2 & 4 \text{ rem. } 0 \\
\hline
2 & 2 \text{ rem. } 0 \\
\hline
2 & 1 \text{ rem. } 0 \\
\hline
& 0 \text{ rem. } 1
\end{array}$$

So $$143_{10} = 10001111_2$$

Calculations using binary notation are easy since there are no tables to learn, but you must remember that in binary $1+1=10$ (read as 'one—nought' not as ten).

Example 11. Add $101_2 + 10101_2 + 110011_2$

$$\begin{array}{r}
101 \\
10101 \\
110011 \\
\hline
1001101_2
\end{array}$$

Work through this addition. Starting with the right hand column, $1+1=10$. $10+1=11$. Write 1 and carry 1. Complete the addition yourself.

Subtraction using binary notation can be a little 'tricky' but practice will soon overcome any difficulty.

Example 12. From 1010101_2 take 110111_2

$$\begin{array}{r}
1010101 \\
110111 \\
\hline
11110_2
\end{array}$$

Starting with the right hand column, $1-1=0$. Write 0. $0-1$. Cannot be done. Borrow 1. The subtraction now becomes $10-1=1$. Write 1. Pay back 1 to lower line, $1+1=10$. Subtraction is now $1-10$. Borrow 1 and it becomes $11-10=1$. Write 1. Complete the subtraction yourself. Check by changing to decimal notation.

Example 13. Work through these examples of multiplication and division. The methods are quite straightforward.

(a) $10111_2 \times 1111_2$

$$
\begin{array}{r}
10111 \\
\times\ 1111 \\
\hline
10111 \\
10111 \\
10111 \\
10111 \\
\hline
101011001_2 \\
\end{array}
$$

(b) $100000111 \div 11100$

$$
\begin{array}{r}
1001 \text{ rem. } 1011 \\
11100)\overline{100000111} \\
11100 \\
\hline
100111 \\
11100 \\
\hline
1011 \\
\end{array}
$$

Exercise 2

(1) The following are decimal numbers: (i) 31 (ii) 125 (iii) 79 (iv) 191
(v) 426. Convert them to:

   (a) base 5   (b) base 8   (c) base 12   (d) base 2.

(2) Convert the following numbers to decimal notation:

   103_5 421_8 35_6 $T7_{12}$ 110101_2
   356_8 $1E3_{12}$ 143_5 10101_2 241_6

(3) Fill in the blank spaces in this table:

	Base 10	Base 8	Base 5	Base 12	Base 2
(i)	24	30	44	20	11000
(ii)		21			
(iii)			33		
(iv)				E4	
(v)					101011

(4) Add:

(a) 324_5
14_5
133_5
201_5

(b) 97_{12}
524_{12}
$10E_{12}$
$T78_{12}$

(c) 37_8
246_8
724_8
66_8

(d) 101_2
1110_2
11_2
1010_2

(e) $23_6 + 135_6 + 321_6 + 5_6$

(f) $48_{12} + 607_{12} + TE_{12} + 94_{12}$

(g) $1010_2 + 111_2 + 10100_2 + 1100_2$

(h) $1101_2 + 11111_2 + 10001_2 + 11011_2$

(5) Subtract:

$$\begin{array}{ll} (a) & 467_8 \\ & -343_8 \\ \hline \end{array} \qquad \begin{array}{ll} (b) & 242_5 \\ & -143_5 \\ \hline \end{array} \qquad \begin{array}{ll} (c) & 97E_{12} \\ & -638_{12} \\ \hline \end{array}$$

$$\begin{array}{ll} (d) & 11011_2 \\ & 10111_2 \\ \hline \end{array}$$

(e) $652_7 - 463_7$

(f) $T79E_{12} - 88T5_{12}$

(g) $10001001_2 - 1011100_2$

(h) $11011011_2 - 1010101_2$

(6) Multiply:

(a) $34_5 \times 23_5$ (d) $1101_2 \times 101_2$ (g) $364_{12} \times 53_{12}$

(b) $73_8 \times 46_8$ (e) $342_5 \times 24_5$ (h) $10010_2 \times 111_2$

(c) $57_{12} \times 13_{12}$ (f) $531_6 \times 35_6$ (i) $111011_2 \times 11101_2$

(7) Divide:

(a) $2134_5 \div 24_5$ (e) $1223_4 \div 131_4$

(b) $637_8 \div 54_8$ (f) $3294_{12} \div 9E_{12}$

(c) $2T612_{12} \div 6T_{12}$ (g) $1347_8 \div 236_8$

(d) $11011_2 \div 101_2$ (h) $1000101_2 \div 110_2$

(8) The following additions and subtractions are to various bases, two are incorrect. Find which are wrong and say what base is used for each of the calculations:

$$\begin{array}{ll} (a) & 23 \\ & 127 \\ & 56 \\ \hline & 230 \\ \hline \end{array} \qquad \begin{array}{ll} (c) & 147 \\ & 36 \\ & 54 \\ & 122 \\ \hline & 463 \\ \hline \end{array} \qquad \begin{array}{ll} (e) & 1111 \\ & 111 \\ & 1111 \\ & 11011 \\ \hline & 20010 \\ \hline \end{array}$$

$$\begin{array}{ll} (b) & 243 \\ & -124 \\ \hline & 114 \\ \hline \end{array} \qquad \begin{array}{ll} (d) & 1539 \\ & -847 \\ \hline & 592 \\ \hline \end{array}$$

(9) Convert:

(a) 1011010_2 to base 8.

(b) 576_8 to binary notation.

(c) 3579_{10} to duodecimal notation.

(d) 764_8 to base 2.

(e) 110110100_2 to octal notation (i.e. base 8).

(10) How many symbols would be needed for a number system to base 16? Convert 79_{10} and 91_{12} to base 16. Invent any new symbols you may need and explain their use.

2 Vulgar Fractions

In our everyday affairs we seldom have to deal with quantities, measurements, weights, amounts, that fall conveniently into whole units. For example, the length of a bookshelf in our room is rarely 1m exactly, more often it is 1m and 'a bit'; the length of a skirt is, more often than not, a certain number of centimetres and 'a bit'. These 'bits' are fractions; and the ability to do calculations involving fractions is a useful skill.

You are already familiar with the use of fractions, and the worked examples that follow are intended to refresh your memory of the way in which the basic processes are performed.

Addition and subtraction

Example 1. $3\frac{1}{4} + 2\frac{7}{10} + 1\frac{1}{8}$

Add the whole numbers and express the fractions in terms of the lowest common denominator

$$= 6\frac{10+28+5}{40} = 6\frac{43}{40} = 7\frac{3}{40}$$

Example 2. $4\frac{1}{2} - 1\frac{7}{8}$

Subtract the whole numbers and express the fractions in terms of the lowest common denominator

$$= 3\frac{4-7}{8}$$

Adjust the fractions to enable subtraction to be done

$$\cancel{3}2\frac{8+4-7}{8} = 2\frac{12-7}{8} = 2\frac{5}{8}$$

Example 3. $2\frac{3}{4} - 1\frac{7}{8} + 2\frac{3}{16} - 1\frac{1}{2}$

Add up the whole numbers $(+4-2)$ and express the fractions in terms of the lowest common denominator

$$= 2\frac{12-14+3-8}{16}$$

12

Collect the numerators thus

$$= 2\frac{+15-22}{16}$$

Adjust the numerators to enable subtraction to be done

$$= 2_1\frac{16+15-22}{16} = 1\frac{9}{16}$$

Multiplication and division

Example 4. $2\frac{5}{8} \times 2\frac{2}{3} \times 1\frac{3}{10}$

Change to improper fractions and cancel where possible

$$= \frac{\overset{7}{\cancel{21}}}{\cancel{8}} \times \frac{\overset{1}{\cancel{8}}}{\cancel{3}} \times \frac{13}{10}$$

Multiply numerators and denominators and express as a mixed number

$$= \frac{91}{10} = 9\frac{1}{10}$$

Example 5. $25 \div 3\frac{3}{4}$

Change to improper fractions

$$= \frac{25}{1} \div \frac{15}{4}$$

Invert divisor and cancel where possible

$$= \frac{\overset{5}{\cancel{25}}}{1} \times \frac{4}{\underset{3}{\cancel{15}}}$$

Multiply and express as a mixed number

$$= \frac{20}{3} = 6\frac{2}{3}$$

13

Example 6. $7\frac{1}{5} \div 5\frac{1}{3} \times 2\frac{2}{9}$

Change to improper fractions:

$$= \frac{36}{5} \div \frac{16}{3} \times \frac{20}{9}$$

Invert divisor and multiply:

$$= \frac{\overset{\overset{3}{9}}{\cancel{36}}}{\underset{1}{5}} \times \frac{\overset{1}{\cancel{3}}}{\underset{4}{16}} \times \frac{\overset{5}{20}}{\underset{1}{9}}$$

Cancel

$$= \frac{3}{1} = 3$$

Sometimes part of a calculation must be done before the whole calculation is completed. That part is bracketed off from the remainder of the calculation and must be done first.

Example 7. $(3\frac{1}{2} - 1\frac{3}{4}) \div 2$

Work the bracket first:

$$= \left(\underset{1}{\overset{}{2}}\frac{4+2-3}{4}\right) \div 2 = 1\frac{3}{4} \div 2$$

Change to improper fractions:

$$= \frac{7}{4} \div \frac{2}{1}$$

Invert divisor and multiply:

$$= \frac{7}{4} \times \frac{1}{2} = \frac{7}{8}$$

In a calculation, if $\times$ and $\div$ signs are mixed with $+$ and $-$ signs then, whether they appear or not, brackets are assumed to be around the quantities to be multiplied or divided.

The expression $4+3\times2$ means

$$4 + \text{twice } 3$$

i.e.
$$4+3+3 = 10$$

So the multiplication must be performed first. Remember that if an 'of' appears in a calculation it is dealt with in the same way as multiplication.

Example 8. $(2\frac{5}{6}+1\frac{1}{12})\div(\frac{5}{8}\text{ of }2\frac{1}{5})$

Work the brackets first. It is convenient to work both brackets at the same time.

$$= \left(3\,\frac{10+1}{12}\right) \div \left(\frac{\overset{1}{\cancel{5}}}{8}\times\frac{11}{\underset{1}{\cancel{5}}}\right)$$

$$= 3\,\frac{11}{12}\div\frac{11}{8}$$

$$= \frac{47}{\underset{3}{\cancel{12}}} \times \frac{\overset{2}{\cancel{8}}}{11}$$

$$= \frac{94}{33} = 2\frac{28}{33}$$

Exercise 1

When working these examples try to present your work as neatly and clearly as possible. Good presentation makes for accurate work.

(1) $\frac{7}{8}+1\frac{3}{4}+2\frac{15}{16}$

(2) $3\frac{5}{8}+1\frac{1}{5}+4\frac{1}{2}$

(3) $4\frac{5}{8}-2\frac{3}{16}$

(4) $8\frac{1}{4}-1\frac{7}{12}$

(5) $5\frac{1}{2}-2\frac{3}{5}+\frac{9}{10}$

(6) $15\frac{11}{12}-4\frac{3}{4}-6\frac{3}{8}$

(7) $4\frac{27}{32}+2\frac{1}{2}-4\frac{3}{8}$

(8) $6\frac{2}{3}-5\frac{7}{8}+2\frac{1}{12}$

(9) $2\frac{1}{4}\times\frac{7}{8}$

(10) $2\frac{11}{16}\times9$

(11) $1\frac{7}{10}\times3\frac{1}{5}\times2\frac{1}{2}$

(12) $\frac{11}{12}\times2\frac{1}{4}\times4\frac{5}{8}$

(13) $5\frac{1}{4}\div1\frac{2}{3}$

(14) $\frac{7}{10}\div2\frac{1}{2}$

(15) $8\frac{1}{3}\div\frac{3}{4}\div2\frac{1}{2}$

(16) $2\frac{3}{8}\times4\frac{1}{16}\div1\frac{3}{16}$

(17) $7\frac{1}{12}\div2\frac{1}{8}\times\frac{3}{5}$

(18) $1\frac{17}{32}\div\frac{7}{16}\div3\frac{1}{2}$

(19) $(1\frac{2}{5}+\frac{3}{10})\times2\frac{1}{2}$

(20) $4\frac{3}{8}\div(\frac{3}{4}-\frac{5}{16})$

(21) $\frac{2}{3}\text{ of }(3\frac{1}{6}+4\frac{1}{4})$

(22) $\frac{7}{8}\text{ of }5\frac{1}{3}+6\frac{1}{4}\div\frac{5}{8}$

(23) $(2\frac{1}{3}+4\frac{1}{4}-3\frac{3}{16})\times(\frac{3}{4}\text{ of }2)$

(24) $(4\frac{1}{4}\div3\frac{3}{16})\times(2\frac{1}{8}\div1\frac{3}{8})$

More complex fractions

Example 9. Remember that $4\frac{1}{4} \div 3\frac{3}{16}$ can be written as

$$\frac{4\dfrac{1}{4}}{3\dfrac{3}{16}}$$

Change to improper fractions

$$= \frac{\dfrac{17}{4}}{\dfrac{51}{16}}$$

Invert divisor and multiply, cancelling where possible

$$= \frac{\overset{1}{\cancel{17}}}{\underset{1}{\cancel{4}}} \times \frac{\overset{4}{\cancel{16}}}{\underset{3}{\cancel{51}}}$$

$$= \frac{4}{3} = 1\frac{1}{3}$$

Example 10. $\dfrac{2\frac{3}{8} + 5\frac{1}{2}}{2\frac{1}{2} - \frac{7}{16}}$

Calculate the numerator and the denominator as two separate calculations

$$\frac{7\dfrac{3+4}{8}}{2\dfrac{8-7}{16}}$$

$$= \frac{7\dfrac{7}{8}}{2\dfrac{1}{16}}$$

Change to improper fractions

$$= \frac{\dfrac{63}{8}}{\dfrac{33}{16}}$$

Invert divisor and multiply

$$= \frac{\overset{21}{\cancel{63}}}{\underset{1}{\cancel{8}}} \times \frac{\overset{2}{\cancel{16}}}{\underset{11}{\cancel{33}}}$$

$$= \frac{42}{11} = 3\tfrac{9}{11}$$

Example 11. $\dfrac{1\frac{3}{4} + 1\frac{7}{16}}{4\frac{1}{4} \div 3\frac{1}{5} \times 3}$

Work out the numerator and prepare the denominator, but **do not** perform the calculation

$$= \frac{2\dfrac{12+7}{16}}{\dfrac{17}{4} \div \dfrac{16}{5} \times \dfrac{3}{1}}$$

Invert $\frac{16}{5}$ and change the sign to $\times$

$$= \frac{3\dfrac{3}{16}}{\dfrac{17}{4} \times \dfrac{5}{16} \times \dfrac{3}{1}}$$

Change the numerator to an improper fraction, invert all fractions in the denominator and multiply

$$= \frac{\overset{1}{\cancel{51}}}{\underset{1}{\cancel{16}}} \times \frac{4}{\cancel{17}} \times \frac{\overset{1}{\cancel{16}}}{5} \times \frac{1}{\cancel{3}} = \frac{4}{5}$$

Exercise 1 *(continued)*

(25) $\dfrac{2\frac{5}{8}}{1\frac{3}{4}}$

(26) $\dfrac{3\frac{3}{10}}{2\frac{1}{5}}$

(27) $\dfrac{\frac{7}{16}}{\frac{35}{64}}$

(28) $\dfrac{2\frac{1}{4} + \frac{19}{32}}{1\frac{7}{8} - 1\frac{1}{16}}$

(29) $\dfrac{3\frac{7}{8} - 2\frac{3}{10}}{2\frac{1}{2} + 1\frac{7}{8}}$

(30) $\dfrac{4\frac{2}{3}}{1\frac{3}{32} \times 1\frac{3}{5}}$

(31) $\dfrac{1\frac{5}{6}}{1\frac{5}{16} \times 3\frac{1}{2}}$

(32) $\dfrac{2\frac{1}{2} \times \frac{5}{6}}{3\frac{3}{4} \div \frac{9}{16}}$

(33) $\dfrac{\frac{7}{8} \text{ of } \frac{1}{54}}{(2\frac{1}{3} - \frac{5}{6}) \times \frac{3}{8}}$

17

Fractions of quantities

Remember that a fraction represents a part of something, $\frac{3}{4}$ of an hour, $\frac{1}{2}$ a kilogramme. We commonly use fractions of quantities in our day-to-day arithmetic; we say that a packet is 'half full', or that we have used 'a quarter of the roll of film'. We must therefore be able to handle fractions, in this way, with some accuracy.

Example 12. Express $7\frac{1}{2}$ minutes as a fraction of 1 hour. Remember that numerator and denominator must both be in the same units.

$$\frac{7\frac{1}{2} \text{ min}}{1 \text{ hour}} \text{ change to minutes} = \frac{7\frac{1}{2} \text{ min}}{60 \text{ min}}$$

cancel the minutes as

$$\frac{7\frac{1}{2}}{60} = \frac{15}{60 \times 2} = \frac{15}{120} = \frac{1}{8}$$

Example 13. The petrol tank of a car holds 45 l when full. How much petrol is in the tank when it is $\frac{2}{3}$ full?

$$\frac{2}{3} \text{ of } \overset{15}{\cancel{45}} \text{ l} = 30 \text{ l}$$

Example 14. $\frac{3}{8}$ of a telegraph pole is buried in the ground. The length of pole above ground is $12\frac{1}{2}$ metres. How long is the pole?

$$\frac{3}{8} \text{ of the pole is buried}$$

$$\therefore \frac{8}{8} - \frac{3}{8} = \frac{5}{8} \text{ of pole is above ground}$$

$$\frac{5}{8} \text{ of pole} = 12\frac{1}{2} \text{ m}$$

$$\therefore \text{ Total length of pole} = 12\frac{1}{2} \times \frac{8}{5}$$

$$= \frac{\overset{5}{\cancel{25}}}{\underset{1}{\cancel{2}}} \times \frac{\overset{4}{\cancel{8}}}{\underset{1}{\cancel{5}}} = 20 \text{ m}$$

Exercise 2

(1) (*a*) What fraction is 625 kg of 5 tonnes?
(*b*) What fraction is 5 kg of $62\frac{1}{2}$ kg?

(2) (*a*) What is $52\frac{1}{2}$ cm as a fraction of 2·80 metres?
(*b*) What is 42 hours as a fraction of 1 week?

(3) A tradesman is paid $31\frac{1}{2}$p per hour. His overtime rate is 'time and a third'. What is his hourly overtime rate? How much will he be paid for $7\frac{3}{4}$ h overtime?

(4) A watering-can holding $11\frac{1}{2}$ l is filled 9 times from a tank holding 230 l of water. What fraction of the contents of the tank is used? How many litres are left in the tank?

(5) From a bolt of material three pieces of $2\frac{3}{4}$ m, $4\frac{1}{2}$ m, and $3\frac{1}{2}$ m are cut. The piece that is left is $\frac{3}{8}$ of the original bolt. Calculate the length of the bolt.

(6) On her journey to school a girl cycles $\frac{3}{4}$ km to the bus stop, and then takes the bus for 3 km, and walks the last 450 m. What fraction of her journey is done on foot?

(7) In a school of 400 pupils, $\frac{1}{5}$ are in the upper school, $\frac{3}{8}$ are in the middle school, and the remainder are in the lower school. How many children are in the lower school?

(8) A strip of wallpaper is 50 cm wide. How many strips will be needed to paper the walls of a room that is 3·60 m wide and 4·20 m long?

(9) Of the weight of an alloy $\frac{9}{10}$ is copper, $\frac{7}{100}$ tin, and $\frac{3}{100}$ zinc. What weight of each metal will be in 450 g of the alloy?

(10) A train from Victoria to the south coast covers a distance of 126 km in $1\frac{3}{4}$ h. What is the average distance that it covers in 1 h?

Farey Series

If a set of proper fractions, with denominators less than a given number, is written down in ascending order the result is called a Farey series. Take this set of fractions with denominators of 5 or less (i.e. less than 6):

$$\frac{1}{2}, \frac{1}{3}, \frac{2}{3}, \frac{1}{4}, \frac{3}{4}, \frac{1}{5}, \frac{2}{5}, \frac{3}{5}, \frac{4}{5}$$

You will notice that fractions equal to simpler fractions have been left out, e.g. $\frac{2}{4}$. Rewritten in ascending order they are,

$$\frac{1}{5}, \frac{1}{4}, \frac{1}{3}, \frac{2}{5}, \frac{1}{2}, \frac{3}{5}, \frac{2}{3}, \frac{3}{4}, \frac{4}{5}$$

which is a Farey series of order 5.

A Farey series has a number of interesting properties but the work of arranging the set of fractions can be rather tiresome, so we shall first look at a way of representing fractions that uses point-lattices. A lattice is simply a series of numbered lines that form squares, as on squared paper, this has been done in the diagram below. The lines have been numbered only as far as five because that is as far as we need to go for our set of fractions.

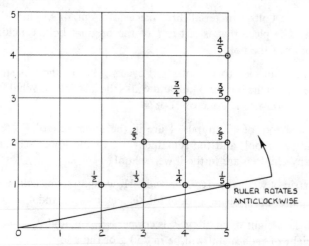

Lattice Point Method of Representing Fractions

Our original set of fractions is now plotted on the lattice in this way: the denominator of the fraction is measured along the horizontal lines and the numerator up the vertical lines. The point at which the horizontal and vertical lines cross is the lattice point that represents a particular fraction. For example $\frac{1}{2}$ is two squares along and one up. Each fraction of the set has been plotted on the figure.

To arrange the set of fractions in ascending order lay the edge of a ruler along the horizontal base line and, with one end anchored at nought, rotate it in an anticlockwise direction, keeping the end firmly on nought. The first 'fraction point' it passes through represents $\frac{1}{5}$, this is the smallest of the set of fractions; the second point represents $\frac{1}{4}$ which is the next fraction in ascending order of size, the next is $\frac{1}{3}$ and so on. The straight edge will pass through all the points in turn in ascending order of size. Writing them down in this order gives us the set of fractions in a Farey series.

Draw your own lattice and find the Farey series of fractions of order 4.

Consider our original Farey series of order 5,

$$\frac{1}{5}, \frac{1}{4}, \frac{1}{3}, \frac{2}{5}, \frac{1}{2}, \frac{3}{5}, \frac{2}{3}, \frac{3}{4}, \frac{4}{5}$$

Take any two consecutive fractions, say $\frac{3}{5}$ and $\frac{2}{3}$, and multiply the denominator of the first fraction by the numerator of the second and the denominator of the second by the numerator of the first. From the first result subtract the second result. This gives us

$$(5 \times 2) - (3 \times 3) = 10 - 9 = 1$$

Check that this result is always obtained by using other pairs of fractions and other series.

If we take any three consecutive fractions from our Farey series, say,

$$\frac{3}{5}, \frac{2}{3}, \frac{3}{4}$$

and add the numerators of the 1st and 3rd fractions, then add the denominator of the 1st and 3rd fractions and express the results as a fraction in this way:

$$\frac{\text{Sum of 1st \& 3rd numerators}}{\text{Sum of 1st \& 3rd denominators}} = \frac{3+3}{5+4} = \frac{6}{9} = \frac{2}{3}$$

we obtain the middle fraction.

Example 16. These fractions, $\frac{1}{4}$, $\frac{2}{7}$, $\frac{1}{3}$, are consecutive members of a Farey series. Find the next member.

Let the next member be $\frac{x}{y}$

Thus $\frac{2}{7}, \frac{1}{3}, \frac{x}{y}$, are consecutive members, and

(i) $$\frac{2+x}{7+y} = \frac{1}{3}$$

(ii) $$(3 \times x) - (1 \times y) = 1$$

21

By inspection we see that $\dfrac{x}{y}=\dfrac{2}{5}$ satisfies both (i) and (ii)

$$\therefore \text{ the next member is } \frac{2}{5}$$

Note: $\dfrac{x}{y}=\dfrac{1}{2}$ would satisfy (i), giving $\dfrac{3}{9}=\dfrac{1}{3}$, but would not satisfy (ii).

Continued Fractions

A fraction in the form

$$\cfrac{1}{2+\cfrac{1}{2+\cfrac{1}{2+\frac{1}{2}}}}$$

is called a continued fraction; it is easy to simplify if we always work from the lowest line upwards:

$$\cfrac{1}{2+\cfrac{1}{2+\cfrac{1}{2+\frac{1}{2}}}}$$
Lowest line is $2+\dfrac{1}{2}=2\dfrac{1}{2}=\dfrac{5}{2}$

$$=\cfrac{1}{2+\cfrac{1}{2+\cfrac{1}{\frac{5}{2}}}}$$
Simplify $\dfrac{1}{\frac{5}{2}}$, which is $1\div\dfrac{5}{2}$

i.e. $\dfrac{1}{1}\times\dfrac{2}{5}=\dfrac{2}{5}$

$$=\cfrac{1}{2+\cfrac{1}{2+\frac{2}{5}}}$$
Lowest line $2+\dfrac{2}{5}=2\dfrac{2}{5}=\dfrac{12}{5}$

Simplify $\dfrac{1}{\frac{12}{5}}=\dfrac{1}{1}\times\dfrac{5}{12}=\dfrac{5}{12}$

$$=\cfrac{1}{2+\frac{5}{12}}$$

$$=\dfrac{1}{2\frac{5}{12}}=\dfrac{1}{\frac{29}{12}}$$
Simplify as above.

$$=\dfrac{12}{29}$$

22

Exercise 3

(1) Use a point lattice to find the larger of the following pairs of fractions,

(*a*) $\frac{7}{8}, \frac{5}{6}$ (*b*) $\frac{3}{4}, \frac{4}{5}$ (*c*) $\frac{7}{8}, \frac{8}{9}$

(2) Use a point lattice to arrange these fractions in a Farey series: $\frac{1}{3}, \frac{1}{2}, \frac{2}{3}, \frac{3}{4}, \frac{1}{4}$. What order is the series?

(3) Work out a Farey series of order 6. Use the properties of Farey series that you know to check your result.

(4) Which of these pairs of fractions are *not* consecutive members of a Farey series?

(*a*) $\frac{1}{4}, \frac{2}{7}$ (*b*) $\frac{2}{3}, \frac{4}{5}$ (*c*) $\frac{3}{4}, \frac{4}{5}$ (*d*) $\frac{4}{7}, \frac{3}{5}$ (*e*) $\frac{3}{5}, \frac{5}{7}$

(5) These are three consecutive members of Farey series. In each case find the next member.

(*a*) $\frac{1}{7}, \frac{1}{6}, \frac{1}{5}$ (*b*) $\frac{1}{2}, \frac{4}{7}, \frac{3}{5}$ (*c*) $\frac{2}{3}, \frac{5}{7}, \frac{3}{4}$

(6) Write out a Farey series of Order 8.

(7) Simplify:
$$\cfrac{1}{1+\cfrac{2}{2+\cfrac{3}{3+4}}}$$

(8) Simplify:
$$\cfrac{1}{1+\cfrac{1}{1+\cfrac{1}{1+1}}}$$

(9) Simplify:
$$\cfrac{1}{1+\cfrac{2}{2+\cfrac{3}{3+\cfrac{4}{4+5}}}}$$

23

3 Decimal Fractions

The decimal point

Take the number

$$333 \cdot 333$$

The position of each figure 3 governs its size in relation to the other figures. Thus 333·333 can be written as:

$$300 + 30 + 3 \cdot + \frac{3}{10} + \frac{3}{100} + \frac{3}{1000}$$

Moving from left to right each figure represents in turn an amount 10 times greater than the figure that comes immediately after it. Any number that is based on a system of tens is in fact a decimal.

In the number,

decimal whole numbers→333·333←decimal fractions

the decimal point is used to separate the decimal whole numbers to the left of the point from the decimal fractions that lie to the right of the point.

The importance of 'place value' in decimals enables us to perform multiplication and division by 10, 100, 1,000, etc. very simply.

Multiplication and division by powers of 10

To multiply by 10 we simply move the decimal point one place to the right, by 100 we move the point two places, by 1,000 three places and so on. Thus

$$9 \cdot 56 \times 10 = 95 \cdot 6$$
$$9 \cdot 56 \times 100 = 956$$

To divide by 10 we move the decimal point one place to the left; by 100 we move the point two places, by 1,000 three places, and so on. Thus

$$23 \cdot 27 \div 10 = 2 \cdot 327$$
$$23 \cdot 27 \div 100 = 0 \cdot 2327$$

Correcting a decimal

To correct for any number of decimal places, when the figure immediately after the last place required is 5 or more, add 1 to the last place required; if the figure is less than 5 the last place required remains

24

unchanged, e.g. 2·7346 becomes 2·735 correct to 3 places of decimals, because the fourth figure is greater than 5.

> 40·036 correct to two places of decimals is 40·04
> 125·3442 correct to three places of decimals is 125·344

Converting vulgar fractions to decimal fractions

To convert a vulgar fraction to a decimal fraction is simply a matter of dividing the numerator by the denominator.

Example 1. Convert $\frac{53}{69}$ to a decimal fraction.

69 is not contained in 53. Add '0' and
introduce the decimal point. Perform
the division in the usual way.
This does not work out exactly so
the answer is 'corrected' to 3 decimal
places, as 0·768.

```
        ·7681
  69)530
      483
      470
      414
      560
      552
       80
       69
       11
```

Example 2. Convert $4\frac{5}{8}$ to a decimal fraction.

Change $4\frac{5}{8}$ to an improper fraction,
i.e. $\frac{37}{8}$, and carry out the division,
inserting the decimal point when '0'
is added.
Answer: 4·625

```
       4·625
  8)37
     32
     50
     48
     20
     16
     40
     40
     ··
```

Decimal fractions are useful when we wish to compare fractions. Take two fractions

$$\frac{63}{79} \quad \text{and} \quad \frac{53}{69}$$

They are difficult to compare; it is not easy to see even which is the larger. The comparison is made simpler when they are converted into decimal fractions.

$$\frac{63}{79} = 0.797 \qquad \frac{53}{69} = 0.768$$

25

Converting decimal fractions into vulgar fractions

The reverse process of changing a decimal into a vulgar fraction is done in this way:

Example 3. Change 0·625 to a vulgar fraction.

$$0·625 = \frac{6}{10} + \frac{2}{100} + \frac{5}{1,000}$$

$$= \frac{600 + 20 + 5}{1,000}$$

$$= \frac{625}{1,000} = \frac{5}{8}$$

Addition, subtraction, multiplication, and division

These examples are intended to review the method of addition, subtraction, multiplication, and division of decimals. Remember that if the decimal points are carefully positioned then the method is exactly the same as that for ordinary numbers.

Example 4.

	Add	46·34	Subtract	12·63
		·06		2·951
		2·451		9·679
		123·7		
		172·551		

In both cases, keep the 'points' in line.

Example 5. 75·03 × 2·7.

Ignore the decimal points and multiply in the usual way. Count the number of decimal places in both numbers, i.e. 2+1=3, and place the point by counting from the right.

$$
\begin{array}{r}
75·03 \\
\times\ 2·7 \\
\hline
52521 \\
150060 \\
\hline
202·581
\end{array}
$$

26

Example 6. 14·93÷2·9. Give your answer correct to two places of decimals.

Make the divisor (2·9) a whole number. This is done by moving the decimal point one place to the right. This multiplies the divisor by 10, so the number it is being divided into (the dividend) must also be multiplied by 10, i.e. the point moved one place to the right. Thus

$$14·93 ÷ 2·9$$

becomes   149·3÷29

Divide in the usual way; when the point is reached place it in the answer. Answer correct to two decimal places = 5·15.

```
          5·148
  29)149·3
      145
      ---
       43
       29
      ---
      140
      116
      ---
      240
      232
      ---
        8
        -
```

Expressing quantities as decimals

Example 7. Express 216·5 kg as a decimal fraction of 1 tonne.
Divide 216·5 kg by 1,000 to convert to a tonne, i.e. move the decimal point three places to the left.

$$\frac{216·5 \text{ kg}}{1,000} = 0·2165 \text{ t}$$

Example 8. Change 0·625 km into metres.
Multiply 0·625 km by 1,000 to convert to metres, i.e. move the decimal point three places to the right.

$$0·625 \text{ km} × 1,000 = 625 \text{ m}$$

These methods used in examples 7 and 8 can be used when working with the other weights and measures, e.g. converting millilitres to litres etc.

Significant figures

It is often necessary to present a decimal as an approximation corrrect to 'so many significant figures'. Significant figures are those that must be retained whatever the position of the decimal point. For example,

$$55·04 \text{ m} = 55,040 \text{ mm} = 0·05504 \text{ km}$$

27

In each of these the nought between 5 and 4 *must* appear, in each case regardless of the unit of length, and is therefore, significant. However the nought at the end of 55,040 mm and the noughts each side of the point of 0·05504 km are necessary only because the decimal point has changed position due to the change in the unit of length and are not significant.

So 38·97, 55·04, 0·03416 are all expressed to 4 significant figures.

However, 57·074 *correct* to 3 significant figures is 57·1.

Exercise 1

(1) Rewrite the following correct to 3 decimal places:

(*a*) 3·0861   (*c*) 0·3748   (*e*) 25·4633

(*b*) 49·0665   (*d*) 1·6666   (*f*) 2·0706

(2) (i) How many significant figures are there in each of the following numbers?

(*a*) 5·36   (*e*) 21·90367

(*b*) 3·506   (*f*) 0·003207

(*c*) 7·935   (*g*) 0·05704

(*d*) 10·0037

(ii) Rewrite them correct to two significant figures.

(3) Multiply each of the following by (i) 10, (ii) 100:

(*a*) 25·17   (*f*) 0·007

(*b*) 0·5127   (*g*) 12·0304

(*c*) 5·0026   (*h*) 0·087

(*d*) 4·7   (*i*) 11·663

(*e*) 3·025   (*j*) 0·7

(4) Find (i) $\frac{1}{10}$, (ii) $\frac{1}{100}$ of the following:

(*a*) 19·4   (*f*) 74·9

(*b*) 0·8   (*g*) 3·25

(*c*) 0·03   (*h*) 240

(*d*) 127·6   (*i*) 36·25

(*e*) 12·03   (*j*) 806·002

(5) Convert the following vulgar fractions to decimal fractions. (Do not go beyond 4 places of decimals.)

(*a*) $\frac{3}{8}$ (*c*) $\frac{9}{5}$ (*e*) $3\frac{5}{12}$ (*g*) $\frac{11}{16}$

(*b*) $\frac{5}{6}$ (*d*) $\frac{3}{7}$ (*f*) $\frac{25}{26}$ (*h*) $\frac{44}{59}$

(6) Convert the following decimal fractions to vulgar fractions, reduced to their lowest terms:

(*a*) 0·12   (*c*) 5·125   (*e*) 7·475   (*g*) 0·65

(*b*) 0·025   (*d*) 0·015   (*f*) 5·0825   (*h*) 0·035

(7) Add:

(*a*)   3·304   (*b*)   29·8
      0·64   0·073
   36   8·93
  64·035   164·8

(*c*) 13·01 + 0·46 + 2·941 + 0·153

(*d*) 15·15 + 49 + 0·063 + 141·6

(*e*) 0·88 + 0·098 + 36·2 + 127·4

(8) Subtract:

(*a*)   6·825   (*b*)   91·02
   − 5·932   − 87·95

(*c*) 11·08 − 0·973   (*d*) 12·001 − 6·03   (*e*) 86·07 − 24·984

(9) Simplify:

(*a*) 4·21 − 4·07 + 2·3 − 0·76

(*b*) 10·07 − 3·08 + 2·7 − 0·005

(*c*) 0·03 + 6·75 − 2·341 + 17

(*d*) 875·6 + 0·006 − 27·05 − 159·371

(*e*) 146·3 − 9·04 − 0·079 − 36·342

(10) Multiply 8·75 by: (*a*) 4·3   (*b*) 8·9   (*c*) 5·74

(11) Multiply 80·07 by: (*a*) 0·07   (*b*) 9·34   (*c*) 21·06

(12) Divide 25·5 by: (*a*) 1·7   (*b*) 3·4

(13) Divide 26·208 by: (*a*) 2·6   (*b*) 7·8

(14) Divide 64 by: (*a*) 5·12   (*b*) 0·08

(15) Divide 112·608 by 1·7, and then write down the values of 112·608 ÷ 17 and 112·608 ÷ 0·017.

(16) Express as a decimal fraction of £1:

(*a*) 45p   (*b*) 336p   (*c*) 64½p   (*d*) 2½p

(17) Express the first of these quantities as a decimal of the second:

    (*a*) 333 kg; 1 tonne   (*c*) 35 cm 8 mm; 1 m

    (*b*) 4,265 litres; m³   (*d*) 2 km 875 m; 1 km

(18) Change:

    (*a*) 0·025 t to grammes   (*c*) 15,450 cm to km

    (*b*) 36,547 mm to metres   (*d*) 0·035 l to cm³

(19) Find the cost of:

    (*a*) 250 g at 26p/kg   (*c*) 300 ml at £1·50/litre

    (*b*) 7·25 m at 66p/m

(20) Which is the greater and by how much?

    0·375 of 5 km; 0·593 of 3 km

4 Metric Weights and Measures

The Metric System is a decimal-based system of weights and measures that is used in most countries throughout the world. Even in those countries that have other measures for everyday use, metric measurements are standard for scientific work and engineering. Now that we are moving over to the full use of metric weights and measures the ability to handle them with ease is an essential skill.

Length

The standard of length used is the metre (m), which is a little longer than the English yard. The 'table' of measures is quite easy since it has a decimal base. For measures smaller than the standard unit the metre is divided into smaller units, thus:

$$\begin{aligned} 1 \text{ metre (m)} &= 10 \text{ decimetres (dm)} \\ &= 100 \text{ centimetres (cm)} \\ &= 1,000 \text{ millimetres (mm)} \end{aligned}$$

These units take their names from the prefixes *deci-* ($\frac{1}{10}$ or 10^{-1}), *centi-* ($\frac{1}{100}$ or 10^{-2}), and *milli-* ($\frac{1}{1,000}$ or 10^{-3}). To provide a unit greater than a metre it is multiplied by 1,000, so that

$$1,000 \text{ metres (m)} = 1 \text{ kilometre (km)}$$

(Note the prefix *kilo-* (1,000).)
The table for measurements of length is then:

$$\begin{aligned} 1 \text{ metre (m)} &= 1,000 \text{ millimetres (mm)} \\ &= 100 \text{ centimetres (cm)} \\ 1,000 \text{ metres (m)} &= 1 \text{ kilometre (km)} \end{aligned}$$

The conversion from one unit to another is easy since it is done by moving the decimal point.

Example 1. Change 17,485 metres to kilometres.
This becomes

$$\frac{17,485}{1,000} \text{ km}$$

which is simplified by placing the decimal point three places in from the right:

$$= 17 \cdot 485 \text{ km}$$

Example 2. Convert 1,285 centimetres to metres.

This becomes

$$\frac{1,285}{100} \text{ m} = 12 \cdot 85 \text{ m}$$

Example 3. Express 1·325 metres as metres, centimetres, and millimetres.

$$1 \cdot 325 = 1 + \frac{32}{100} + \frac{5}{1,000}$$

Therefore

$$1 \cdot 325 \text{ m} = 1 \text{ m } 32 \text{ cm } 5 \text{ mm}$$

Weight

The metric unit of weight is the kilogramme (kg), which is defined as the weight of 1,000 cubic centimetres of pure water. The kilogramme is divided into $\frac{1}{1,000}$ths to give the gramme (g). The gramme, in turn, is divided into $\frac{1}{1,000}$ths to obtain the milligramme (mg). The gramme and the milligramme are used for small quantities. The box of weights used with a chemical balance will give you a good idea of their size. For weighing very large amounts the kilogramme is multiplied by 1,000 to obtain the megagramme (Mg) or tonne (t). Note the prefix *mega-* (1,000,000 or 10^6).

The table for weights is then:

1 megagramme (Mg) or tonne (t)	= 1,000 kilogrammes (kg)
1 kilogramme (kg)	= 1,000 grammes (g)
1 gramme (g)	= 1,000 milligrammes (mg)

Conversion from one unit to another unit of weight is merely a matter of placing a decimal point.

Example 4   2,546 grammes = 2·546 kilogrammes
                     435 mg = 0·435 g

Capacity

The international basic unit for measuring capacity or volume is the cubic metre (m^3). This is a large amount, and so for everyday use it is broken down into smaller, more convenient units. Thus:

1 cubic metre (m^3) = 1,000 litres (l) i.e. 1,000 cubic decimeters (dm^3)
 1 litre (l) = 1,000 millilitres (ml)

Since   1 m^3 = 1,000,000 cubic cm (cm^3) = 1,000,000 ml

then   1 cm^3 = 1 ml

You will remember that one kilogramme = the weight of 1,000 cm^3 of water, and that 1 kg = 1,000 g. Therefore 1 cm^3 of water = 1 ml = 1 g. The litre is used for everyday use, buying milk, petrol etc. In this context two further multiple units may be met with:

the hectolitre (*hecto-* = 100 or 10^2) = 100 litres
and the centilitre (*centi-* = $\frac{1}{100}$ or 10^{-2}) = 10 millilitres

Volume

For precision work with volume the litre is not used, and the table of volumes is obtained directly from the table of length. The cubic metre is still the basic unit.

1 cubic metre (m^3) = 1,000 cubic decimetres (dm^3)
1 cubic decimetre (dm^3) = 1,000 cubic centimetres (cm^3)
1 cubic centimetre (cm^3) = 1,000 cubic millimetres (mm^3)

Area

The metric tables for square measure are also obtained from the linear tables. The basic unit of area is the square metre (m^2). Small areas are measured in square millimetres (mm^2) or square centimetres (cm^2), while for very large areas square kilometres (km^2) are used.
Thus:

1 square kilometre (km^2) = 1,000,000 square metres (m^2)
1 square metre (m^2) = 1,000 square centimetres (cm^2)
1 square centimetre (cm^2) = 100 square millimetres (mm^2)

For measuring land, building plots, playing fields, farms, etc., the hectare (ha) = 10^4 m^2 (i.e. 10,000 square metres) is useful, since one hectare is a little larger than a full size soccer pitch.

33

Basic Calculations

The basic calculations using the metric system are quite straightforward. They simply follow the rules of decimals.

Example 5.

(*a*) Add:

$$
\begin{array}{r}
250 \text{ g} \\
35 \text{ g} \\
500 \text{ g} \\
750 \text{ g} \\
\hline
1{,}585 \text{ g} \\
= 1{\cdot}585 \text{ kg}
\end{array}
$$

(*b*) Subtract:

$$
\begin{array}{r}
56{\cdot}93 \text{ m} \\
37{\cdot}75 \text{ m} \\
\hline
19{\cdot}18 \text{ m} \\
= 19 \text{ m } 18 \text{ cm}
\end{array}
$$

(*c*) Multiply:

$$
\begin{array}{r}
3{\cdot}125 \text{ litres} \\
\times 24 \\
\hline
12500 \\
62500 \\
\hline
75{\cdot}000 \text{ litres}
\end{array}
$$

(*d*) Divide: How many pieces 2 m 7 cm long can be cut from 30 metres?

$$30 \text{ m} \div 2{\cdot}07 \text{ m}$$

$$
\begin{array}{r}
207)\overline{3000}(\ 14 \text{ rem. } 1{\cdot}02 \text{ m} \\
207 \\
\hline
930 \\
828 \\
\hline
102
\end{array}
$$

14 pieces rem. 1·02 metres

Time

The measurement of time is the familiar

$$
\begin{aligned}
1 \text{ day (d)} &= 24 \text{ hours (h)} \\
1 \text{ hour (h)} &= 60 \text{ minutes (min)} \\
1 \text{ minute (min)} &= 60 \text{ seconds (s)}
\end{aligned}
$$

The basic unit for scientific work is the second (s).

Speed

Following from the above, velocity in scientific work is measured in metres per second (m/s), but the speed of a vehicle is more conveniently referred to in kilometres per hour (km/h).

Example 6. The circumference of a motor tyre is 1,050 mm. The car's wheel is turning at the rate of 10 revolutions per second. Assuming that there is no wheel slip, what is the speed of the car in km/h?

Distance travelled by wheel in 1 s $= 1,050 \times 10$
$$= 10,500 \text{ mm}$$
$$= 10 \cdot 5 \text{ m}$$

$\therefore$ Distance travelled by wheel in 1 h $= (10 \cdot 5 \times 60 \times 60) \text{ m}$

$$= \frac{10 \cdot 5 \times 60 \times 60}{1,000} \text{ km}$$

$$= 37 \cdot 8 \text{ km}$$

Speed of the car is 37·8 km/h

Example 7. A certain type of oil weighing 800 g per litre is packed in 10 litre cans. Find the total weight of a full can of oil if the can itself weighs 550 g. A lorry is loaded with 460 cans of this oil. Find the total weight of its load in tonnes.

Weight of 1 l of oil $= 800 \text{ g}$
$\therefore$ Weight of 10 l of oil $= 8,000 \text{ g} = 8 \text{ kg}$
Weight of oil plus can $= 8,000 \text{ g} + 550 \text{ g}$
$$= 8,550 \text{ g}$$
$$= 8 \cdot 55 \text{ kg}$$
So weight of load of 460 cans $= (8 \cdot 55 \times 460) \text{ kg}$
$$= \frac{8 \cdot 55 \times 460}{1,000} \text{ t}$$
$$= 3 \cdot 933 \text{ t}$$

Exercise 1

(1) Change 4 m 54 cm into (*a*) metres, (*b*) centimetres.

(2) Change 3 km 320 m into (*a*) kilometres, (*b*) metres.

(3) Change 2·64 m into (*a*) centimetres, (*b*) millimetres.

(4) Change 4 kg 155 g into (*a*) kilogrammes, (*b*) grammes.

(5) Change 2,355 ml into litres.

(6) Change 75 cm into (*a*) metres, (*b*) millimetres.

(7) Express the following in kilometres and metres:
(*a*) 4·836 km	(*c*) 5,794 m	(*e*) 9,450 m
(*b*) 27·04 km	(*d*) 33·671 km	

(8) Express as metres, centimetres, and millimetres:

    (*a*) 12·473 m   (*c*) 348·6 cm   (*e*) 2·00714 km

    (*b*) 5·901 m   (*d*) 0·007 km   (*f*) 3,462 mm

(9) Change 0·05 litres into cubic centimetres.

(10) Change 6,400 square centimetres into square metres.

(11) Change 0·5 cubic metres into litres.

(12) How many cubic centimetres of water weigh 125 grammes?

(13) Add together: 4 m 54 cm, 2 m 50 cm, 30·05 m, 45 cm, 0·005 m. Give your answer (*a*) in metres, (*b*) in centimetres.

(14) (*a*) From 3·650 litres take 1·983 litres.

    (*b*) From 3·685 kg take 947 grammes.

(15) Multiply (*a*) 14·75 m (*b*) 3 kg 195 g by 5, 12, and 26.

(16) Divide 42·60 m by (*a*) 24, (*b*) 2·4, (*c*) 0·24.

(17) Calculate:

    (*a*) 55 g + 3·2 kg + 16·75 kg + 0·45 kg

    (*b*) 36 m − 315 cm   (*f*) 46 h 30 min − 3 h 45 min

    (*c*) 0·35 l × 25   (*g*) 25 h 30 min − 125 min

    (*d*) 695 ml ÷ 5   (*h*) 51·85 m ÷ 17

    (*e*) 56½ h ÷ 10   (*i*) the weight of 6,750 cm³ of water

(18) Four lengths, 3·45 m, 2·50 m, 90 cm, and 85 cm long are cut from a 10 metres roll of material. How much of the roll is left?

(19) At the start of a journey a car's tank holds 45·5 litres of petrol. After a run of 265 km the tank holds 20·5 litres. What is the average petrol consumption of the car in kilometres per litre?

(20) Multiply (*a*) 0·765 m by 250 (answer in km)

    (*b*) 441 ml by 8 (answer in litres)

(21) A flagstone has an area of 5,625 cm². Express its area in m². How many similar stones, to the nearest hundred, will be needed to pave an area of 500 m²?

(22) Change (*a*) 50 km/h (kilometres per hour) to m/s (metres per second)

    (*b*) 3 m³/min to litres per second

    (*c*) 200 m²/min to hectares per 8 hours

(23) A tank has a capacity of 2·5 m³. What weight of water will it hold in tonnes, assuming that 1 litre of water weighs 1 kg?

(24) Calais to Barcelona is approximately 1,440 km. A car averages 49·4 km on 4·5 l of petrol. How much petrol would be needed for this journey? What would it cost at 6½p/litre?

(25) A recipe for a cake requires 230 g of flour, 115 g of butter, and 115 g of sugar. What would be the quantities needed to make enough mixture for

(*a*) four such cakes,
(*b*) a cake 1·25 times larger?

(26) Convert a velocity of (*a*) 30 km/h to m/s,
(*b*) 16·6 m/s to km/h.

(27) A particle has a velocity of 0·35 m/s. Find the distance it travels in 4·5 seconds in (*a*) metres, (*b*) millimetres.

(28) A racing car does 60·8 laps of a 5 km racing circuit in exactly 2 hours. Calculate its average speed in (*a*) km/h, (*b*) m/s.

(29) A pump empties a water tank with a capacity of 4 m³ in 16 minutes. Express this rate of flow in litres per minute. What weight of water is removed each second?

(30) The average weight of the passengers and crew of a bus is 66 kg. If there are 32 people aboard the vehicle and the 'all-up' weight of the bus is 12·75 t find the weight of the bus when empty.

5 Money

The change to decimal coinage has, at last, brought us into line with nearly all the other countries in the world. The decimal system has a number of advantages: people from abroad will find our currency easier to understand, calculations are easier to perform, and only two units are needed, pounds and pence.

British decimal currency is based, as was the old system, on the pound sterling, but the pound is now divided into 100 pence.

Although calculations are easier, speed and accuracy only come through practice.

Remember:

(i) Only two symbols are used, £ for pounds and p for pence. These two symbols are *never* used together. The amount of two pounds and sixty-five pence is written as £2·65 (read as 'two pounds sixty-five'). A decimal point is used to separate pounds from pence because the pence are a decimal fraction of a pound, e.g. £2·65 = £2 + £0·65, that is, $\frac{65}{100}$ of £1.

(ii) For amounts written in pence only, two methods can be used:

$$97p \quad \text{or} \quad £0·97$$
$$6p \quad \text{or} \quad £0·06$$

The halfpenny is always shown as a vulgar fraction:

$$3\tfrac{1}{2}p \quad \text{or} \quad £0·03\tfrac{1}{2}$$
$$98\tfrac{1}{2}p \quad \text{or} \quad £0·98\tfrac{1}{2}$$
$$\tfrac{1}{2}p \quad \text{or} \quad £0·00\tfrac{1}{2}$$

Addition and Subtraction

Example 1. (*a*) Add: £4·10½ + £6·08 + £24·95 + £0·76½
(*b*) From £27·50 take £19·75

(*a*)	£	(*b*)	£
	4·10½		27·50
	6·08		− 19·75
	24·95		£ 7·75
	0·76½		
	£35·90		

Work through these examples following the normal rules for decimals.

Example 2.

(a) £2·17 × 26

$$\begin{array}{r} £\ 2·17 \\ \times\ \ 26 \\ \hline 13\ 02 \\ 43\ 40 \\ \hline £\ \overline{56·42} \end{array}$$

(b) £125·70 ÷ 15

$$\begin{array}{r} £8·38 \\ 15\overline{)£125·70} \\ 120 \\ \hline 57 \\ 45 \\ \hline 120 \\ 120 \\ \hline \cdots \end{array}$$

Perform the multiplication and place the 'point' by counting two places from the right.

Follow the normal rules for division of decimals.

Exercise 1

(1) Add:

    (a) £0·87½ + £0·33 + £0·55 + £0·25
    (b) £17·76 + £3·35 + £18·98 + £6·73
    (c) £125·08 + £234·96 + £297·45 + £98·15
    (d) £3·65 + 38p + £2·18 + 63½p

(2) Subtract:

    (a) £37·45 − £28·64
    (b) £124·08 − £67·39
    (c) £1·08 − 87p
    (d) 56p − 39½p
    (e) £49·67 − £0·97

(3) Multiply:

    (a) 76p × 12   (c) £12·20 × 4   (e) £0·61 × 156
    (b) 56p × 52   (d) £14·52 × 24   (f) 96p × 26

(4) Divide:

    (a) £2·76 ÷ 3   (c) 91p ÷ 13   (e) £47·25 ÷ 30
    (b) £16·98 ÷ 12   (d) £132·48 ÷ 36   (f) £87·56 ÷ 156

(5) Express (i) 96p (ii) £2·25 (iii) £4·40 (iv) £0·86 as decimal and vulgar fractions of (*a*) £1 (*b*) £5.

(6) A secretary is paid £546 per annum. What amount will she receive (*a*) each month, (*b*) each week?

(7) A bicycle is priced at £26 cash or 12 instalments of £2·44. How much is saved by paying cash?

(8) A painter is paid £16·94 for a working week of 44 hours. What is his rate of pay per hour?

Foreign Money

Trade with other countries and the growth of foreign travel and holidays abroad make a working knowledge of foreign money systems and the ability to convert from one currency to another an essential skill. Our own decimal currency does not remove the need to convert from foreign, but it does make it easier.

Rates of exchange

Here is a table that gives the exchange rates at the time of writing of a number of foreign currencies; remember that they are all based on a system of decimal coinage. Thus $2·40 means $2\frac{40}{100}$ dollars, or 2 dollars and 40 cents.

FOREIGN EXCHANGE

Country	Rate of Exchange (1970)		
Austria	61·50	Schillings	= £1
Belgium	120·00	Francs	= £1
Canada	2·55	Dollars	= £1
Denmark	18·00	Kroner	= £1
France	13·40	Francs	= £1
Germany (West)	10·30	Marks	= £1
Italy	1,500·00	Lire	= £1
Norway	17·10	Kroner	= £1
Spain	165·00	Pesetas	= £1
Sweden	12·35	Kronor	= £1
Switzerland	10·30	Francs	= £1
U.S.A.	2·40	Dollars	= £1

Conversion

Example 3. A family decide to take a holiday abroad visiting France, Switzerland, and Italy. They estimate the total cost as £160, made up in this way—France £30, Switzerland £45, Italy £85. Calculate the amount of Swiss, French, and Italian currency they will obtain, using the rates of exchange given in the Table.

France	*Switzerland*
£1 = 13·40 francs	£1 = 10·30 francs
∴ £30 = 13·40 francs × 30	∴ £45 = 10·30 francs × 45
= 402 francs	= 463·50 francs

Italy

£1 = 1,500·00 lire

∴ £85 = 1,500·00 lire × 85

= 127,500 lire

Example 4. Compare the value in pence, to the nearest $\frac{1}{2}$p, of a Danish krone and a Swedish krona.

18·00 kroner (Danish) = 100p   12·35 kronor (Swedish) = 100p

$$\therefore 1 \text{ krone} = \frac{100p}{18} \qquad \therefore 1 \text{ krona} = \frac{100p}{12\cdot35}$$

$$= 5\tfrac{1}{2}p \qquad\qquad\qquad = 8p$$

Exercise 2

(1) Find the value to the nearest penny of:

    (*a*) 1 dollar (U.S.A.)   (*d*) 1 franc (France)

    (*b*) 1 dollar (Canada)   (*e*) 1 peseta

    (*c*) 1 franc (Belgium)   (*f*) 1 schilling

(2) Which are the cheaper and by how much:

    (*a*) Nylons in Britain at 42p or in France at 6·50 francs?

    (*b*) Shoes in Britain at £2·50 per pair, or in Italy at 4,540 lire per pair, or Spain at 400 pesetas per pair?

    (*c*) A record from France costing 12·50 francs, or one from America costing 2 dollars?

(3) Change 145·10 schillings into West German marks.

(4) A boy on holiday in Denmark has £5 pocket money which he changes into kroner. At the end of his holiday he has 4·85 kroner left. How much has he spent in Danish money and how much has he left in British money?

(5) A Swiss hotel charges 12 francs a day, to which is added a service charge of 10%. A man starts a holiday with £50, his travelling expenses amount to £7·50; he books for ten days. How much can he spend in francs, apart from his hotel expenses, if he wishes to have £5 left at the end of his holiday?

6 Averages

If the total number of runs scored by a batsman throughout a season is divided by the number of times he has batted, the result will be his **average** score for each innings.

Again, if the heights of a group of people are added together and the result is divided by the number of people in the group then the height obtained will be the **average** or **mean** height of the people in the group. Briefly,

$$\text{average} = \frac{\text{sum of quantities}}{\text{number of quantities}}$$

Example 1. The heights of six people are 1·83 m, 1·6 m, 1·66 m, 1·80 m, 1·58 m, 1·78 m. Calculate the average height of this group.

$$\text{Average height} = \frac{\text{sum of heights}}{\text{number of heights}}$$

$$= \frac{10\cdot26 \text{ m}}{6}$$

$$= 1\cdot71 \text{ metres.}$$

	1·83 m
	1·61 m
	1·66 m
	1·80 m
	1·58 m
	1·78 m
Sum of heights	10·26 m

If

$$\text{average} = \frac{\text{sum of quantities}}{\text{number of quantities}}$$

then

$$\text{sum of quantities} = \text{average} \times \text{number of quantities.}$$

Example 2. A man's average weekly wage for 8 weeks is £15·62½. If he averages £14·25 a week for the first four weeks, what will his average wage be for the last four weeks?

$$\text{Average for 8 weeks} = £15\cdot62\tfrac{1}{2}$$
$$\therefore \text{Total earned} = £15\cdot62\tfrac{1}{2} \times 8$$
$$= £125\cdot00$$

$$\text{Average for first 4 weeks} = £14\cdot25$$
$$\therefore \text{Total for first 4 weeks} = £14\cdot25 \times 4$$
$$= £57\cdot00$$

$$\text{Total earned in second 4 weeks} = £125 - £57$$
$$= £68$$

$$\therefore \text{ Average for second 4 weeks} = £68 \div 4$$
$$= £17$$

Exercise 1

(1) Below is a table of the heights, weights, and ages of 12 boys. Calculate (i) the average height of the group, (ii) the average weight, (iii) the average age to the nearest month.

	Height	Weight	Age
A	1·52 m	47·45 kg	13 yr. 10 m.
B	1·55 m	50·34 kg	14 yr. 2 m.
C	1·725 m	63·95 kg	13 yr. 11 m.
D	1·70 m	60·32 kg	14 yr. 9 m.
E	1·67 m	76·20 kg	14 yr. 7 m.
F	1·57 m	53·05 kg	14 yr. 0 m.
G	1·47 m	43·09 kg	13 yr. 11 m.
H	1·54 m	42·18 kg	13 yr. 10 m.
I	1·65 m	52·62 kg	14 yr. 1 m.
J	1·55 m	50·80 kg	14 yr. 3 m.
K	1·77 m	64·84 kg	14 yr. 8 m.
L	1·725 m	64·40 kg	14 yr. 8 m.

(2) By how much do A, G, and L differ, above or below, from the group averages for height, weight, and age?

(3) The following readings were obtained in an experiment, 345, 341, 343, 335, 340, 344, 337, 345. All the readings were taken in millimetres. Express the average reading in centimetres.

(4) On a housing estate the houses are rented as follows:

> 60 two-bedroom houses at £3·05 per week
> 120 three-bedroomed houses at £4·12½ per week
> 80 four-bedroomed houses at £5·15 per week

Calculate the average rent paid on the estate. Compare this average with the rent paid in each type of house, and say how much it is above or below the average.

(5) In an examination six girls had an average mark of 54, the average of the first five was 51. What is the sixth girl's mark?

(6) In 10 min a car travels 2·6 km, in the next 12 min it travels 10·4 km, and in the next 8 min reaches its destination, a further 10·4 km. What is its average speed in km/h?

(7) A factory used 845 m, 975 m, 868 m, and 898 m of material in 4 consecutive working weeks. Each week is made up of 5 working days. What is the average amount of material used each working day? How much more material will be needed if the order being completed lasts a further 10 working weeks?

(8) Twenty-five litres of petrol at 31p for 5 litres, are mixed with 15 litres at 27p per 5 litres. What is the value of the mixture per litre? (Work to the nearest halfpenny.)

(9) At a sports meeting the 5 fastest times for the 100 metres were 10·9, 11·1, 11·1, 11·2, 11·2 seconds. Work out the average time and use this time to calculate an average speed for the distance in km/h, to the nearest km.

(10) A boy cycles for 8 km at 16 km/h and then stops for 20 minutes. He continues for a further 24 min at 16 km/h, and then stops for 15 min. He finishes his journey by riding 9·6 km in 30 min. The boy's sister sets out at the same time as he does and maintains a steady speed of 14·4 km/h, without stopping, for the same journey. Who finishes the journey first, and by how many minutes?

7 Ratio and Proportion

Ratio

One way of comparing two quantities is to divide one quantity into the other.

If a boy gets 10p pocket money and his elder brother gets 50p, we can say that the younger boy gets $\frac{1}{5}$ as much pocket money as his brother.

This can be expressed as:

$$\frac{\text{Younger boy's money}}{\text{Older boy's money}} = \frac{10p}{50p} = \frac{1}{5}$$

Thus the ratio of the young boy's pocket money to the older boy's pocket money is 1 to 5, or 1:5.

Looking at the problem from the other way, it can be said that the older boy gets 5 times the pocket money of his younger brother.

So

$$\frac{\text{Older boy's money}}{\text{Younger boy's money}} = \frac{50p}{10p} = \frac{5}{1}$$

Thus the ratio of the older boy's pocket money to the younger boy's pocket money is 5:1.

When two quantities are compared by means of a ratio it is essential to establish clearly the *order* in which the comparison is being made.

You will have noticed that a ratio can be expressed as 3:4 or as $\frac{3}{4}$, that is to say as a fraction, and when we deal with ratios it is often more convenient to treat them as fractions. Remember, in order to reduce a ratio to its simplest form both quantities must be expressed in the same units.

Example 1. Express 68·40 kg as a ratio of 114 kg.

$$\text{Ratio} = \frac{68 \cdot 40 \text{ kg}}{114 \text{ kg}}$$

$$= \frac{684}{1140} \qquad \text{Multiply top and bottom by 10.}$$

$$= \frac{3}{5}$$

$$\therefore \text{Ratio} = 3:5 \text{ or } \tfrac{3}{5}$$

Example 2. Divide £45 between two people in the ratio of 4:5.

$$\text{Number of parts} = 4 + 5$$
$$= 9$$
$$\therefore \text{ Each part} = \frac{£45}{9} = £5$$

Then   1st person receives £5 × 4 = £20

and   2nd person receives £5 × 5 = £25

Check: £20 + £25 = £45, the original sum of money.

Ratio expressed as a decimal

Since decimal fractions are convenient to use it is sometimes an advantage to express a ratio as a decimal.

Example 3. In the △ABC (Fig. 1), BC = 5 cm, AB = 6 cm. Express the ratio of the length of side BC to length of side AB as a decimal fraction.

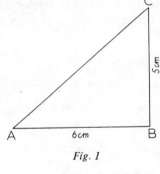

Fig. 1

Convert $\frac{5}{6}$ to decimal

```
       ·8333
    6)50
      48
      ──
       20
       18
       ──
       20
       18
       ──
       20
       18
       ──
        2
       ──
```

$$\text{Ratio} = \frac{\text{BC}}{\text{AB}} = \frac{5 \text{ cm}}{6 \text{ cm}}$$

$$= 0\cdot8333$$

Scale

When a model ship is made it is constructed to scale. For example a model built to a scale of $\frac{1}{30}$ means 10 cm on the model represents 300 cm or 3 m on the actual ship. The expressing of a ratio in the form of '1: something' is very useful; it is used on maps to show the relationship or ratio of a distance on the map to the actual distance on the ground. On a map this ratio is called the Representative Fraction.

47

Example 4. The scale of a map is 2·5 cm to 1 km. What is its Representative Fraction?

$$\text{Scale is } 2{\cdot}5 \text{ cm:} 1 \text{ km}$$

$$\therefore \text{ Ratio} = \frac{2{\cdot}5 \text{ cm}}{1 \text{ km}} = \frac{2{\cdot}5}{1{,}000 \times 100} = \frac{1}{40{,}000}$$

$$\therefore \text{ R.F.} = \frac{1}{40{,}000} \text{ or } 1{:}40{,}000$$

Exercise 1

(1) Simplify the following ratios by expressing them as fractions in their simplest form:

(a) 150 mm:3 m   (c) $\frac{3}{4}:\frac{11}{12}$ (e) 5 m/s:90 km/h
(b) 40 kg:0·16 t   (d) 56p:£2·24

(2) The sides of two squares are 3 cm and 5 cm. What are (a) the ratio of their sides; (b) the ratio of their perimeters; (c) the ratio of their areas?

(3) Divide £140 into two parts in the ratio of 3:4.

(4) Divide £54 into three parts in the ratio of 9:8:1.

(5) The lengths of the sides of a triangle are in the ratio of 3:4:5, its perimeter is 60 cm. Calculate the lengths of its sides.

(6) ABC is a triangle. AB=7·5 cm, AC=12·5 cm and BC=10 cm. Express the ratios (i) $\frac{BC}{AB}$ (ii) $\frac{AC}{AB}$ as decimals.

(7) In a rectangle the ratio of the long side to the short side is 5:3. The perimeter is 1·20 m. What is the length of the long side?

(8) What is the representative fraction of a map drawn to a scale of (a) 10 cm to 1 km, (b) 10 cm to 5 km?

(9) The R.F. of a map is 1:80,000. What is the distance in kilometres between two places that are 112·5 mm apart on the map?

(10) The scale of a map is 5 cm to 1 km. What is the R.F. of the map, and what length on the map will represent 12·5 km?

Proportion

If we take two equal ratios,

$$\frac{3}{6} = \frac{5}{10}$$

it is clear that the relationship between 3 and 6 is the same as the relationship between 5 and 10, i.e.

3 is to 6 as 5 is to 10

in other words, 3, 6 and 5, 10 are in proportion.

Thus when two ratios are equal, the numbers or amounts that make up these ratios are said to be in proportion.

Example 5. Three metres of material cost £2·25. What is the cost of 8 metres?

$$\text{Ratio of Lengths} = \frac{\text{New length}}{\text{Old length}} = \frac{8}{3}$$

But Ratio of Lengths = Ratio of Prices, therefore lengths and prices are in proportion. So

$$\text{price of 8 m} = \frac{8}{\cancel{3}} \text{ of } \cancel{£2·25}^{£0·75}$$
$$\quad\quad\quad\quad\quad\;\; 1$$

$$= £6$$

Example 6. The school flag pole is 9·60 m high. It casts a shadow of 3·20 m when the shadow cast by the cathedral spire is 28 m long. What is the height of the spire?

$$\text{Ratio } \frac{\text{Pole}}{\text{Shadow of Pole}} = \frac{9·60 \text{ m}}{3·20 \text{ m}} = \frac{3}{1}$$

$$\therefore \text{ Height of Spire} = \frac{3}{1} \times 28 \text{ m}$$

$$= 84 \text{ m}$$

Exercise 1 (continued)

(11) A plan is drawn to a scale of $\frac{1}{50}$. What are the actual lengths of dimensions shown on the plan as (a) $2\frac{1}{2}$ cm, (b) 47 mm, (c) 0·85 m, (d) 64·32 mm?

(12) Ten litres of oil weigh 8 kg, a litre of water weighs 1 kg. Express as a ratio the relative density of oil and water.

(13) In a class the ratio of successes to failures in an examination was 9:2. If there were 18 passes, how many pupils failed the examination?

(14) A spring increases in length by 36 mm when carrying a weight of 7·2 kg. What will be the increase in length when the load is 9·2 kg?

(15) The ratio of the salaries of a manager and his deputy is 9:7. If the manager is paid £1,260 per annum, what is the deputy paid?

(16) During a sale a television set is reduced in price from £64 to £48. If all other goods are reduced at the same rate, what will be the sale price of a tape-recorder priced at £32?

(17) A concrete mix is made of cement, sand, and ballast in the ratio of 2:5:8. What weight of each is there in 6 tonnes of concrete?

(18) In a room there are two windows. Both are the same width but one is 2·4 m long and the other 1·5 m long. The smaller window needs 12 m of curtain material. Calculate the length of material needed to curtain the larger window. (Work to the nearest metre.)

(19) At the Motor Show there were 4 times as many saloon cars as convertibles. If there were 335 cars on show, how many were convertibles?

(20) On a tour a driver does 336 km in a day of 7 h driving, and his car uses 27 litres of petrol. Assuming similar road conditions, and the same average speed, calculate the distance he would cover and the amount of petrol that would be used if he drove for 10 h.

8 Percentages

A percentage as a vulgar fraction

A percentage, as you will remember, is really a fraction with a denominator of 100.

'Cent' is short for 'centum' which means 100, so per cent means 'per 100'.

Thus 60 per cent (written as 60%) $= \frac{60}{100}$ and

$$60\% = \frac{60}{100} = \frac{3}{5}$$

$$25\% = \frac{25}{100} = \frac{1}{4}$$

$$50\% = \frac{50}{100} = \frac{1}{2}$$

$$125\% = \frac{125}{100} = 1\frac{1}{4}$$

When a percentage is not easily convertible to a fraction the following method is useful:

Example 1. Convert $22\frac{1}{2}\%$ to a fraction.

$$22\frac{1}{2}\% = \frac{22\frac{1}{2}}{100}$$

$$= \frac{45}{2} \div \frac{100}{1}$$

$$= \frac{\overset{9}{\cancel{45}}}{2} \times \frac{1}{\underset{20}{\cancel{100}}} = \frac{9}{40}$$

A vulgar fraction as a percentage

The process is reversed when converting a fraction to a percentage.

Example 2. Convert $\frac{5}{8}$ to a percentage.

$$\frac{5}{\underset{2}{8}} \text{ of } \frac{\overset{25}{\cancel{100}}}{1} = \frac{125}{2} = 62\frac{1}{2}\%$$

Remember

To convert a percentage to a fraction divide by 100.
To convert a fraction to a percentage multiply by 100.

A decimal fraction as a percentage

Example 3. Express 0·875 as a percentage.

Multiply by 100 to change decimal fraction to a percentage.

$$0·875 \times 100 = 87·5\%$$

Quantities as a percentage

Example 4. Express £5·50 as a percentage of £200.

Percentage is

$$\frac{£5·50}{\underset{2}{£200}} \times \overset{1}{\cancel{100}}$$

$$= \frac{5·5}{2} = 2\frac{3}{4}\%$$

Percentages of quantities and amounts

Example 5. Find $12\frac{1}{2}\%$ of £5.

$$\frac{12\frac{1}{2}}{100} \text{ of } £5$$

$$= \frac{1}{8} \times £5$$

$$= \frac{500\text{p}}{8} = 62\frac{1}{2}\text{p}$$

Example 6. Find $6\frac{1}{4}\%$ of 88 kg.

$$\frac{6\frac{1}{4}}{100} \text{ of } \frac{88}{1}$$

$$\frac{\overset{1}{\cancel{25}}}{\underset{\underset{2}{16}}{\cancel{400}}} \times \frac{\overset{11}{\cancel{88}}}{1} = \frac{11}{2} = 5 \cdot 5 \text{ kg}$$
$$= 5 \text{ kg } 500 \text{ g}$$

Example 7. Find the whole amount if $15\% = 90\text{p}$.

$$15\% = 90\text{p}$$

$$\therefore 100\% = \cancel{90}\text{p} \times \frac{100}{\cancel{15}}$$

$$= 600\text{p}$$
$$= £6$$

Percentage changes

If a number is increased by 10% then the number is made larger by $\frac{10}{100}$ of itself. Thus the ratio of the new number to the old number is $\frac{110}{100}$, so the new number is obtained by multiplying the old number by $\frac{110}{100}$.

Example 8. Increase 180 by 10%.
$$100\% = 180$$
Then $$110\% = 18\cancel{0} \times \frac{11\cancel{0}}{10\cancel{0}} = 198$$

Example 9. Decrease 240 by $12\frac{1}{2}\%$.
$$100\% = 240$$
Then $$87\frac{1}{2}\% = 2\cancel{40} \times \frac{\overset{\overset{7}{\cancel{87\frac{1}{2}}}}{\cancel{87\frac{1}{2}}}}{\underset{\underset{1}{\cancel{8}}}{\cancel{100}}} = 210$$

Exercise 1

(1) Convert the following percentages to vulgar fractions:

    (*a*) 45% (*d*) 130% (*g*) $12\frac{1}{2}\%$ (*j*) $8\frac{1}{4}\%$
    (*b*) 70% (*e*) 11% (*h*) $2\frac{1}{2}\%$ (*k*) $66\frac{2}{3}\%$
    (*c*) 95% (*f*) 57% (*i*) $33\frac{1}{3}\%$ (*l*) $3\frac{3}{4}\%$

(2) Convert the following fractions to percentages:

    (*a*) $\frac{3}{4}$ (*d*) $\frac{1}{8}$ (*g*) $2\frac{1}{3}$ (*j*) $0 \cdot 85$
    (*b*) $\frac{7}{10}$ (*e*) $\frac{1}{12}$ (*h*) $4\frac{5}{8}$ (*k*) $0 \cdot 625$
    (*c*) $\frac{11}{50}$ (*f*) $2\frac{1}{2}$ (*i*) $0 \cdot 6$ (*l*) $3 \cdot 125$

(3) What percentage is:

    (*a*) £7 of £35?   (*e*) 250 g of 1 kg?

    (*b*) £7·50 of £150?   (*f*) 300 ml of 5 litres?

    (*c*) $2\frac{1}{2}$p of £1?   (*g*) 248 g of 1·24 kg?

    (*d*) 100 cm of 12 m?   (*h*) £1·25 of £5?

(4) Find:

    (*a*) $12\frac{1}{2}\%$ of £32·40   (*d*) $33\frac{1}{3}\%$ of 3·3 kg

    (*b*) $2\frac{1}{2}\%$ of £78   (*e*) 8% of 24 m

    (*c*) $6\frac{1}{4}\%$ of £9·50   (*f*) $33\frac{1}{3}\%$ of £76·17

(5) Of what amount is:

    (*a*) £1·50, 75%?   (*c*) 405, 81%?   (*e*) £192, 6%?

    (*b*) 1200 m, 60%?   (*d*) 75p, 40%?

(6) Increase:

    (*a*) 300 by 15%   (*c*) 500 g by $2\frac{1}{2}\%$

    (*b*) £72 by 10%   (*d*) £50 by 4·2%

(7) Decrease:

    (*a*) 500 by 3%   (*c*) £75 by 8%

    (*b*) 416 by $12\frac{1}{2}\%$ (*d*) £67 by 15%

 (8) The population of a town increases from 15,000 to 16,750. What is the increase per cent?

 (9) A secretary's wages are £9·50 per week; she receives a rise of 5%. What is her new wage?

(10) A brick weighing 4 kg absorbs 750 g of water. What is the percentage increase in the weight of the brick?

(11) The tax paid on a suitcase was 8% of its value. If the tax paid was 36p, find the value of the case.

(12) If 17% of a number is 85, calculate 7% of it.

(13) From London to Dover is 104 km. Dover to Calais across the channel is 35 km, from Calais to Barcelona by road is 1,440 km. What percentage of the journey from London to Barcelona is a sea trip?

(14) At an election there were two candidates. The candidate elected gained 56% of the total votes cast, and he had 192 more votes than his opponent. What was the total number of votes cast?

Percentage profit and loss

When a number of things are bought and sold, the profit or loss on the transaction is usually expressed as a percentage of the **cost price**. This is done so that the profit or loss margins can be more easily compared.

The calculation of profit or loss as a percentage is simply a case of expressing the difference between the **cost price** and the **selling price** as a fraction of the cost price and then converting this fraction to a percentage.

Thus: profit or loss per cent

$$= \frac{\text{Difference of S.P. and C.P.}}{\text{C.P.}} \times \frac{100}{1}$$

If the selling price is greater than the cost price, then a percentage **profit** is shown. If the selling price is less than the cost price, then a percentage **loss** is shown.

Example 1. A bicycle is bought for £18 and is sold for £19·80. Calculate the profit as a percentage of the cost price.

Actual Profit is £19·80 − £18 = £1·80

$$\therefore \% \text{ Profit} = \frac{\text{Profit}}{\text{C.P}} \times \frac{100}{1}$$

$$= \frac{\overset{1}{\cancel{£1·80}}}{\underset{10}{\cancel{£18}}} \quad \frac{\overset{10}{\cancel{100}}}{1}$$

$$= 10\%$$

Example 2. A book is bought for $62\frac{1}{2}$p and sold for 50p. What is the loss per cent?

Actual Loss = $62\frac{1}{2}$p − 50p = $12\frac{1}{2}$p

$$\therefore \text{ Loss } \% = \frac{\text{Loss}}{\text{C.P.}} \times \frac{100}{1}$$

$$\frac{12\frac{1}{2}\text{p}}{62\frac{1}{2}\text{p}} \times \frac{100}{1}$$

$$= \frac{1}{\cancel{5}} \times \frac{\overset{20}{\cancel{100}}}{1} = 20\%$$

Example 3. If the Cost Price is 36p and the profit is $12\frac{1}{2}\%$, calculate the Selling Price.

$$\text{Profit} = 12\frac{1}{2}\% \text{ of } 36p$$

$$= \frac{12\frac{1}{2}}{100} \text{ of } 36p$$

$$= \frac{\overset{1}{\cancel{25}}}{\underset{8}{\cancel{200}}} \text{ of } \overset{4\frac{1}{2}p}{\cancel{36}p}$$

$$\underset{1}{}$$

$$= 4\frac{1}{2}p$$

$$\therefore \text{ Selling price} = 36p + 4\frac{1}{2}p$$

$$= 40\frac{1}{2}p$$

Another way of working this example is as follows:

Selling Price (S.P.) = Cost Price (C.P.) increased by 12%

$$\therefore \text{ S.P.} = \text{C.P.} \times \frac{112\frac{1}{2}}{100}$$

$$= \overset{4\frac{1}{2}p}{\cancel{36}p} \times \frac{\overset{9}{112\frac{1}{2}}}{\underset{8}{\cancel{100}}}$$

$$\underset{1}{}$$

$$= 40\frac{1}{2}p$$

Example 4. The Selling Price is £25 and the profit margin is 15%, calculate the Cost Price.

If Profit is 15%

$$\therefore \text{ Cost Price} = \frac{100}{115} \text{ of Selling Price}$$

$$= \frac{100}{\underset{23}{\cancel{115}}} \times £\frac{\overset{5}{\cancel{25}}}{1}$$

$$= £\frac{500}{23} = £21\frac{17}{23}$$

$$= £21 \cdot 74 \text{ to nearest penny}$$

Exercise 2

(1) Calculate the profit or loss on the following:

    (*a*) C.P. 50p, S.P. 62½p   (*d*) C.P. 80p, S.P. 90p

    (*b*) C.P. £1, S.P. £1·25   (*e*) C.P. £15, S.P. £18·75

    (*c*) C.P. 22½p, S.P. 18½p   (*f*) C.P. £1·80, S.P. £1·65

(2) Apples bought at 9p per kg are sold at 13½p per kg. What is the profit per cent on (*a*) 1 kg, (*b*) 50 kg?

(3) The Cost Price of a cooker is £63 and it is sold for £75. Calculate the percentage profit on (*a*) the Cost Price, (*b*) the Selling Price.

(4) A man paid £850 for a car and later sold it for £725. Calculate the loss per cent to two decimal places.

(5) A dress manufacturer sells to a wholesaler, who sells to a shop-keeper, who in turn sells to the public. A dress costs £1·80 to make. Calculate the price at which the dress will be sold to the public if the manufacturer's profit is 12½%, the wholesaler's 20%, and the shopkeeper's 33⅓%.

(6) When the dry ingredients of concrete are mixed with water their volume decreases by 35%. What volume of dry mix will be needed to fill a trench requiring 240 m³ of concrete?

(7) A shopkeeper buys goods valued at £200. He is given a trade discount of 25%. He pays this bill promptly and obtains a further 2½% discount. How much does he pay for the goods and what will his percentage profit be if he sells all the goods?

(8) A bottle of perfume costs 20 francs in Paris and import duty is paid on it at the rate of 25% of the cost price. If 1 franc = 8½p what is the total amount paid for the perfume in English money?

(9) Wine which costs 2·7 francs per litre in France increases in price by 33⅓% when it is sold in England. Calculate its price per litre in England. Take £1 = 12 francs.

(10) A builder estimates that to build a garage will cost him £150 for labour and £120 for materials. To these costs he adds 15% as his profit and tenders this amount for the job. His costs increase, however, by 7½%. Work out his actual profit and express it as a percentage of costs.

9 Interest

Simple Interest

When we pay money into a bank we are, in effect, lending our savings to the bank, and the bank is prepared to pay us for the loan of our money. Similarly, if we borrow money from a bank we, in turn, are expected to pay the bank for the loan. This payment is over and above any money we may lend or borrow, just as we pay rent for the use of a house, so we pay 'rent' for the use of a sum of money. The 'rent' we pay for the use of money is called **interest**.

Interest is always expressed as a percentage. For example, the National Savings Bank pays interest at the rate of $2\frac{1}{2}\%$ per annum on money deposited. You will remember that $2\frac{1}{2}\%$ means '$2\frac{1}{2}$ for every hundred' and 'per annum' means for each year. Thus, interest at the rate of $2\frac{1}{2}\%$ per annum means that for every £100 deposited or lent to the bank for a whole year, £2·50 will be paid in interest, that is to say, $\frac{2\frac{1}{2}}{100}$ or $\frac{1}{40}$ of £100 will be paid in interest. Also £200 at $2\frac{1}{2}\%$ p.a. means that at the end of a year $\frac{2\frac{1}{2}}{100}$ or $\frac{1}{40}$ of £200, or £5 will be paid in interest. Further, £200 at $2\frac{1}{2}\%$ p.a. will have earned £15 in interest at the end of 3 years.

Example 1. Find the Simple Interest on £240 at 4% for 3 years.

$$\text{Rate of interest} = 4\% = \frac{4}{100}$$

Thus $\qquad$ Simple Interest for 1 year $= \frac{4}{100}$ of £240

and $\qquad$ Simple Interest for 3 years $= \frac{4}{100}$ of £240 × 3

$$= £\frac{\overset{2}{\cancel{4}} \times 240 \times 3}{\underset{5}{\cancel{100}}}$$

$$= £\frac{144}{5} = £28\frac{4}{5}$$

$$= £28·80$$

58

The money that is put in the bank or is borrowed is called the **principal**. In this example it is £240.

Thus the calculation of Simple Interest can be expressed as

$$\frac{\text{Principal} \times \text{Rate per cent} \times \text{Time in Years}}{100}$$

or
$$\text{S.I.} = \frac{P \times R \times T}{100}$$

where P = Principal R = Rate per cent T = Time in years

Example 2. Find the simple interest on £125 at $5\frac{1}{2}\%$ for 2 yr. 6 mth.

$$\text{S.I.} = \frac{P \times R \times T}{100}$$

$$= £\frac{125 \times 5\frac{1}{2} \times 2\frac{1}{2}}{100}$$

$$= £\frac{\overset{5}{\cancel{125}}}{1} \times \frac{11}{2} \times \frac{5}{2} \times \frac{1}{\underset{4}{\cancel{100}}}$$

$$= £\frac{275}{16} = £17\frac{3}{16}$$

$$= £17 \cdot 18 \text{ to nearest penny}$$

In the formula,

$$\text{Interest } (I) = \frac{P \times R \times T}{100}$$

if any three of the values are known, then the fourth can be found by substitution and changing the subject of the formula. Thus:

if
$$I = \frac{PRT}{100}$$

then
$$R = I \div \frac{PT}{100}$$

$$= \frac{100I}{PT}$$

and
$$P = \frac{100I}{RT}$$

also
$$T = \frac{100I}{PR}$$

Example 3. The Simple Interest on £225 for $2\frac{1}{2}$ years is £25·31. Find the rate per cent.

$$I = \frac{PRT}{100}$$

$$\therefore R = \frac{100I}{PT}$$

$$= \frac{100 \times £25 \cdot 31}{£225 \times 2\frac{1}{2} \text{ yr.}}$$

$$= \frac{£2,531}{£562 \cdot 5}$$

$$= 4\frac{1}{2}\% \text{ to nearest } \frac{1}{2}\%$$

When Interest is added to the Principal the result is called the Amount. Thus £200 + £15 interest amounts to £215.

Example 4. What sum of money will amount to £428 in 2 years at $2\frac{1}{2}\%$ Simple Interest? (Work to the nearest penny.)

$$\text{Interest} = \text{Amount} - \text{Principal} \quad \text{or} \quad A - P$$

$$P = \frac{100I}{RT}$$

$$\therefore P = \frac{100(A - P)}{RT}$$

By substitution $$P = \frac{100(428 - P)}{2\frac{1}{2} \times 2}$$

$$P = \frac{42,800 - 100P}{5}$$

By cross multiplication $5P = 42,800 - 100P$

$$\therefore 5P + 100P = 42,800$$

$$105P = 42,800$$

$$P = \frac{42,800}{105}$$

$$= £407 \frac{13}{21}$$

Principal = £407·62 to nearest penny

Exercise 1

(1) Find the Simple Interest on:

    (*a*) £350 for 3 yr. at 5%   (*b*) £225 for 2 yr. at $6\frac{1}{2}\%$

           (*c*) £140 for 1 yr. 6 mth. at $2\frac{1}{2}\%$

(2) Find, to the nearest penny, the Simple Interest on:

    (*a*) £96 for 3 mth. at 7%

    (*b*) £35 for 9 mth. at 6½%

    (*c*) £216 for 2 yr. 2 mth. at 5½%

(3) What rate per cent is being paid if the Simple Interest for 3 yr. on £450 is £81?

(4) In what length of time will the Simple Interest on £160 at 2½% amount to £2?

(5) To obtain an income of £1 per week, how much money must be invested at an interest rate of 3½% per annum? (Work to the nearest £1.)

(6) £250 was invested at 7% on 1 January, on 1 October the rate of interest dropped to 5½%. What will be the total amount of Simple Interest for the whole year?

Compound Interest

When money is deposited in a Savings Bank the interest is not usually paid out at the end of each year, it is simply added on to the Principal. For example, £100 deposited in a Savings Bank at 2½% Interest, at the end of the year will have earned £2·50 in interest so that the Principal becomes £100 + £2·50 = £102·50. Interest for the second year will be 2½% of £102·50 = £2·56, and the Principal becomes £102·50 + £2·56 = £105·06. Thus Interest for the third year will be 2½% of £105·06. Interest calculated in this way is called Compound Interest.

Example 1. Calculate the Interest and the Amount of £250 at 5% p.a. Compound Interest for 3 years.

$$\text{Principal 1st year} \qquad\qquad = \text{£250}$$

$$\text{Interest 1st year} \quad = \frac{\text{£250}}{100} \times 5$$

$$= \text{£2·50} \times 5 \quad = \quad \text{£12·50}$$

$$\text{Principal 2nd year} \qquad\qquad = \text{£262·50}$$

$$\text{Interest 2nd year} \quad = \frac{\text{£262·50}}{100} \times 5$$

$$= \text{£2·625} \times 5 \quad = \quad \text{£13·12}\tfrac{1}{2}$$

$$\text{Principal 3rd year} = £275 \cdot 62\tfrac{1}{2}$$
$$\text{Interest 3rd year} = \frac{£275 \cdot 625}{100} \times 5$$
$$= £2 \cdot 756 \times 5 = £13 \cdot 78$$
$$\text{Amount at end of 3rd year} = £289 \cdot 40\tfrac{1}{2}$$
$$\text{Compound Interest} = £39 \cdot 40\tfrac{1}{2}$$

Compound Interest is often calculated half-yearly. The calculation is done in the usual way except that for half-yearly periods the percentage increase for the half-period is half the percentage per annum, i.e. 5% p.a. becomes $2\tfrac{1}{2}$% for each half-year period.

Exercise 2

Find the amount and the Compound Interest, to the nearest penny, of:

(1) £450 for 3 yr. at 5%

(2) £240 for 2 yr. at $12\tfrac{1}{2}$%

(3) £1,500 for 3 yr. at 3%

(4) £695 for 2 yr. at 4%

(5) £2,250 for 4 yr. at $2\tfrac{1}{2}$%

(6) £220 for $1\tfrac{1}{2}$ yr. at $3\tfrac{1}{2}$%

(7) £1,000 for $2\tfrac{1}{2}$ yr. at 5%

(8) £40 for 5 yr. at 3%

(9) £30 for $3\tfrac{1}{2}$ yr. at $2\tfrac{1}{2}$%

(10) £1,000 for 4 yr. at 1%

The Compound Interest Table

Calculating Compound Interest is made easier by the use of the table shown below. It gives the amount that £1 will become in from 1 to 12 years at various rates of interest per cent per annum, expressed as a decimal correct to 5 places.

Year	$2\tfrac{1}{2}$%	3%	$3\tfrac{1}{2}$%	4%	$4\tfrac{1}{2}$%	5%	6%
1	1·02500	1·03000	1·03500	1·04000	1·04500	1·05000	1·06000
2	1·05063	1·06090	1·07123	1·08160	1·09203	1·10250	1·12360
3	1·07689	1·09273	1·10872	1·12486	1·14117	1·15763	1·19102
4	1·10381	1·12551	1·14752	1·16986	1·19252	1·21551	1·26248
5	1·13141	1·15927	1·18769	1·21665	1·24618	1·27628	1·33823
6	1·15969	1·19405	1·22926	1·26532	1·30226	1·34010	1·41852
7	1·18869	1·22987	1·27228	1·21593	1·36086	1·40710	1·50363
8	1·21840	1·26677	1·31681	1·36857	1·42210	1·47746	1·59385
9	1·24886	1·30477	1·36290	1·42331	1·48610	1·55133	1·68948
10	1·28008	1·34392	1·41060	1·48024	1·55297	1·62889	1·79085
11	1·31209	1·38423	1·45997	1·53945	1·62285	1·71034	1·89630
12	1·34489	1·42576	1·51107	1·60103	1·69588	1·79586	2·01220

Example 3. Calculate the Amount and Compound Interest of £280 for 7 years at 3% p.a. (Work to the nearest penny.)

From the table

$$£1 \text{ in 7 years at } 3\% = £1\cdot22987 \approx £1\cdot23$$
$$\therefore £280 \text{ in 7 years at } 3\% = £1\cdot22987 \times 280$$
$$= £344\cdot3636 \approx £344\cdot36$$

Amount £344·36:   Interest £64·36

This table can be extended to cover longer periods than 12 years, e.g.

£1 at 4% for 21 years is $1\cdot60103 \times 1\cdot42331 = 2\cdot279 \times £1 \approx £2\cdot28$.

When the interest is calculated for half-yearly periods, the table is used by halving the percentage and doubling the number of years; so, 6% for 4 years paid half-yearly becomes 3% for 8 years.

The Compound Interest formula

£1 at 3% Compound Interest in 1 year amounts to

$$£\frac{100+3}{100} = £\frac{103}{100} = £1\cdot03$$

£1 at 3% Compound Interest in 2 years amounts to

$$£1\cdot03\left(\frac{100+3}{100}\right) = £1\cdot03 \times 1\cdot03 = £(1\cdot03)^2$$

$\therefore$ £1 at r% Compound Interest in n years amounts to

$$£\left(\frac{100+r}{100}\right)^n$$

Hence £x at r% Compound Interest in n years amounts to

$$£x\left(\frac{100+r}{100}\right)^n$$

So   Amount $(A) = x\left(\dfrac{100+r}{100}\right)^n$

where r = rate %, n = number of years, and x = Principal.

This formula for the calculation of Compound Interest should be used with logarithms as this greatly simplifies the calculation; the result, however, is a little less accurate than when the table is used.

Example 4. Find the Amount of £845 at 4% for 6 years.

$$A = £x \left(\frac{100+r}{100}\right)^n$$

$$= £845 \left(\frac{100+4}{100}\right)^6$$

$$= £845 \left(\frac{104}{100}\right)^6$$

$$= £845 (1·04)^6$$

Amount = £1,069

Interest = £1,069 − £845 = £224

No.	log.
1·04	0·0170
	×6
	0·1020
845	2·9269
1069	3·0289

Exercise 3

(1) Find the Amount of £250 for 4 yr. at $2\frac{1}{2}$% using, (*a*) the arithmetical method, (*b*) the table, (*c*) the formula.

(2) Use the formula to find the Amount at Compound Interest of £5 at $2\frac{1}{2}$% for 10 yr.

(3) Using the formula calculate the Amount and the Compound Interest, to the nearest penny of:
 (*a*) £325 for 4 yr. at 5%
 (*b*) £165 for 5 yr. at 6%
 (*c*) £420 for 3 yr. at 4%

(4) Use the formula to calculate, to the nearest £1, the Compound Interest on:
 (*a*) £300 for 2 yr. at 5% payable half-yearly.
 (*b*) £420 for 3 yr. at 4% payable half-yearly.

(5) £100 is invested for a girl the day she is born. What will it amount to, if 3% Compound Interest is allowed, by her 18th birthday?

10 Area and Volume

Areas

As we look about us we see surfaces, floors, ceilings, walls, roads, roofs, fields; some of these surfaces are simple shapes, others are extremely complicated. The complicated shapes can be divided into a number of simple shapes. If, then, we learn about the simple shapes we will be in a position to handle the more complex ones.

Figures 2, 3, and 4 show three simple shapes that you will have seen before; they are **quadrilaterals**, that is to say, four-sided figures. The methods for finding their **areas** and **perimeters** (distance around the figure) are revised in order to refresh your memory.

Area of a rectangle

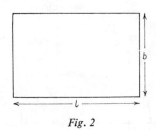

Fig. 2

$$\text{area of rectangle} = \text{length} \times \text{breadth}$$
$$\therefore A = l \times b = lb$$

If
$$A = lb$$

then
$$l = \frac{A}{b}$$

and
$$b = \frac{A}{l}$$

$$\text{perimeter} = l + b + l + b$$
$$= 2l + 2b$$
$$= 2(l + b)$$

Example 1. A rectangular yard is 15 m wide and 22·5 m long (see Fig. 3). What area of paving will be required to cover it, and what is the length of the fence that surrounds it?

65

Area of yard $= lb$
$$= 22 \cdot 5 \times 15$$
$$= 337 \cdot 5 \text{ m}^2$$

Perimeter of yard $= 2(l+b)$
$$= 2(22 \cdot 5 + 15)$$
$$= 2 \times 37 \cdot 5$$
$$= 75 \text{ m}$$

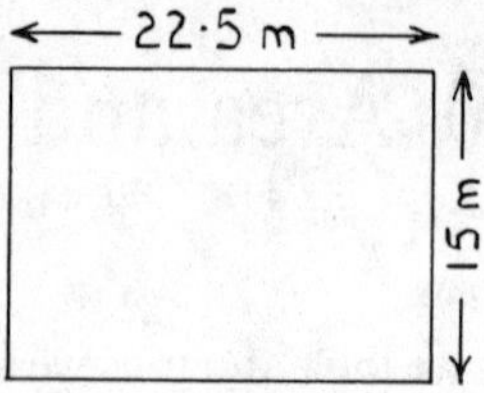

←——— 22·5 m ———→

15 m

Fig. 3

Example 2. The area of a rectangle is 16·5 cm², its width is 2·75 cm. Find its length.

$$\text{Area} = lb$$
$$\therefore l = \frac{A}{b}$$
$$= \frac{16 \cdot 5}{2 \cdot 75}$$
$$= 6 \text{ cm}$$

Area of a parallelogram

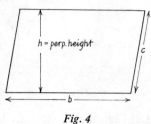

Fig. 4

area of parallelogram = base × perp. ht.

$$\therefore A = bh \quad \text{also} \quad b = \frac{A}{h} \quad \text{and} \quad h = \frac{A}{b}$$

The perimeter is the distance *round* the figure, so

$$\text{perimeter} = 2(b+c)$$

Example 3. Find the area of a parallelogram with a base of 0·6875 m and a perpendicular height of 24 cm.

area of parallelogram $= bh$

Change to same units
$$= 0 \cdot 6875 \text{ m} \times 24 \text{ cm}$$
$$= 0 \cdot 6875 \text{ m} \times 0 \cdot 24 \text{ m}$$
$$= 0 \cdot 165 \text{ m}^2$$

Area of a trapezium

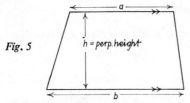

Fig. 5

You will remember that a trapezium (Fig. 5) is a quadrilateral with only two sides parallel.

$$\text{area of trapezium} = \tfrac{1}{2}\text{ sum of parallel sides} \times \text{perp. ht.}$$

a and b are parallel sides

$$\therefore A = \tfrac{1}{2}(a+b)h$$

and

$$h = \frac{A}{\tfrac{1}{2}(a+b)} = \frac{2A}{a+b}$$

Since the four sides of a trapezium are all different lengths then the perimeter is found by simply adding together the lengths of the sides.

Example 4. In the trapezium ABCD, AB is parallel to CD and AB = 9·4 cm, CD = 15·4 cm. The distance between AB and CD is 5·8 cm.

$$\begin{aligned}
\text{area of trapezium ABCD} &= \tfrac{1}{2}(AB+CD)h \\
&= \tfrac{1}{2}(9\cdot4+15\cdot4)5\cdot8 \\
&= \frac{1}{\underset{1}{2}} \times \underset{1}{\overset{12\cdot4}{24\cdot8}} \times 5\cdot8 \\
&= 71\cdot92 \text{ cm}^2
\end{aligned}$$

Area of a triangle

Another common shape is the triangle (see Fig. 6) which is, of course, a three-sided plane figure.

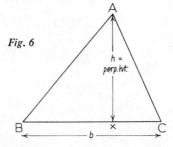

Fig. 6

The method of finding the area of a triangle is similar to that for finding the area of a parallelogram.

$$\text{area of triangle} = \tfrac{1}{2} \text{ base} \times \text{perp. ht.}$$

$$\therefore A = \frac{bh}{2}$$

and

$$b = \frac{2A}{h}, \quad h = \frac{2A}{b}$$

Example 5. Find the area of triangle ABC with BC=8·75 cm and AX=4 cm.

$$\text{area of triangle} = \frac{bh}{2}$$

$$= \frac{8 \cdot 75 \times \overset{2}{\cancel{4}}}{\underset{1}{\cancel{2}}}$$

$$= 17 \cdot 5 \text{ cm}^2$$

When the three sides of a triangle are known its area can be calculated by using this formula,

$$\text{area} = \sqrt{s(s-a)(s-b)(s-c)}$$

where *a*, *b*, and *c* are the lengths of the three sides, and *s* is the semi-perimeter, that is, half the perimeter, of the triangle, or

$$s = \frac{a+b+c}{2}$$

Example 6. A triangle has sides of 4·5 cm, 2·3 cm, and 3·7 cm. Calculate its area.

$$\text{area} = \sqrt{s(s-a)(s-b)(s-c)}$$

but $s = \dfrac{a+b+c}{2}$

$$= \sqrt{5 \cdot 25(5 \cdot 25 - 4 \cdot 5)(5 \cdot 25 - 2 \cdot 3)(5 \cdot 25 - 3 \cdot 7)}$$

$$= \frac{4 \cdot 5 + 2 \cdot 3 + 3 \cdot 7}{2}$$

$$= \sqrt{5 \cdot 25 \times 0 \cdot 75 \times 2 \cdot 95 \times 1 \cdot 55}$$

$$= \frac{10 \cdot 5}{2}$$

$$= \sqrt{18 \cdot 004}$$

$$s = 5 \cdot 25$$

$$A = 4 \cdot 24 \text{ cm}^2$$

Exercise 1

(1) In the following table each figure is a rectangle. Calculate the missing dimensions.

	Length	Breadth	Area	Perimeter
(*a*)	9 cm	5·5 cm		
(*b*)		8·75 cm	175 cm²	
(*c*)	4·75 m	2·5 m		
(*d*)		15 cm		80 cm
(*e*)	9·5 m			25·5 m
(*f*)	2·5 m		4·25 m²	

(2) Fill in the blank spaces in this table:

	Shape	Base	Height	Area
(*a*)	Parallelogram	0·3 m	0·06 m	
(*b*)	Triangle	14·8 cm	9 cm	
(*c*)	Parallelogram		3·75 cm	9·375 cm²
(*d*)	Triangle	0·5 m		0·625 m²
(*e*)	Triangle	4·4 cm		16·06 cm²

(3) In a trapezium the parallel sides are 9 cm and 3·5 cm respectively. The distance between them is 4 cm. Find the area of the trapezium.

(4) The area of a trapezium is 16·875 m², the parallel sides are 2·5 m and 1·25 m. Find the perpendicular height between the parallel sides.

(5) Find the area of these figures (Fig. 7). In (ii) and (iii) find the area of the shaded portion.

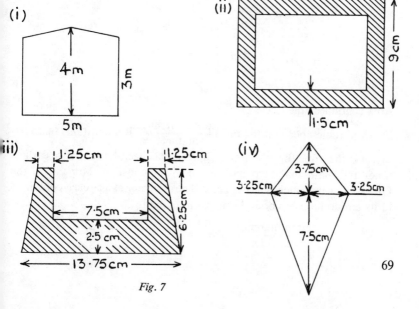

Fig. 7

(6) Find the area of a triangle with sides of 2·1 m, 1·8 m, and 0·9 m.

(7) A rectangular metal sheet is 75 cm by 25 cm. When heated its area increases by $2\frac{1}{2}\%$. What will be the area of the plate when hot?

(8) A room is 5 m wide by 6 m long and 3 m high. Calculate the total surface area of the walls. If the windows, door, and fireplace make up 20% of the wall area, how much paint will be needed to give the walls two coats of paint if a litre of paint covers 18 m²?

(9) Calculate the area of the shaded part of Fig. 8.

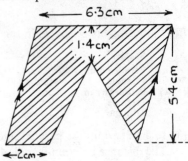

Fig. 8

(10) Find the area of Fig. 9.

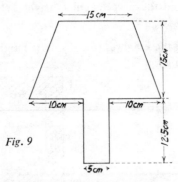

Fig. 9

Area continued: the circle

You will remember that the ratio $\dfrac{\text{circumference}}{\text{diameter}}$ is a constant, that is to say, it is the same for any circle. This fact has been known since earliest times and mathematicians have given to the constant the name of the Greek letter pi, which is written as π. The diameter of a circle is contained in its circumference about $3\frac{1}{7}$ times, thus the ratio

$$\frac{\text{circumference}}{\text{diameter}} \text{ (or } \pi) = 3\frac{1}{7} = \frac{22}{7} = 3\cdot142$$

Fig. 10

Circumference of a circle

Since
$$\pi = \frac{\text{circumference}}{\text{diameter}}$$

then   circumference $= \pi \times$ diameter

or $c = \pi d$

also $\text{diameter} = \dfrac{\text{circumference}}{\pi}$

or $d = \dfrac{c}{\pi}$

since   diameter $= 2 \times$ radius

then $\text{radius} = \dfrac{\text{circumference}}{2 \times \pi}$

or $r = \dfrac{c}{2\pi}$

Example 1. What is the circumference of a wheel of diameter 28 cm?

$$\text{circumference} = \pi d$$

$$= \frac{22}{\overset{}{7}_1} \times \frac{\overset{4}{28}}{1}$$

$$= 88 \text{ cm}$$

Remember, since diameter $= 2 \times$ radius then $\pi d = 2\pi r$.

Example 2. The circumference of a circle is 133·45 cm. Calculate its radius, taking $\pi = 3·14$

$$\text{diameter} = \frac{c}{\pi}$$

$$= \frac{133·45}{3·14}$$

$$= 42·5 \text{ cm}$$

$$\text{radius} = \tfrac{1}{2} \text{ diameter} \quad \therefore \text{ radius} = \frac{42·5}{2} = 21·25 \text{ cm}$$

Sectors of a circle

A circle can be divided into sectors and the angle at the centre in a sector can be used to describe the sector as a fraction of the whole circle.

Thus a semicircle (see Fig. 11) has an angle of 180° at the centre, so a semicircle is $\frac{180}{360} = \frac{1}{2}$ of the whole circle.

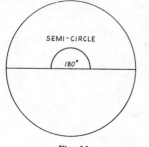

Fig. 11

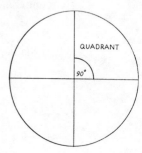

Fig. 12

Again a quadrant (see Fig. 12) has an angle of 90° at the centre, so a quadrant is $\frac{90}{360} = \frac{1}{4}$ of the whole circle.

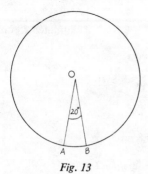

Fig. 13

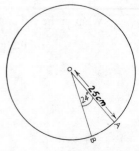

Fig. 14

A sector AOB (see Fig. 13) that has an angle of 20° at O, the centre of the circle, is $\frac{20}{360} = \frac{1}{18}$ of the whole circle and the arc AB will be $\frac{1}{18}$ of the circumference of the circle.

Example. In the circle ABC (Fig. 14), O is the centre of the circle and AOB is a sector with angle AOB=24°. Calculate the length of the arc AB if the radius of the circle is $2\frac{1}{2}$ cm.

$$\text{circumference} = \pi d$$
$$d = 2 \times r = 5 \text{ cm}$$
$$\therefore \pi d = \frac{22}{7} \times \frac{5}{1}$$
$$= \frac{110}{7} \text{ cm}$$

but
$$\text{sector AOB} = \frac{24}{360} = \frac{1}{15}$$
$$\therefore AB = \frac{1}{15} \text{ of circumference of circle}$$
$$= \frac{1}{15} \text{ of } \frac{110}{7} \text{ cm}$$
$$= \frac{22}{21} = 1\frac{1}{21} \text{ cm} = 1.05 \text{ cm}$$

Area of a circle

Draw any circle ABCD with centre O and radius$=r$. Divide into 4 quadrants, by drawing diameters AC and BD at right angles.

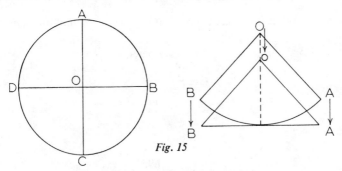

Fig. 15

In the quadrant AOB (see Fig. 15) the length of the arc
$$AB = \frac{\text{circumference}}{4} = \frac{\pi d}{4}$$

73

but
$$\text{diameter} = 2r$$

$$\therefore \text{ AB} = \frac{\pi \times \overset{1}{2}r}{\underset{2}{4}}$$

$$= \frac{\pi r}{2}$$

The area of quadrant AOB is equal to the area of a triangle with base = AB and height = r. The area of this triangle will be $\frac{\text{AB} \times r}{2}$, but

$$\text{AB} = \frac{\pi r}{2}$$

$$\therefore \text{ area of triangle} = \frac{\frac{\pi r}{2} \times r}{2}$$

$$= \frac{\pi r}{2} \times \frac{r}{2} = \frac{\pi r^2}{4}$$

$$\therefore \text{ area of triangle} = \frac{\pi r^2}{4} = \text{area of quadrant AOB}$$

and
$$\text{area of circle} = 4 \times \text{area of quadrant}$$

$$\therefore \text{ area of circle} = \frac{\pi r^2}{\underset{1}{4}} \times \overset{1}{4}$$

$$= \pi r^2$$

Remember
$$Area\ of\ Circle = \pi r^2$$

Example 1. What is the area of a circular disc of 21 mm diameter?

$$\pi = \frac{22}{7} \qquad r = \frac{1}{2} \text{ diameter} = \frac{21}{2} \text{ mm}$$

$$\text{area of circle} = \pi r^2$$

$$= \frac{\overset{11}{22}}{\underset{1}{7}} \times \frac{\overset{3}{21}}{2} \times \frac{21}{2}$$

$$= \frac{693}{2} \text{ mm}^2$$

$$= 346\tfrac{1}{2} \text{ mm}^2$$

$$= 3 \cdot 465 \text{ cm}^2$$

Example 2. In a circular metal plate of radius 26 cm, two round holes are cut each of radius 3·8 cm (Fig. 16). What area of metal remains after the holes have been cut?

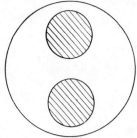

area of circular plate $= \pi r^2$
$$= 3\cdot14 \times 26 \times 26$$
$$= 2{,}122\cdot64 \text{ cm}^2$$

Fig. 16

area of round hole $= \pi r^2$
$$= 3\cdot14 \times 3\cdot8 \times 3\cdot8$$
$$= 45\cdot34 \text{ cm}^2$$
$\therefore$ area of both holes $= 90\cdot68 \text{ cm}^2$

then   area of remaining metal $= 2{,}122\cdot64 - 90\cdot68$
$$= 2{,}031\cdot96 \text{ cm}^2$$

Example 3. The area of a wheel is 86·625 cm². What will be the length of a spoke (i.e. the radius)?

area of circle $= \pi r^2$
$\therefore$ $86\cdot625 = \pi r^2$

so $86\cdot625 = 3\cdot14 \times r^2$

and $r^2 = \dfrac{86\cdot625}{3\cdot14}$

$$= 27\cdot6$$

$$r = \sqrt{27\cdot6} = 5\cdot25 \text{ cm}$$

When you are not given a value for π use $\frac{22}{7}$ or 3·14, as seems best, i.e. 3·14 would probably be used in questions with decimal values.

Exercise 2

(1) Find the circumference of a circle of diameter:

     (*a*) 7 cm   (*b*) 125 mm   (*c*) 1·5 m   (*d*) 2·1 cm

(2) Calculate the circumference of a circle of radius:

    (*a*) 0·35 m   (*b*) 3·5 cm   (*c*) 10·5 cm   (*d*) 52 mm

(3) Find the diameter of a circle of circumference:

    (*a*) 2·2 m   (*b*) 25 cm   (*c*) 14·13 cm   (*d*) 14·6 m

(4) Calculate the radius of a circle of circumference:

    (*a*) 66 cm   (*b*) 9·5 mm   (*c*) 7·85 cm   (*d*) 4·62 m

(5) Calculate the area of a circle of radius:

    (*a*) 14 cm   (*b*) 35 mm   (*c*) 2·4 cm   (*d*) 5 m

(6) Find the radius and diameter of a circle of area:

    (*a*) 14 mm²   (*b*) 38·5 cm²   (*c*) $346\frac{1}{2}$ cm²   (*d*) 7·065 m²

(7) A circular roundabout of diameter 14 m is built at a cross-roads. What length of curb will be needed to surround it? ($\pi = 3\frac{1}{7}$)

(8) A large wheel of radius 21 cm is driven by a smaller wheel of radius 4 cm. How many times will the small wheel revolve in turning the large wheel through one revolution? ($\pi = 3\frac{1}{7}$)

(9) Take the radius of the earth as 6,370 km, calculate the length of the equator. ($\pi = 3·14$)

(10) A well rope winds on an axle of 22·5 cm diameter. The distance for the bucket to reach the water is 9·9 m. How many times will the axle have to be turned to lower the bucket to water level?

(11) The radius of a record is 9 cm; calculate its area. ($\pi = 3·14$)

(12) On a map drawn to a scale of 25 mm to 1 km, a circle of radius 87·5 mm is drawn. How many square kilometres will be represented by that part of the map contained in the circle?

(13) Calculate the area of a sector of a circle with a radius of 11·5 cm that has an angle at the centre of 45°.

(14) A circular flower bed of radius 2·5 m is surrounded by a paved path 0·5 m wide. What is the area of the path? What length of metal strip will be needed to edge both sides of the path?

(15) Find the area of Fig. 17.

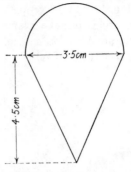

Fig. 17

(16) Calculate the perimeters and areas of the shaded part of the shapes in Fig. 18. ($\pi = 3\cdot14$)

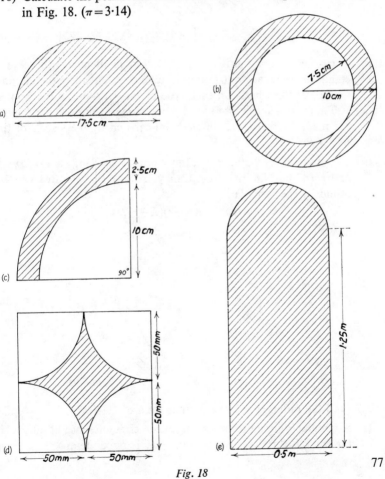

Fig. 18

77

(17) In Fig. 19 ABCD is a piece of material cut from DOC, the sector of a circle, to make a lamp shade. If $\angle$AOB$=36°$ and the length of the arc AB$=275$ mm, and the length of arc DC$=385$ mm, calculate the length of AD.

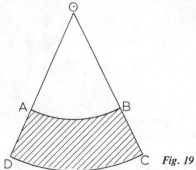

Fig. 19

(18) The wheels of a mini-car are 475 mm in diameter, those of a standard-sized car are 675 mm in diameter. Calculate the circumference of the wheels on each type of car, working to the nearest 100 mm. At a speed of 40 km/h how many revolutions per minute are made by the wheels of the mini-car and by the wheels of the larger car?

(19) The shape in Fig. 20 is called an Annulus or Ring. If $R=70$ cm and $r=42$ cm, find its area. Can you show that its area can be found by the formula

$$\text{Area} = \pi(R+r)(R-r)?$$

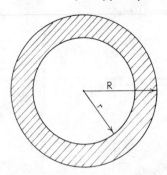

Fig. 20

(20) Find the radius of a circle with an area of $15\cdot4$ m².

(21) A circular running track has an inside circumference of 400 m. If the track is 8 m wide, what is its outside circumference?

Surface area of solids

If a rectangular cardboard box, with a lid, is cut so that it can be laid out in one piece, then the shape of the cardboard when it is laid flat is called the **net** of the box.

Prisms

Any regular solid which has the same cross section throughout its length is a **prism**. Thus our box can be called a rectangular prism and the shape of the laid-out cardboard is the net of a rectangular prism.

Figures 21, 22, and 23 are sketches of three prisms with diagrams of their corresponding nets:

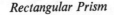

Rectangular Prism

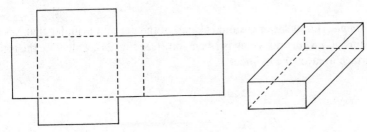

Fig. 21

Triangular Prism

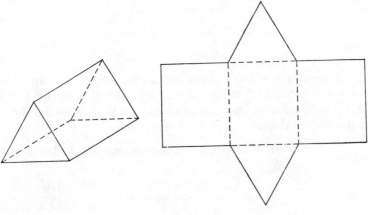

Fig. 22

79

Circular Prism or Cylinder

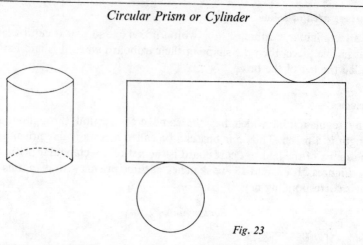

Fig. 23

Example. Draw a dimensional sketch of the net of a cylinder that has a radius of 3·5 cm and which is 14 cm long (see Fig. 24). Calculate the total surface area of the cylinder.

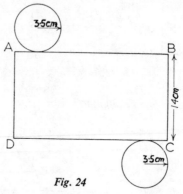

Fig. 24

The net of the cylinder shows that its surface is made up of two circles with radii of 3·5 cm, and a rectangle with breadth equal to the height of the cylinder, i.e. 14 cm, and length AB, equal to the circumference of the cylinder.

$$\text{length AB of rectangle} = \text{circumference of cylinder}$$
$$= \pi d$$
$$= \frac{22}{7} \times \frac{7}{1}$$
$$= 22 \text{ cm}$$

therefore area of curved surface of cylinder, i.e.

$$\text{rectangle ABCD} = l \times b$$
$$= 22 \times 14$$
$$= 308 \text{ cm}^2$$
$$\text{area of circle} = \pi r^2$$
$$\therefore \text{ area of 2 ends of cylinder} = 2 \times \frac{22}{7} \times 3{\cdot}5 \times 3{\cdot}5$$
$$= 77 \text{ cm}^2$$
$$\therefore \text{ total surface area of cylinder} = 308 + 77$$
$$= 385 \text{ cm}^2$$

Volume of a prism

When we find the volume of a rectangular box we use the following formula:

$$\text{volume} = \text{length} \times \text{breadth} \times \text{height}$$

What we are doing in effect is to find the *area* of the end face or cross section of the box and to multiply this by the length (see Fig. 25).

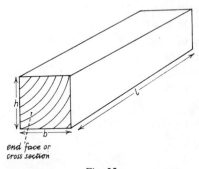

end face or
cross section

Fig. 25

The area of the cross section $= b \times h$ and the volume $= bh \times l$. Thus the volume of a prism is,

area of cross section × length

81

Example. Calculate the volume and capacity of a cylinder of radius 10 cm and 26·5 cm long.

$$\text{volume of cylinder} = \text{area of cross section} \times \text{length}$$
$$\text{area of cross section} = \pi r^2$$
$$\therefore \text{ volume} = \pi r^2 \times l$$
$$= 3\cdot14 \times 10 \times 10 \times 26\cdot5$$
$$= 8{,}321 \text{ cm}^3$$
$$= 8\cdot321 \text{ litres}$$

The net of a pyramid

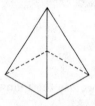

Fig. 26

The faces of a pyramid (Fig. 26) are triangles that meet at a point called a vertex. The number of faces that make up a pyramid depends on the shape of the base of the pyramid. Thus a pyramid on a square base will have a net of the shape shown in Fig. 27:

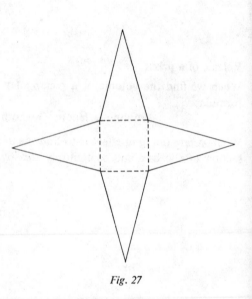

Fig. 27

A pyramid on a triangular base will have a net of the following shape (Fig. 28):

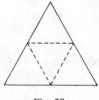

Fig. 28

The calculation of the surface area of a pyramid is really the calculation of the areas of a number of triangles. Thus an important dimension is the slant height (*s*) of the pyramid.

The **slant height** (*s*) should always be distinguished from the **perpendicular height** (*h*). (See Fig. 29.)

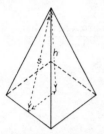

Fig. 29

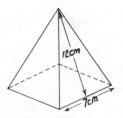

Fig. 30

Example. Calculate the surface area of a square pyramid with a 7 cm base and a slant height of 12 cm (Fig. 30).

The net of the pyramid shows that the surface area is made up of four equal triangles and a square. (See Fig. 31.)

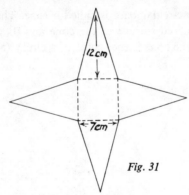

Fig. 31

$$\text{area of triangle} = \frac{s \times b}{2}$$

$$= \frac{12 \times 7}{2} = 42 \text{ cm}^2$$

$$\therefore \text{ area of four faces} = 42 \times 4$$
$$= 168 \text{ cm}^2$$
$$\text{area of base} = a^2$$
$$= 7 \times 7 = 49 \text{ cm}^2$$
$$\therefore \text{ total surface area} = 42 + 49$$
$$= 91 \text{ cm}^2$$

The volume of a pyramid

The volume of a pyramid $= \frac{1}{3}$ area of base × perpendicular ht.

Example. Find the volume of a pyramid with a rectangular base 5 cm by 4 cm, and a perpendicular height of 6 cm.

$$\text{volume of pyramid} = \frac{\text{area of base} \times \text{perp. ht.}}{3}$$

$$= \frac{(5 \times 4) \times 6}{3}$$

$$= \frac{20 \times 6}{3}$$

$$= \frac{120}{3}$$

$$= 40 \text{ cm}^3$$

The cone

A pyramid with a circular base is called a **cone**. The net of a cone is made up of the curved surface of the cone and its circular base. The curved surface of the cone is the sector of a circle. (See Fig. 32.)

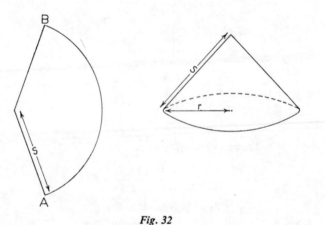

Fig. 32

The radius of the sector is *s* and this becomes the slant height of the cone, while the arc AB becomes the circumference of the circular base of the cone.

The area of the curved surface of a cone can be found by πrs where r = radius of base and s = slant height.

Therefore the total surface area of a cone

$$= \pi rs + \pi r^2$$
$$= \pi r(s+r)$$

Example. Calculate the total surface area of a cone with a slant height of 10 cm and a base diameter of 7 cm.

$$\text{total surface area of cone} = \pi r(s+r)$$

$$= \frac{22}{7} \times 3\tfrac{1}{2}(10 + 3\tfrac{1}{2})$$

$$= \frac{\overset{11}{\cancel{22}}}{7} \times \frac{\overset{1}{\cancel{7}}}{2} \times \frac{27}{2}$$

$$= \frac{297}{2} = 148\tfrac{1}{2} \text{ cm}^2$$

$$= 148 \cdot 5 \text{ cm}^2$$

Volume of a cone

Since a cone is a circular pyramid then the

$$\text{volume of cone} = \frac{\text{area of base} \times \text{perpendicular height}}{3}$$

$$= \tfrac{1}{3}\pi r^2 h$$

Example. A cone is 12 cm high and has a radius of 5 cm. What is its volume?

$$\text{volume of cone} = \frac{1}{3}\pi r^2 h$$

$$= \frac{1}{\cancel{3}} \times \frac{22}{7} \times \frac{5}{1} \times \frac{5}{1} \times \frac{\overset{4}{\cancel{12}}}{1}$$

$$= \frac{2200}{7}$$

$$= 314\tfrac{2}{7} \text{ cm}^3$$

$$= 314 \cdot 3 \text{ cm}^3$$

The sphere

Soccer and tennis balls, the moon, the planets, the earth itself are all spherical in shape or at least nearly so. The sphere is, then, a very common shape.

The formula for finding its volume V, is

$$V = \tfrac{4}{3}\pi r^3$$

and for finding its surface area S is

$$S = 4\pi r^2$$

where r is the radius of sphere, that is, the distance from any point on the surface to the centre.

Example. What is the volume and surface area of a ball that has a diameter of 10·5 cm?

$$V = \tfrac{4}{3}\pi r^3 \quad (r = 5\!\cdot\!25)$$

$$= \frac{4}{\cancel{3}} \times \frac{22}{\cancel{7}} \times \overset{1\cdot75}{\cancel{5\!\cdot\!25}} \times \overset{0\cdot75}{\cancel{5\!\cdot\!25}} \times 5\!\cdot\!25$$

$$= 606\!\cdot\!375 \text{ cm}^3$$

$$S = 4\pi r^2$$

$$= 4 \times \frac{22}{\cancel{7}} \times \overset{0\cdot75}{\cancel{5\!\cdot\!25}} \times 5\!\cdot\!25$$

$$= 346\!\cdot\!5 \text{ cm}^2$$

Exercise 3

(1) Draw a scale diagram of the net of a cube with a 3·5 cm side, and use this diagram to find its surface area.

(2) Copy this table into your exercise book and complete it by filling in the required information:

Solid	Number of faces	Number of faces of these shapes			
		Square	Rectangle	Triangle	Circle
Rectangular Prism					
Triangular Prism					
Square Prism					
Cylinder					
Pyramid Sq. base					
Pyramid Triangular base					

(3) Calculate the surface areas and the volumes of these prisms:

    (*a*) A square prism with a 150 mm end and length 375 mm.

    (*b*) A cylinder with radius 6·3 cm and height 38·1 cm.

    (*c*) A triangular prism, base 10 cm, slant sides 6·25 cm, length 40 cm.

(4) A cylindrical petrol tank has a radius of 68·5 cm and is 3 m long. Find the capacity of the tank. What area of sheet metal will be used in its construction?

(5) Figure 33 is a dimensional sketch of a canvas tent. Calculate the amount of canvas needed to make it. Work to the nearest m² and allow 10% for joins, etc.

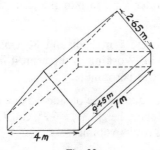

Fig. 33

(6) A metal pipe has an inside diameter of 9·1 cm and an outside diameter of 10·8 cm. Find the volume of metal in a 3 m length of the pipe ($\pi = 3\cdot14$).

87

(7) A swimming bath is 1 m deep at the shallow end and 2 m deep at the other end. It is 15 m long and 6 m wide. The bottom of the bath is concrete and the sides are glazed tiles. Find (i) the area that is tiled, and (ii) its capacity in m³.

(8) Figure 34 is a rough dimensional sketch of a barn. If the barn can be completely filled with hay what volume of hay will it contain?

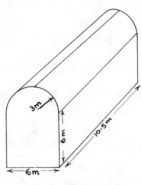

Fig. 34

(9) A steel girder weighs 1,620 kg, the area of its cross-section is 850 cm². If steel weighs 8 g per 1 cm³, what is the length of the girder?

(10) A rectangular water tank measures 1 m long by 0·65 m wide. If 227·5 litres of water are run into the tank, find the depth of the water.

(11) A cylindrical tank 1·5 m high and 80 cm in diameter can be emptied in 2½ min. Working to the nearest litre, express this as a rate of flow in litres per minute.

(12) A pyramid has a square base of side 7·5 cm, perpendicular height $(h)=5$ cm, and slant height $(s)=6·25$ cm. Calculate (a) its total surface area and (b) its volume.

(13) The volume of a pyramid is 500 cm³. If the area of its base is 37·5 cm², what is its height?

(14) Calculate the volume of a cone with radius $(r)=125$ mm and height $(h)=250$ mm.

(15) A cone has a base radius of 4·5 cm and a slant height of 7·5 cm. Find the total surface area of the cone.

(16) An open cone made of sheet metal has a base diameter of 0·5 m and a slant height of 0·66 m. Find the area of sheet metal needed to make it.

(17) A cylinder has a diameter of 12·5 cm, and a height of 12·5 cm. What is the diameter of a sphere that will fit inside the cylinder? Calculate the volume of the cylinder and of the sphere and express the volume of the sphere as a fraction of the volume of the cylinder.

(18) A casting is in the form of a cylinder of radius 15 cm, with a hemisphere of the same radius at each end. The overall length of the casting is 55 cm. Calculate its surface area.

(19) A pipe has an internal diameter of 5·7 cm, and water flows along it at the rate of 0·61 m per second. Calculate (i) correct to two decimal places, the volume of water that flows through the pipe in 1 min, (ii) the number of litres to the nearest 10 litres, that flow through the pipe in 1 h ($\pi = 3\cdot14$).

(20) A sphere, of radius 375 mm, is placed in a cylinder, of radius 875 mm, that contains 1,000 mm of water. How far will the water in the cylinder rise?

11 The Techniques of Algebra

Since the earliest times people have used tools to enable them to do things more easily and quickly. Imagine how difficult it would be to take out a screw without a screwdriver or to cut out a dress pattern without scissors. The techniques used in Algebra provide us with some of the most useful mathematical tools that enable us to do things fairly easily, that would be extremely difficult, or even impossible, without their aid.

Our algebraic tool kit enables us to reduce multiplication and division sums in arithmetic to simple addition and subtraction. A long-winded explanation can be reduced to half-a-dozen signs and letters that can be understood by anyone, regardless of language, who can also use the tools from the kit.

When we are taught to use a tool—spanner, scissors, or soup spoon —we are shown it, its use is explained and demonstrated, and then we must take it and try to use it. In effect we are called upon to make a real effort on our own behalf. This section shows us some of the tools of mathematics, it demonstrates their use, but we must be prepared to make an effort if we are to acquire the skill to use them.

Substitution

Example 1. Find the value of $4xy^2 - 2z$ when $x = 7$, $y = 5$, and $z = 3$.
$4xy^2 - 2z$ written in full becomes

$$4 \times x \times y \times y - 2 \times z$$

Substituting for x, y, and z

$$4 \times 7 \times 5 \times 5 - 2 \times 3 = 700 - 6$$
$$= 694$$

Note: $2 \times z$ is sometimes written as $2.z$, and $4xy^2$, that is, $4 \times x \times y \times y$ as $4.x.y.y$ especially if the multiplication sign might be confused with x.

Example 2. Find the value of $\dfrac{3}{p^2-q}-\dfrac{p}{4}$ when $p=2$ and $q=0$.

$$\dfrac{3}{p^2-q}-\dfrac{p}{4}$$

rewritten, becomes

$$\dfrac{3}{p\times p-q}-\dfrac{p}{4}$$

Substituting

$$\dfrac{3}{2\times2-0}-\dfrac{2}{4}=\dfrac{3}{4}-\dfrac{2}{4}$$

$$=\tfrac{1}{4}$$

Exercise 1

The expression $\dfrac{3x^2-y}{2}$ means: Take y from $3\times x\times x$ and divide the result by 2.

Write down what each of the following expressions means:

(1) $2a+7$ (3) $\dfrac{a+b}{4}$ (5) $\dfrac{p^2-q}{z}$

(2) $5x-3$ (4) $\dfrac{10}{2a+3}$ (6) $\dfrac{4b+2}{a}-d^2$

Find the value of the following expressions:

(7) $3x+2$ when $x=4$.   (9) $\dfrac{2z+6}{3}$ when $z=6$.

(8) $5a-7$ when $a=2$.   (10) $\dfrac{24}{a+9}$ when $a=3$.

(11) $\dfrac{m}{2n-4}$ when $m=3$ and $n=5$.

(12) $\dfrac{x^2}{y+3}$ when $x=4$ and $y=5$.

(13) $\dfrac{2}{a^2-4}+\dfrac{2b^2}{3}$ when $a=4$ and $b=2$.

(14) $\dfrac{a^3}{3}\times\dfrac{2b^2}{3}$ when $a=2$ and $b=1$.

(15) $4xy-3y-2xz$ when $x=2$, $y=3$, and $z=0$.

(16) $\dfrac{p}{q}+\dfrac{r}{q}-\dfrac{3}{4}$ when $p = 7$, $q = 8$, and $r = 0$.

(17) $\dfrac{x^3}{4}+\dfrac{y}{3}-\dfrac{1}{y}$ when $x = 2$, $y = 3$.

(18) $\dfrac{a^2-5}{5}-\dfrac{3}{b^2-11}$ when $a = 3$, $b = 4$.

(19) $\dfrac{p^2}{q^2}-\dfrac{p-3}{q}$ when $p = 9$, $q = 10$.

(20) $\dfrac{xyz-z^2}{y}$ when $x = 2$, $y = 4$, and $z = 6$.

Signed or directed numbers

Addition

When we think of a number, say 9, we tend to think of it only as a positive quantity. If we have £9 it is a positive amount. On the other hand, if we owe £9, although the amount of money is just as real, it has an entirely different meaning for us. We could, in fact, regard having £9 as $+£9$, and owing £9 as $-£9$. The ability to do calculations using $+$ and $-$ amounts is an essential skill in mathematics.

Example 1.

$$\begin{array}{r} \text{Add} \quad +7 \\ -6 \\ +2 \\ +5 \\ \underline{-3} \end{array}$$

Add together all the numbers with $+$ signs	Add together all the numbers with $-$ signs
$\begin{array}{r} +\ 7 \\ +\ 2 \\ \underline{+\ 5} \\ +14 \end{array}$	$\begin{array}{r} -6 \\ \underline{-3} \\ -9 \end{array}$

93

The result will carry the sign of the larger number and will be their difference, i.e.

$$\begin{array}{r} +14 \\ -\ 9 \\ \hline +\ 5 \end{array}$$

Example 2. Add $3y$; $-6y$; $14y$; $-2y$; $-7y$; $-4y$.

Remember where no sign is given, as in $14y$, this means $+14y$. Arrange in order

$$\begin{array}{r} +\ 3y \\ -\ 6y \\ +14y \\ -\ 2y \\ -\ 7y \\ -\ 4y \end{array}$$

<table>
<tr><td>Add together all $+$'s</td><td>Add together all $-$'s</td></tr>
<tr><td>

$$\begin{array}{r} +\ 3y \\ +14y \\ \hline +17y \end{array}$$

</td><td>

$$\begin{array}{r} -\ 6y \\ -\ 2y \\ -\ 7y \\ -\ 4y \\ \hline -19y \end{array}$$

</td></tr>
</table>

The result carries the sign of the larger number and will be their difference, i.e.

$$\begin{array}{r} +17y \\ -19y \\ \hline -\ 2y \end{array}$$

Example 3. Add $4b^2+3c-2$; $7-5c-b^2$; $2b^2+6$; $-12c-3$.

Arrange in this way keeping the like terms in order:

$$\begin{array}{r} 4b^2+\ 3c-2 \\ -\ b^2-\ 5c+7 \\ 2b^2\qquad +6 \\ -12c-3 \\ \hline 5b^2-14c+8 \end{array}$$

Subtraction

The simple rule for subtraction is—*change the sign of the number to be subtracted and then add.*

Example 4.

$$\text{From} \quad +9 \qquad\qquad +\ 9$$
$$\text{Take} \quad \underline{-5} \quad \text{change sign} \quad \underline{+\ 5}$$
$$\qquad\qquad\qquad\qquad\qquad +14 \quad \text{and add.}$$

Example 5.

$$\text{From} \quad -12 \qquad\qquad -12$$
$$\text{Take} \quad \underline{-\ 7} \quad \text{change sign} \quad \underline{+\ 7} \quad \text{and add.}$$
$$\qquad\qquad\qquad\qquad\qquad -\ 5$$

(Note that the result has the sign of the larger number and is the difference of the two numbers.)

Example 6.

$$\text{From} \quad -3y \qquad\qquad -\ 3y$$
$$\text{Take} \quad \underline{+9y} \quad \text{change sign} \quad \underline{-\ 9y} \quad \text{and add.}$$
$$\qquad\qquad\qquad\qquad\qquad -12y$$

Example 7.

$$\text{From} \quad 6x-7y$$
$$\text{Take} \quad \underline{-3x-12y} \quad \text{change signs and add.}$$
$$\qquad +9x+\ 5y$$

Example 8. What must be added to $7x^2-8$ to make $3-4xy-9x^2$?

Arrange in order and subtract $\qquad\qquad\qquad -9x^2-4xy+3$
(change signs and add) $\qquad\qquad\qquad\qquad \underline{7x^2 \qquad -8}$
$$\qquad\qquad\qquad\qquad\qquad\qquad\qquad -16x^2-4xy+11$$

Exercise 2

(1) Add:

$$
\begin{array}{llll}
\text{(a)} +3 & \text{(b)} -4 & \text{(c)} +5 & \text{(d)} -9 \\
\quad -4 & \quad +3 & \quad -3 & \quad +3 \\
\quad +6 & \quad -6 & \quad -6 & \quad +4 \\
\quad \underline{-2} & \quad \underline{+12} & \quad \underline{+1} & \quad -2 \\
& & & \quad \underline{+4}
\end{array}
$$

(2) Add:

(a) $+3x$ (b) $-4y$
$-2x$ $+y$
$+6x$ $+3y$
$-x$ $-5y$
———   ———

(c) $4a$; $-6a$; $-9a$; $3a$. (d) $5x^2$; $3x^2$; $-x^2$; $-2x^2$.

(e) 5; b; $-2b$; -2.

(3) Add:

(a) $2x-3y$ (b) $7p-6q$
      $4x+5y$ $4p-5q$
      $-3x+2y$ $-8p+3q$
      ————————   ————————

(c) $4t+6$ (d) $5-3a^2$
      $t-7$ $2+a^2$
      $2t+3$ $-7-5a^2$
      —————— $6+2a^2$
                      ————————

(4) Add:

(a) $2a^2+3a-7$
    $7a^2-4a+3$
    $5a+2$
    a^2-a-2
    ——————————

(b) x^2-2x+5; $5x-7$; $3x^2-x+1$; x^2+x-3.

(c) p^2+3p-q; $4p^2-5p+2q$; $2p^2-2p-3q$; $5q+p-9p^2$.

(d) $2b+3$; b^2-5b; $4-2b^2$.

(e) a^3+2a^2-4a+6; a^2+3a-7; $4a^3-6a^2-2a+9$;
    $2+3a+a^2-5a^3$.

(5) | | (a) | (b) | (c) | (d) | (e) | (f) |
|---|---|---|---|---|---|---|
| From | $+8$ | -7 | -19 | $+5x$ | $-10a$ | $+16r^2$ |
| Take | $+5$ | -3 | $+8$ | $+3x$ | $-4a$ | $-7r^2$ |
| | — | — | — | — | — | — |

(6) Subtract:

(a)	(b)	(c)	(d)	(e)	(f)
$+11$	$+8$	-15	$+14y$	$-27a^2$	$+21a^2b$
$+\ 6$	-3	$-\ 7$	$+\ 9y$	$-14a^2$	$-6a^2b$

(7)

	(a)	(b)	(c)
From	$4x+5y$	$12m+9$	$2a-4b$
Take	$3x-2y$	$5m-4$	$2a-5b$

	(d)	(e)	(f)
From	$5z-7$	r^2-s^2	$-7p^2-2q^2$
Take	$-4z-3$	$-2r^2+3s^2$	$-3p^2-6q^2$

(8)

	(a)	(b)	(c)
From	$4a^2-5a+6$	$9x^2+2x-5$	$6y^2-4y-8$
Take	$2a^2+\ a-7$	$-3x^2+3x+7$	$-3y^2\quad+2$

	(d)	(e)	(f)
From	$-2b^2+5b-9$	$6x^2-10x+18$	$14p^3-6p\ +7$
Take	$3b^2-2b+11$	$-4x^2+\ 8x-16$	$11p^3-5p^2+2$

(9) From $4a^2-2a+3$ take $6-2a^2$.

(10) What must be added to $2a^2-a+b^2$ to make $4a^2+3a-2b^2$?

(11) How much greater is $6x+2y-16z$ than $3x-4y-z$?

(12) Take the sum of $5y^2-6y+3$; $3y^2+2y-8$; $4y^2-4y+2$; from $14y^2-7y+1$.

Multiplication and division

If two numbers with *like* signs are multiplied together then the result or product will have a **positive** sign, i.e. a $+$.

If two numbers with *unlike* signs are multiplied together then the result or product will have a **negative** sign, i.e. a $-$.

If two numbers with like signs are divided, then the result or **quotient** will have a **positive** sign, i.e. a $+$.

If two numbers with unlike signs are divided, then the result will have a **negative** sign, i e. a $-$.

Example 1.

$$(-7) \times (+12) = -84$$
$$(-4) \times (-9) = +36$$
$$(-6) \times (+d) = -6d$$
$$(+16) \div (+4) = +4$$
$$(-27) \div (+3) = -9$$
$$(-14x) \div (-2x) = +7$$

Exercise 3

Work the following:

(1)
(a)	(b)	(c)
$(-5) \times (+2)$	$(+6) \times (-3)$	$(+4) \times (+6)$

(d)	(e)	(f)
$(-7) \times (-4)$	$(-1) \times (+8)$	$(+4) \times (-5)$

(g)	(h)	(i)
$(3x) \times (5)$	$(-7a) \times (-3)$	$(9) \times (-4a)$

(j)	(k)	(l)
$(-5y) \times (6)$	$(12p) \times (-5)$	$(-8) \times (5k)$

(2)
(a)	(b)	(c)
$(+8) \div (-4)$	$(-27) \div (-9)$	$(-15) \div (+3)$

(d)	(e)	(f)
$(+18d) \div (+9d)$	$(+12) \div (-6)$	$(+21b) \div (-3b)$

(g)	(h)	(i)
$(-42x) \div (-7x)$	$(+64a) \div (-8a)$	$(-32y) \div (+4y)$

(j)	(k)	(l)	(m)
$\dfrac{(-9)}{(-3)}$	$\dfrac{(+16a)}{(-4a)}$	$\dfrac{(-28x)}{(+7x)}$	$\dfrac{(5y)}{(-y)}$

12 Indices or Powers

a^3 is a more convenient way of writing $a \times a \times a$.
$3y^2$ is a more convenient way of writing $3 \times y \times y$.

Multiplying

If $a^3 \times a^2$ is written out fully it becomes $a \times a \times a \times a \times a$ which gives a^5.

Again $3y^2 \times y^4$ becomes $3 \times y \times y \times y \times y \times y \times y$ which gives $3y^6$.

The rule for multiplying powers or indices is *add the indices.*

Example 1.

$$a^4 \times a^2 = a^{4+2} = a^6$$
$$3x^3 \times 2x = 6x^{3+1} = 6x^4$$
$$-2y^2 \times 3y^4 = -6y^{2+4} = -6y^6$$

Dividing

If $a^3 \div a^2$ is written out fully it becomes

$$\frac{a \times a \times \cancel{a}}{\cancel{a} \times \cancel{a}} \quad \text{which gives } a.$$

Again $4z^5 \div 2z^3$ becomes

$$\frac{\overset{2}{\cancel{4}} \times z \times z \times \cancel{z} \times \cancel{z} \times \cancel{z}}{\cancel{2} \times \cancel{z} \times \cancel{z} \times \cancel{z}} = 2z^2$$

The rule for dividing powers or indices is *subtract the indices.*

Example 2.

$$a^5 \div a^2 = a^{5-2} = a^3$$
$$9x^3 \div 3x = 3x^{3-1} = 3x^2$$
$$-14z^6 \div 7z^2 = -2z^{6-2} = -2z^4$$

Note how the number part of the expression is dealt with separately from the letter part.

When working the following exercise remember the rules for signs.

Exercise 1

(1) Simplify:

(a)	(b)	(c)	(d)
$x^2 . x^3$	$a . a^3$	$4y^2 . 3y^4$	$4b^2 . 2b^2$

(e)	(f)	(g)	(h)
$(x^3)(-x^2)$	$(-a)(a^3)$	$(-2b^2)(-b^3)$	$(3m^2)(-4m^3)$

(i)
$(4p^3)(-2p^3)$

(2) Simplify:

(a)	(b)	(c)	(d)
$a^3 \div a^2$	$x^5 \div x^2$	$9x \div 3x$	$8y^2 \div 4y^2$

(e)	(f)	(g)	(h)
$(-6a^3) \div (a^2)$	$(4x^2) \div (-2x)$	$(16z^5) \div (-4z^3)$	$(-9x^4) \div (-3x^2)$

(i)	(j)	(k)	(l)	(m)
$\dfrac{10x^4}{5x^3}$	$\dfrac{27a^5}{9a^3}$	$\dfrac{-8m^2}{2m}$	$\dfrac{-16k^4}{-4k^3}$	$\dfrac{24x^6}{-12x^4}$

(3) Simplify:

(a)	(b)	(c)	(d)
$\dfrac{4x^2 \times 3x}{9x^3}$	$\dfrac{-2b(-4b^2)}{4b^2}$	$\dfrac{-3m^3(5m^4)}{5m^3}$	$\dfrac{k(5k^4)}{(-k^2) \times (3k^3)}$

(4) Simplify:

(a)	(b)	(c)	(d)
$6a^2 + 3a^2$	$6a^2 \times 3a^2$	$6a^2 - 3a^2$	$6a^2 \div 3a^2$

Powers

The expression $(x^2)^3$ when written out fully becomes

$$(x.x).(x.x).(x.x) \quad \text{which gives } x^6$$

Again $(2y^3)^2$ becomes

$$(2.y.y.y).(2.y.y.y) \quad \text{which gives } 4y^6$$

The rule for raising a power to a power is *multiply the indices*.

Example 3.

$$(a^4)^3 = a^{4 \times 3} = a^{12}$$
$$(5z^2)^2 = 25z^{2 \times 2} = 25z^4$$
$$(-3y^2)^3 = -3^{1 \times 3} \times y^{2 \times 3} = -3^3 \times y^6 = -27y^6$$
$$(2xy)^4 = 2^{1 \times 4} \times x^{1 \times 4} \times y^{1 \times 4} = 2^4 \times x^4 y^4 = 16x^4 y^4$$

Roots

$\sqrt{64}$ means the square root of 64, which is 8, since 8×8 or $8^2 = 64$.
Stated another way:

$$\sqrt{64} = \sqrt{8^2} = 8$$

Again, $\sqrt[3]{27}$ means the cube root of 27 which is 3 since $3 \times 3 \times 3$, or $3^3 = 27$. Alternatively, $\sqrt[3]{27} = \sqrt[3]{3^3} = 3$.

Again $\sqrt[5]{a^{10}}$ means the 5th root of a^{10} which is a^2, since

$$a^2 \times a^2 \times a^2 \times a^2 \times a^2 \quad \text{or} \quad (a^2)^5 = a^{10}$$

Alternatively $\sqrt[5]{a^{10}} = \sqrt[5]{(a^2)^5} = a^2$.

In each of these examples the correct result could have been obtained by dividing the root into the power.

From the last example we get

$$\sqrt[5]{a^{10}} = a^{10 \div 5} = a^2$$

Example 4. Find $\sqrt[3]{x^9}$.

$$\sqrt[3]{x^9} = x^{9 \div 3} = x^3$$

The rule for finding a root is, *divide the index by the required root.*

Rules

The rules for indices can be expressed in a simplified standard form:

(1) *Multiplying powers—add the indices, e.g.:*

$$a^m \times a^n = a^{m+n}$$

(2) *Dividing powers—subtract the indices, e.g.:*

$$a^m \div a^n = a^{m-n}$$

(3) *To raise a power to a power—multiply the indices, e.g.:*

$$(a^m)^n = a^{m \times n} = a^{mn}$$

(4) *To find a root—divide the index by the root, e.g.:*

$$\sqrt[n]{a^m} = a^{m \div n} = a^{\frac{m}{n}}$$

Exercise 2

(1) Write these examples in full to explain how the result is obtained.

(a) $(a^3)^2 = a^6$ (c) $\left(\dfrac{c}{4}\right)^2 = \dfrac{c^2}{16}$

(b) $(2z)^3 = 8z^3$ (d) $(pq)^2 = p^2 q^2$

(2) Simplify:

(a) $(b^2)^3$ (d) $(-x)^3$ (g) $(ab)^2$

(b) $(x^4)^2$ (e) $(-3m)^2$ (h) $(3x^2y^2)^3$

(c) $(2a)^2$ (f) $(-2b^2)^3$ (i) $(-4m^2n)^2$

(3) Simplify:

(a) $\sqrt{x^2}$ (d) $\sqrt{4x^4}$ (g) $\sqrt{a^2b^2}$

(b) $\sqrt[3]{b^3}$ (e) $\sqrt[3]{8a^6}$ (h) $\sqrt[3]{8x^6y^9}$

(c) $\sqrt[5]{a^5}$ (f) $\sqrt{16b^2}$ (i) $\sqrt[4]{m^4n^8}$

Fractional indices

If we consider $\sqrt[3]{x^2}$, then applying Rule 4: $\sqrt[3]{x^2}=x^{2/3}$, so that the cube root of x^2 is $x^{2/3}$. This can be checked in this way,

$$(x^{2/3})^3 = x^{2/3} \times x^{2/3} \times x^{2/3} = x^{2/3 + 2/3 + 2/3} = x^2$$

Using this method in reverse any fractional index can be expressed as a root.

Example.

$$y^{3/4} = \sqrt[4]{y^3} \qquad 16^{1/2} = \sqrt{16} = 4$$
$$x^{1/2} = \sqrt{x} \qquad 27^{1/3} = \sqrt[3]{27} = 3$$

Negative indices

In the case of

$$\frac{x^2}{x^4} = \frac{x.x}{x.x.x.x} = \frac{1}{x^2}$$

An alternative solution is obtained by applying Rule 2:

$$\frac{x^2}{x^4} = x^{2-4} = x^{-2}$$

thus

$$\frac{x^2}{x^4} = \frac{1}{x^2} = x^{-2}$$

and x^{-3} can be restated as $\dfrac{1}{x^3}$

Again $\quad n^{-5} = \dfrac{1}{n^5}, \quad 3^{-2} = \dfrac{1}{3^2} = \dfrac{1}{9}, \quad 2^{-4} = \dfrac{1}{2^4} = \dfrac{1}{16}$

The special case of x^0

Example 5

$$x^3 \div x^3 = \frac{x^3}{x^3} = 1$$

This can be done in this way, Rule 2.

$$x^3 \div x^3 = x^{3-3} = x^0 \quad \therefore \quad x^0 = 1$$

Any number or expression to the power of 0 (nought) is equal to 1, e.g.:

$$27^0 = 1, \quad (3x)^0 = 1, \quad 3x^0 = 3$$

$A \times 10^n$

A useful way of writing large or small numbers makes use of indices.

For example:
$$93,000 = 9 \cdot 3 \times 10,000$$
$$= 9 \cdot 3 \times 10^4$$
$$0 \cdot 000035 = \frac{3 \cdot 5}{100,000}$$
$$= \frac{3 \cdot 5}{10^5} = 3 \cdot 5 \times 10^{-5}$$

In this way a number can be expressed as the product of a number between 1 and 10 and a power of 10, i.e. $A \times 10^n$, where n is either positive or negative. This is the standard form of a number and is particularly useful when handling decimal fractions with a lot of noughts after the decimal point.

Exercise 3

(1) Write down the values of:

    (a) $9^{1/2}$ (c) $25^{1/2}$ (e) $36^{1/2}$

    (b) $8^{1/3}$ (d) $16^{1/4}$ (f) $64^{1/3}$

(2) Rewrite the following as a root:

    (a) $x^{1/2}$ (c) $a^{2/3}$ (e) $c^{1/2}$

    (b) $y^{1/6}$ (d) $b^{3/4}$ (f) $m^{0 \cdot 5}$

(3) Write down the values of:

    (a) 2^{-2} (d) 2^{-3} (f) 3^{-3}

    (b) 5^{-1} (e) 7^0 (g) 25^0

    (c) 4^{-2}

(4) Rewrite the following as fractions:

    (a) x^{-3} (b) n^{-2} (c) b^{-5} (d) a^{-4}

(5) Write down the values of:

    (a) y^0 (c) 126^0 (e) $5y^0$

    (b) $(5a)^0$ (d) 10^0 (f) $12z^0$

(6) Convert to standard form:

    (*a*) 3,000,000   (*c*) 180,000,000

    (*b*) 275,000   (*d*) 38,000

(7) Rewrite in the form $A \times 10^n$:

    (*a*) 0·00046   (*c*) 0·000037

    (*b*) 0·000009   (*d*) 0·0000156

(8) Use the form $A \times 10^n$ to perform these calculations. Give your answer in standard form.

    (*a*) $350,000 \times 30,000$

    (*b*) $75,000,000 \times 220,000$

    (*c*) $0·000048 \div 0·0012$

    (*d*) $0·000000828 \div 0·000023$

Multiplication

Algebraic multiplication is similar to long multiplication in arithmetic. For example:

$$(6b+3) \times 4 = \begin{array}{r} 6b+3 \\ 4 \\ \hline 24b+12 \end{array}$$

again the same example can be written in this form:

$$4(6b+3) = 24b+12$$

Also
$$(3x^2 - y) \times -4xy = \quad 3x^2 - y$$
$$-4xy$$
$$\overline{-12x^3y + 4xy^2}$$

or in the form
$$-4xy(3x^2 - y) = -12x^3y + 4xy^2$$

A more difficult example is $(5x+7)(2x-3)$. This is read as $5x+7$ into $2x-3$, and means $(5x+7) \times (2x-3)$.

The method is as follows:
$$5x+7$$
$$2x-3$$
$$(5x+7) \times 2x = 10x^2 + 14x$$
$$(5x+7) \times -3 = \quad -15x - 21$$
$$\overline{10x^2 - \quad x - 21}$$

Division

Algebraic division is similar to long division in arithmetic.

For example:
$$6a - 3 \div 3$$
$$3 \;|\; \underline{6a - 3}$$
$$2a - 1$$

Again
$$a^3b^2 + 4a^2b - 6ab^3 \div ab$$

$$ab \;|\; \underline{a^3b^2 + 4a^2b - 6ab^3}$$
$$a^2b + 4a \quad -6b^2$$

A more difficult example is

$$(3x^2 - 10x - 8) \div (x - 4)$$

The method is as follows: Divide $3x^2$ by x. It goes exactly $3x$ times; write $3x$ in the answer. Multiply $x-4$ by $3x$. The result is $3x^2 - 12x$ which is written here. Subtract (change the sign and add). Bring down the -8. Divide $2x$ by x and repeat the last stage.

$$
\begin{array}{r}
3x+2 \\
x-4 \;\overline{\big)\; 3x^2 - 10x - 8} \\
3x^2 - 12x \\
\hline
+\; 2x - 8 \\
2x - 8 \\
\hline
\end{array}
$$

105

Exercise 4

(1) Write the answers to the following:

(a)	(b)	(c)
$2a+3$	$4b-2$	$5a+6b$
$\times 4$	$\times 3$	$\times 2$

(d)	(e)	(f)
$3p+6$	$5p-3$	$7p+4q$
$\times\ p$	$\times -p$	$\times -3p$

(g)	(h)	(i)
c^2-4c	$3z^2-2z$	$4ab-7$
$\times c$	$\times -2z$	$\times 3ab$

(j)	(k)	(l)
$5m^2n-8$	$2a^2-3a+4$	$5a^2+2ab-3b^2$
$\times -3mn$	$\times 5a$	$\times -4a$

(2) Find the products of:

(a) $5(2a-3)$ (f) $-6(4b+7)$

(b) $7(3b+4)$ (g) $2c(3c-4)$

(c) $4(3x-2)$ (h) $-4b(b^2-2b)$

(d) $3r(2r+4)$ (i) $7(2x^2-4xy+y^2)$

(e) $-3(4a+5)$ (j) $-8(3b^2-7bc+2c^2)$

(3) Use the long multiplication method to find the products of the following:

(a) $(a+4)(a+2)$ (f) $(5y+4z)(2y-3z)$

(b) $(b-3)(b-1)$ (g) $(6a-b)(3a-4b)$

(c) $(r-5)(r-3)$ (h) $(7m-4n)(3m+2n)$

(d) $(3a+2)(4a+5)$ (i) $(6+3r)(4+2r)$

(e) $(2z+6)(3z-4)$ (j) $(9-3y)(4+4y)$

(4) Divide:

    (a) $6x - 4$ by 2

    (b) $9a - 27$ by 9

    (c) $12x^2 - 8x$ by $4x$

    (d) $10a^2b + 15a$ by $5a$

    (e) $14r^2 + 7r$ by $-7r$

    (f) $6a^3 - 4a^2 + 8a$ by $-2a$

    (g) $4b^4 + 8b^3 - 12b^2$ by $-4b^2$

    (h) $x^4y^2 - 4x^2y + 3xy^2$ by xy

(5) Divide, using the long division method:

    (a) $a^2 + 4a + 4$ by $a + 2$

    (b) $3b^2 + 15b + 12$ by $b + 4$

    (c) $x^2 + 3x - 4$ by $x + 1$

    (d) $4r^2 - 2r - 30$ by $r - 3$

    (e) $x^2 - x - 2$ by $x - 2$

    (f) $6m^2 - 24mn - 72n^2$ by $2m - 12n$

Brackets

If the statement

       'subtract $4a^2$ from 10 and multiply the result by $2a$'

is worked out, then $10 - 4a^2$ must be completed first and if the statement is written as an algebraic expression then this fact must be made clear. This is done by using brackets, and the statement written as an algebraic expression is

$$(10 - 4a^2) \times 2a \quad \text{or} \quad 2a(10 - 4a^2)$$

Sometimes, instead of brackets, a line called a **vinculum** is used, so

$$2x - (4y + z)$$

can be written as

$$2x - \overline{4y + z}$$

Brackets are sometimes used inside other brackets in which case different kinds are used, e.g. { } and [ ], so that confusion does not arise.

Remember, when simplifying an expression, the inside bracket is removed first and the working is continued outwards.

When each bracket is removed, the rule for signs must be applied. This rule states that if there is a + outside the brackets, when they are removed the signs within them remain *unchanged*; if there is a − outside the brackets, on removal the signs within them *change*. That is:

> \+ *outside: signs remain the same*
> − *outside: signs change*

Example 1. Simplify $3x(x-4)$.

Multiply by $3x$. The sign is + so the sign in the brackets is unchanged

$$3x^2 - 12x$$

Example 2. Simplify $-2a(3a+5)$.

Multiply by $2a$. The sign is −, so the sign in brackets is changed

$$-6a^2 - 10a$$

Example 3. Simplify $4b(3b^2 - \overline{2b-5})$.

Remove the vinculum. A − before the bracket changes the sign

$$4b(3b^2 - 2b + 5)$$

Multiply by $4b$. The sign is +, so the signs in the brackets are unchanged

$$12b^3 - 8b^2 + 20b$$

Example 4. Remove the brackets from $3a(2a-6)-4(a^2+7a)$ and simplify by collecting the terms.

Multiply the first bracket by $3a$. The sign is + so the signs are unchanged. Multiply the second bracket by -4. The sign is − so the signs are changed

$$6a^2 - 18a - 4a^2 - 28a$$

Collect the terms

$$6a^2 - 4a^2 - 18a - 28a = 2a^2 - 46a$$

Exercise 5

(1) Simplify:

(a) $2a(4a+3)$ (e) $2xy(3x-4y)$

(b) $4r(3r-6)$ (f) $-4t(5t-6)$

(c) $-7(6b+3)$ (g) $\frac{1}{2}(4x-8)$

(d) $-3x(2x-4)$ (h) $\frac{2}{3}(12a+15)$

(2) Simplify:

(a) $3a(2a^2+\overline{7a+3})$

(b) $4y(5y^2-\overline{3y+12})$

(c) $-7x(x^2-\overline{4x+10})$

(d) $-12r(3r^2+\overline{4r-6})$

(e) $2xy(4x^2y^2-\overline{3xy+4y^2})$

(f) $-3p(\overline{5p^2-6p}+3)$

(3) Remove the brackets and simplify each expression by collecting the terms.

(a) $(3a+5)+(2a-4)$

(b) $2x(3x-4)-3(x+5)$

(c) $(2b+7)-(b-2)-6$

(d) $2(4-3y)-3(2y+5)$

(e) $3(4p-6-\overline{2p-9})$

(f) $4x^2+6x-\overline{3x^2+4x}-9$

(g) $\frac{1}{4}(8a+4)-7(2a-2)+4(a-1)$

(h) $c-2(c-\overline{6c-3}+5)$

(i) $\frac{1}{3}(6x+9)-\frac{1}{2}(8x+4)+5(2x+2)$

(j) $(6m-4n)-(4m-6n)$

13 Factors

Single term factors

If the expression $3x(3x-5)$ is expanded, that is to say, multiplied out, the result

$$9x^2-15x \quad \text{is obtained}$$

If the expression $9x^2-15x$ is factorised the above process is reversed and the result

$$3x(3x-5) \quad \text{is obtained}$$

$3x$ is in fact the greatest expression that goes, exactly, into both $9x^2$ and $-15x$, i.e. the highest factor common to both expressions.

When factorising, it is essential to discover the **highest common factor**. Without it the expression will not be completely factorised.

Example 1. Factorise: $6p-9q$.

H.C.F.$=3$.

$$6p-9q = 3(2p-3q)$$

Example 2. Factorise $2x^3+4x^2y^2-6xy$.
H.C.F.$=2x$.

$$2x^3+4x^2y^2-6xy = 2x(x^2+2xy^2-3y)$$

In an expression where it is difficult to discover the H.C.F. it is useful to use a technique of factorising by grouping the terms.

Factors by grouping the terms

Example 3. Factorise $ax-ay+bx-by$.

In this expression $ax-ay+bx-by$ can be grouped repeatedly and factorised separately

$$a(x-y)+b(x-y)$$

Here $(x-y)$ is a common factor, thus by factorising again this result is obtained

$$(x-y)(a+b)$$

110

Example 4. Factorise $2ab+2a+c+bc$.

Group and factorise

$$2a(b+1)+c(1+b)$$

$(b+1)$ is the same as $(1+b)$, so factorise again

$$(2a+c)(b+1)$$

Exercise 1

(1) Expand the following (i.e. work out fully):

    (a) $2(4a^2-3)$ (d) $xy(2x-y)$

    (b) $b(3c+7)$ (e) $-3a(2a^2-a-4)$

    (c) $-3x(2x-6)$ (f) $ab(2a+2b-2)$

(2) Complete the following:

    (a) $3a+6b = 3(\qquad)$

    (b) $l^2+lm = l(\qquad)$

    (c) $-a^2b^2-b^2 = -b^2(\qquad)$

    (d) $5d-25d^2 = 5d(\qquad)$

    (e) $8x^3-6x^2y^2-4xy = \qquad(4x^2-3xy^2-2y)$

    (f) $4a^3+2a^2b^2-2a^2b = \qquad(-2a-b^2+b)$

(3) Factorise the following:

    (a) $6x^2+9x$ (f) $3x^3-9x^2y-6x^2$

    (b) $4x-8y$ (g) $R-R^2$

    (c) a^2-4a (h) $4b^3-8b^2c^2+12bc$

    (d) $20p-15q$ (i) $3a^2b+6ab-9ab^2$

    (e) $6x^2-12xy$ (j) $2x^4-4x^3+2x^2$

(4) Factorise by grouping the terms:

    (a) $x(z+2)+y(z+2)$

    (b) $a(2b-4)-2c(2b-4)$

    (c) $ab-ac+db-dc$

    (d) $4x+2z+2xy+yz$

    (e) $pq-q^2+3pr-3rq$

    (f) $6+3a+2b+ab$

    (g) $2x^2-3x+6xy-9y$

Products of binomials

If two or more terms are multiplied together the result obtained is called the **product** of these terms.

If an algebraic expression is made up of two terms, e.g. $(x+3)$, $(a-2)$, $(p-q)$, or $(2y+4)$ it is called a **binomial**.

The product of two binomials can always be found by long multiplication.

Example 1. Expand (multiply) $(a+5)(a-2)$.

$$\begin{array}{r} a+5 \\ \times\, a-2 \\ \hline a^2+5a \\ -2a-10 \\ \hline a^2+3a-10 \end{array}$$

It is extremely useful to be able to obtain binomial products mentally. The following method should enable this to be done fairly easily.

Example 2.

Expand $(x+3)(x+5)$.

Multiply together the first term in each bracket $\qquad x \times x = x^2$

Multiply the two inside terms $(3 \times x)$ and the two outside terms $(5 \times x)$ and add the results together $\qquad 3x+5x = 8x$

Multiply the last term in each bracket $\qquad 3 \times 5 = 15$

Add these results together and we obtain the product $\qquad x^2+8x+15$

Example 3. Expand $(x-3)(x-5)$.

First terms $x \times x = x^2$ Inside terms $-3 \times x = -3x$
Last terms $-3 \times -5 = +15$ Outside terms $-5 \times x = -5x$ $\bigg\}-8x$
Product $= x^2-8x+15$

Example 4. Expand $(3x-2)(4x+7)$.

$$(3x-\ 2)(4x+\ 7)$$

$$12x^2 \quad -14$$

$$-8x$$

$$+21x$$

$$+13x$$

Product $= 12x^2+13x-14$

Exercise 2

Expand (i.e. multiply out) the following, using the 'short' method:

(1) $(x+2)(x+3)$

(2) $(x+1)(x+2)$

(3) $(a+4)(a+5)$

(4) $(b+4)(b+5)$

(5) $(m+2)(m+6)$

(6) $(y+5)(y+7)$

(7) $(4+x)(3+x)$

(8) $(5+a)(2+a)$

(9) $(a-3)(a-1)$

(10) $(x-5)(x-2)$

(11) $(z-3)(z-7)$

(12) $(p-8)(p-1)$

(13) $(5-a)(3-a)$

(14) $(6-d)(4-d)$

(15) $(2x+3)(3x+2)$

(16) $(5x+1)(x+6)$

(17) $(3y+1)(2y+2)$

(18) $(3+3a)(5+2a)$

(19) $(1+7c)(3+3c)$

(20) $(5+3y)(10+2y)$

(21) $(3a-2)(2a-4)$

(22) $(3k-5)(2k-4)$

(23) $(2b-1)(b-8)$

(24) $(2m-6)(3m-4)$

(25) $(6-3a)(5-a)$

(26) $(7-3r)(5-4r)$

(27) $(x-2)(x+4)$

(28) $(x-7)(x+3)$

(29) $(a+4)(a-5)$

(30) $(b+10)(b-1)$

(31) $(9-s)(3+s)$

(32) $(5+p)(7-p)$

(33) $(2a-4)(a+6)$

(34) $(6y+3)(2y-4)$

(35) $(5x-3)(2x+10)$

(36) $(8b+5)(3b-1)$

(37) $(10-3a)(2+4a)$

(38) $(8+2p)(1-3p)$

(39) $(2y-b)(2y-b)$

(40) $(3x-4)^2$

(41) $(2r-s)(3r+2s)$

(42) $(3a+2b)(a-4b)$

(43) $(2b-c)(b+6c)$

(44) $(5x+3y)(9x-2y)$

Factors of trinomials

An algebraic expression that is made up of three terms, e.g. $x^2 - 8x + 15$, $12x^2 + 13x - 4$, is called a **trinomial**. It has been shown that the product of two binomials gives this result, thus the factors of a trinomial can be expressed as the product of two binomials.

Example 1. Factorise $x^2 + 8x + 15$.

Since this is a trinomial expression its factors can be expressed as the product of two binomials. Hence the factors of $x^2 + 8x + 15$ will be in this pattern: $(* \overset{+}{\underset{-}{\text{or}}} *)(* \overset{+}{\underset{-}{\text{or}}} *)$. When the first term in each bracket is multiplied together the result is the first term of the trinomial. In this example the first term is x^2, so the first factor in each bracket must be x, since only $x \times x = x^2$.

At this stage, then, the factor pattern is $(x \pm *)(x \pm *)$. The last term in each bracket, when multiplied together, give as a result the last term of the trinomial expression, in this case $+15$. The possible combinations that will give this result are:

$$+15 \times +1, \quad +5 \times +3, \quad -15 \times -1, \quad -5 \times -3$$

This gives four possible factor patterns:

(i) $(x+15)(x+1)$ (ii) $(x+5)(x+3)$
(iii) $(x-15)(x-1)$ (iv) $(x-5)(x-3)$

Multiply these out, using the 'short' method:

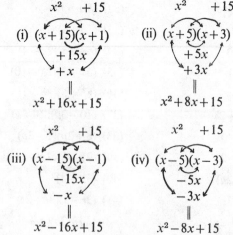

Since only (ii) gives the original expression the factors of
$$x^2 + 8x + 15 = (x+5)(x+3)$$

Example 2. Factorise $x^2 - 8x + 15$.

The first term is x^2 so the factor pattern must be

$$(x \pm *)(x \pm *)$$

The product of the second factor in each bracket must give $+15$. The possible combinations are

$$+15 \times +1, \quad +5 \times +3, \quad -15 \times -1, \quad -5 \times -3$$

However a negative (minus) value is required for the middle term of the original expression, i.e. $-8x$; $+15 \times +1$ and $+5 \times +3$ cannot give a negative result and can be discarded. This leaves as possible solutions:

(i) $(x-15)(x-1)$ (ii) $(x-5)(x-3)$

which when multiplied give

(i) $x^2 - 16x + 15$ (ii) $x^2 - 8x + 15$

Therefore the factors of $x^2 - 8x + 15 = (x-5)(x-3)$.

Example 3. Factorise $y^2 + 2y - 8$.

The factor pattern, since the first term is y^2, will be

$$(y \pm *)(y \pm *)$$

The possible combinations for the last term, -8, are

$$-4 \times +2, \quad +4 \times -2, \quad +8 \times -1, \quad -8 \times +1$$

Looking again at the original expression, $y^2 + 2y - 8$ it is clear that the correct combination of numbers must give $+2y$ as a middle term. By inspection (by trying each pair of numbers mentally) $+4 \times -2$ are shown to be the correct numbers. Therefore the factors of $y^2 + 2y - 8$ are $(y+4)(y-2)$.

Example 4. Factorise $y^2 - 2y - 8$.

Follow the method of the previous example. This time the middle term is $-2y$ and the combination that gives this result is $-4 \times +2$. Thus, the factors of $y^2 - 2y - 8$ are

$$(y-4)(y+2)$$

115

Rules

Here are some rules that may help with the signs. Remember it is far better to try and understand what you are doing than to follow a rule blindly.

(1) *If the last term of a trinomial is + then the signs in each bracket of its factors will be alike, both + or both −.*

(2) *If the middle term is also + then the signs in the brackets will both be +.*

(3) *If, however, the middle term is − the signs in the brackets will be −.*

(4) *If the last term of a trinomial is − then the signs in the brackets will be unlike.*

Exercise 3

Factorise

(1) $x^2 + 6x + 8$

(2) $y^2 + 7y + 10$

(3) $a^2 + 5a + 6$

(4) $b^2 + 9b + 8$

(5) $x^2 + 8x + 15$

(6) $x^2 - 6x + 8$

(7) $a^2 - 3a + 2$

(8) $b^2 - 6b + 9$

(9) $r^2 - 8r + 12$

(10) $s^2 - 8s + 15$

(11) $a^2 + a - 2$

(12) $x^2 + x - 6$

(13) $b^2 + 2b - 8$

(14) $t^2 + 2t - 24$

(15) $a^2 + 9a - 36$

(16) $a^2 - 2a - 3$

(17) $x^2 - 2x - 24$

(18) $b^2 - 6b - 27$

(19) $y^2 - 4y - 5$

(20) $n^2 - 8n - 9$

A trinomial of the form $3b^2 - 10b + 8$ is more difficult to factorise than trinomials of the type found in Exercise 3. The difficulty is caused by the fact that the first term is not simply b^2 but has a numerical coefficient, e.g. 3.

Example 1. Factorise $3b^2 - 10b + 8$.

The factor pattern, since the first term is $3b^2$, will be

$$(3b \pm *)(b \pm *)$$

The possible combinations for the last term $+8$ are

$$+8 \times +1, \quad +4 \times +2, \quad -8 \times -1, \quad -4 \times -2$$

Since the middle term is $-10b$ the combinations with $+$ signs only ($+8 \times +1$ and $+4 \times +2$) can be disregarded, leaving -8×-1 and -4×-2.

The possible alternatives now become

(i) $(3b - 8)(b - 1)$ Multiply by the short method, con-
$-11b$ centrating on the results that give the
middle term of the trinomial.

(ii) $(3b - 1)(b - 8)$
$-25b$

(iii) $(3b - 4)(b - 2)$
$-10b$

(iv) $(3b - 2)(b - 4)$
$-14b$

Alternative (iii) gives the required result, so the factors of $3b^2 - 10b + 8 = (3b - 4)(b - 2)$.

Exercise 4

Factorise:

(1) $2x^2 + 8x + 8$

(2) $3a^2 + 9a + 6$

(3) $2x^2 - 6x - 20$

(4) $2b^2 - 2b - 12$

(5) $3y^2 + 3y - 18$

(6) $2x^2 + 2x - 12$

(7) $2r^2 - 9r + 4$

(8) $6s^2 - 14s + 8$

(9) $2c^2 + 5c + 3$

(10) $2z^2 - yz - y^2$

(11) $2a^2 - 5ab + 2b^2$

(12) $2p^2 + pq - q^2$

(13) $6 - 8x + 2x^2$

(14) $6 + 3y - 3y^2$

(15) $2 - a - 6a^2$

Squares of binomials

Take the binomial $(a + b)$. To multiply it by itself, e.g. $(a + b)(a + b)$ is to square it and this can be written as $(a + b)^2$.

Example 1. Expand $(a+b)^2$.

$$(a+b)^2 = (a+b)(a+b)$$
$$= a^2+2ab+b^2 \quad \text{or} \quad a^2+b^2+2ab$$

Example 2. Expand $(a-b)^2$.

$$(a-b)^2 = (a-b)(a-b)$$
$$= a^2-2ab+b^2 \quad \text{or} \quad a^2+b^2-2ab$$

These two results are the standard form for squaring the sum of two terms, and squaring the difference of two terms. They should be memorised.

Example 3. Expand $(x+5)^2$.

$$(x+5)^2 = (x+5)(x+5)$$
$$= x^2+5^2+(5x+5x)$$
$$= x^2+25+10x \quad \text{or} \quad x^2+10x+25$$

Example 4. Expand $(2-x)^2$.

$$(2-x)^2 = (2-x)(2-x)$$
$$= 2^2+x^2-(2x+2x)$$
$$= 4+x^2-4x \quad \text{or} \quad x^2-4x+4$$

Difference of two squares

Consider the binomial product $(a+b)(a-b)$

$$
\begin{array}{r}
a+b \\
\times\, a-b \\
\hline
a^2+ab \\
-ab-b^2 \\
\hline
a^2 \qquad -b^2 \\
\end{array}
$$

Thus the factors of $a^2-b^2=(a+b)(a-b)$ which is the standard form for the factors of the difference of two squares since a^2 is a perfect square, b^2 is a perfect square and to subtract them is to find their difference. Again

$$a^2-b^2 = (a+b)(a-b)$$

This should be memorised.

118

Example 5. Factorise $x^2 - 9$.

$$x^2 - 9 = x^2 - 3^2$$

Using the standard form, the factors are $(x + 3)(x - 3)$ as above.

Example 6. Factorise $16y^2 - 81$.

$$16y^2 - 81 = (4y)^2 - 9^2$$

Factors are $(4y + 9)(4y - 9)$.

We have seen that the factors of

$$a^2 - b^2 = (a + b)(a - b)$$

and this fact can be used as an aid in certain calculations.

Example 7. Find the value of $45^2 - 29^2$.

The factors of $a^2 - b^2 = (a + b)(a - b)$. Thus the factors of

$$\begin{aligned}
45^2 - 29^2 &= (45 + 29)(45 - 29) \\
&= 74 \times 16 \\
&= 1{,}184
\end{aligned}$$

Example 8. Find the value of $7{\cdot}4^2 - 3{\cdot}8^2$.

$$\begin{aligned}
7{\cdot}4^2 - 3{\cdot}8^2 &= (7{\cdot}4 + 3{\cdot}8)(7{\cdot}4 - 3{\cdot}8) \\
&= 11{\cdot}2 \times 3{\cdot}6 \\
&= 40{\cdot}32
\end{aligned}$$

Exercise 5

Expand (i.e. multiply out) the following:

(1) $(x + 3)^2$

(2) $(2x + 5)^2$

(3) $(3a + 2)^2$

(4) $(x - 2)^2$

(5) $(3a - 4)^2$

(6) $(4c - 3)^2$

(7) $(2b + 3c)^2$

(8) $(3x - 4y)^2$

(9) $(4p - 2q)^2$

(10) $(4c + 7d)^2$

(11) $(4 + 2r)^2$

(12) $(3 - 4k)^2$

Factorise the following:

(13) $x^2+2xy+y^2$

(14) $9a^2+18ab+9b^2$

(15) x^2-4x+4

(16) $4a^2-12a+9$

(17) $p^2+4pq+4q^2$

(18) $4m^2-4mn+n^2$

(19) x^2-y^2

(20) $4a^2-9b^2$

(21) b^2-16

(22) a^2-1

(23) $4-b^2$

(24) x^4-100

(25) $4p^2-9q^2$

(26) $36-16a^2$

(27) $9a^2b^2-25$

(28) $49-36k^2$

(29) y^4-4z^4

(30) $4x^4-121$

Use factors to find the value of:

(31) 17^2-8^2

(32) 28^2-22^2

(33) 43^2-35^2

(34) 97^2-57^2

(35) 86^2-67^2

(36) 176^2-6^2

(37) $4.6^2-2.5^2$

(38) $9.8^2-7.4^2$

(39) $14.3^2-8.8^2$

(40) $(2\frac{1}{3})^2-(\frac{2}{3})^2$

(41) $(3\frac{1}{4})^2-(\frac{3}{4})^2$

14 Algebraic Fractions

Algebraic fractions obey the same rules as ordinary vulgar fractions. However when dealing with fractions in algebra the rules for multiplication and division of signed numbers and powers should not be forgotten.

If the numerator and denominator of a fraction is multiplied or divided by the same quantity, then the value of the fraction is unchanged.

Example 1.

$$\frac{3}{4} \text{ multiply top and bottom by } 7 = \frac{21}{28}$$

$$\frac{56}{64} \text{ divide top and bottom by } 8 \quad = \frac{7}{8}$$

$$\frac{4}{9} \text{ multiply top and bottom by } y = \frac{4y}{9y}$$

$$\frac{7a}{14} \text{ divide top and bottom by } 7 \quad = \frac{a}{2}$$

$$\frac{x-3}{y} \text{ multiply top and bottom by } x^2 \quad = \frac{x^2(x-3)}{x^2y} = \frac{x^3-3x^2}{x^2y}$$

$$\frac{c^2-2cd^2}{3c-6d^2} \text{ divide top and bottom by } c-2d^2 = \frac{c(c-2d^2)}{3(c-2d^2)} = \frac{c}{3}$$

Exercise 1

(1) Complete the following:

(a)   (b)   (c)

$$\frac{2}{3} = \frac{}{15} \qquad \frac{7}{8} = \frac{}{56} \qquad \frac{5}{4} = \frac{}{24}$$

(d)   (e)   (f)

$$\frac{2a}{4} = \frac{}{8} \qquad \frac{5x}{8} = \frac{}{32} \qquad \frac{3c^2}{ab} = \frac{}{4ab}$$

(2) Complete the following:

(a)
$$\frac{3}{4} = \frac{12}{}$$

(b)
$$\frac{y}{5} = \frac{y^2}{}$$

(c)
$$\frac{2x}{3y} = \frac{2x^2}{}$$

(d)
$$\frac{2b}{5c} = \frac{2bd}{}$$

(e)
$$\frac{x-2y}{x} = \frac{}{xy}$$

(f)
$$\frac{r}{p-q} = \frac{}{2r(p-q)}$$

(3) Simplify the following by reducing them to their lowest terms:

(a) $\dfrac{45}{63}$ (b) $\dfrac{56}{72}$ (c) $\dfrac{4x}{16}$ (d) $\dfrac{6a}{18a}$

(e) $\dfrac{16a^2}{24a^3}$ (f) $\dfrac{21x^2}{7x}$ (g) $\dfrac{2xy}{6xy}$ (h) $\dfrac{9ab}{27abc}$

(i) $\dfrac{2(p+q)}{3r(p+q)}$ (j) $\dfrac{(a-b)(a+b)}{a+b}$ (k) $\dfrac{(a+b)^2}{4(a+b)}$

Addition and subtraction

Fractions to be added or subtracted must have the same denominator. The work is made easier if this common denominator is the lowest one.

Example 2. $\frac{3}{5} + \frac{9}{10}$.

The lowest number that will contain the denominators 5 and 10 is 10. So each fraction is changed into 10ths and then added together.

$$\frac{3}{5} + \frac{9}{10} = \frac{6+9}{10} = \frac{15}{10} = 1\frac{5}{10} = 1\frac{1}{2}$$

Example 3. Simplify $\dfrac{2x}{5} + \dfrac{x}{3} - \dfrac{3y}{5}$.

The lowest common denominator (L.C.M.) is 15. Convert to a common denominator of 15.

$$\frac{6x}{15} + \frac{5x}{15} - \frac{9y}{15}$$

This can be rewritten as

$$\frac{6x+5x-9y}{15}$$

122

Simplify by collecting like terms

$$\frac{11x - 9y}{15}$$

Note: Do not try to cancel $9y$ and 15 because 3 is not a common factor of the numerator.

Example 4. Simplify $\dfrac{5x}{y} + \dfrac{3y}{x} - \dfrac{2}{xy}$.

L.C.M. $= xy$.

$$\frac{5x}{y} + \frac{3y}{x} - \frac{2}{xy} = \frac{5x.x + 3y.y - 2.1}{xy}$$

$$= \frac{5x^2 + 3y^2 - 2}{xy}$$

Example 5. Simplify $6 - \left(\dfrac{1}{x} + \dfrac{2}{x^2}\right)$.

Remove brackets, noting the $-$ sign outside brackets. L.C.M. $= x^2$.

$$6 - \left(\frac{1}{x} + \frac{2}{x^2}\right) = \frac{6}{1} - \frac{1}{x} - \frac{2}{x^2}$$

$$= \frac{6x^2 - x - 2}{x^2}$$

Exercise 2

Simplify:

	(a)	(b)	(c)	(d)
(1)	$\dfrac{5}{6} + \dfrac{7}{12}$	$\dfrac{2x}{3} + \dfrac{x}{6}$	$\dfrac{4a}{8} + \dfrac{3a}{4}$	$\dfrac{9y}{5} + \dfrac{3y}{10}$
(2)	$\dfrac{3}{b} + \dfrac{7}{2b}$	$\dfrac{4}{3x} + \dfrac{2}{x}$	$\dfrac{a}{3} + \dfrac{2b}{a}$	$\dfrac{4x}{2y} + \dfrac{z}{y}$
(3)	$\dfrac{5}{8} - \dfrac{1}{4}$	$\dfrac{3x}{6} - \dfrac{x}{3}$	$\dfrac{9p}{10} - \dfrac{3p}{5}$	$\dfrac{4n}{3} - \dfrac{n}{6}$
(4)	$\dfrac{6}{b} - \dfrac{1}{2b}$	$\dfrac{4x}{3} - \dfrac{x}{2y}$	$\dfrac{2a}{b} - \dfrac{b}{a}$	$\dfrac{9x}{5y} - \dfrac{4y}{x}$

123

(5) (a) $\dfrac{5x}{3}+\dfrac{3x}{2}+\dfrac{9y}{4}$ (b) $\dfrac{x}{3}+4$ (c) $2+\dfrac{4}{5x}$

(6) (a) $\dfrac{x}{4}+\dfrac{y}{5}+\dfrac{z}{2}$ (b) $\dfrac{x}{4}+\dfrac{x}{6}+\dfrac{x}{12}$ (c) $\dfrac{b}{3}+\dfrac{c}{6}+2$

(7) (a) $\dfrac{3}{c^2}+\dfrac{2}{c}+3$ (b) $\dfrac{x}{8}+\dfrac{2x}{2}-\dfrac{3x}{4}$ (c) $\dfrac{a}{2}+\dfrac{a}{3}-\dfrac{a}{4}$

(8) (a) $\dfrac{3}{x^2}-\dfrac{2}{x}+4$ (b) $5-\dfrac{1}{a}+\dfrac{3}{b}$ (c) $\dfrac{5}{4}-\dfrac{x}{4y}+\dfrac{y}{6x}$

(9) (a) $5-\left(\dfrac{2}{c}+\dfrac{2}{c^2}\right)$ (b) $3a-\left(\dfrac{b}{4}+\dfrac{c}{6}\right)$ (c) $2p+\left(\dfrac{1}{q}-\dfrac{1}{r}\right)$

(10) (a) $\dfrac{2a-6}{a}+\dfrac{4a+3}{a}$ (b) $\dfrac{x}{x-2}-\dfrac{2y}{x-2}$

(11) (a) $\dfrac{2b-2}{3}+\dfrac{3b}{6}$ (b) $\dfrac{r-5}{2}-\dfrac{r}{8}$

(12) (a) $\dfrac{3x}{x+2}-\dfrac{x+3}{x+2}$ (b) $\dfrac{2p}{p+2}-\dfrac{5q}{p}$

(13) (a) $\dfrac{S-3}{2}+\dfrac{S+1}{6}$ (b) $\dfrac{3b+2}{c}-\dfrac{c-1}{b}$

(14) (a) $\dfrac{2a}{d-3}+\dfrac{3}{d-3}-\dfrac{1}{4}$ (b) $\dfrac{5a+6}{a}+\dfrac{3a-7}{a}-\dfrac{2}{3}$

(15) (a) $\dfrac{2c+1}{c}+\dfrac{2c}{3}-\dfrac{c}{2}$ (b) $4p-\dfrac{q}{2}-\dfrac{r}{5}$

Multiplication and division

To multiply a fraction by a fraction, multiply the numerators and then the denominators to obtain the required result. Take every opportunity to cancel common factors as this makes the work easier.

Example 8. Simplify $\dfrac{7}{16} \times \dfrac{4}{14}$

$$\dfrac{\overset{1}{\cancel{7}}}{\underset{4}{\cancel{16}}} \times \dfrac{\overset{1}{\cancel{4}}}{\underset{2}{\cancel{14}}} = \dfrac{1}{8}$$

Example 9. Simplify $\dfrac{5a}{8b} \times \dfrac{4}{a}$

$$\dfrac{\overset{5}{\cancel{5a}}}{\underset{2b}{\cancel{8b}}} \times \dfrac{\overset{1}{\cancel{4}}}{\underset{1}{\cancel{a}}} = \dfrac{5}{2b}$$

Example 10. Simplify $\dfrac{12x^2}{3x-3y} \times \dfrac{x-y}{3x}$

$$\dfrac{12x^2}{3x-3y} \times \dfrac{x-y}{3x} = \dfrac{\overset{4x}{\cancel{12x^2}}}{\underset{1}{3\cancel{(x-y)}}} \times \dfrac{\cancel{x-y}}{\underset{1}{\cancel{3x}}} = \dfrac{4x}{3}$$

Factorise to make cancelling easier.

To divide a fraction by a fraction invert the divisor and change the division sign to multiplication.

Example 11. Simplify $\dfrac{9}{21} \div \dfrac{3}{7}$

$$\dfrac{9}{21} \div \dfrac{3}{7} = \dfrac{\overset{\overset{1}{\cancel{3}}}{\cancel{9}}}{\underset{\underset{1}{\cancel{3}}}{\cancel{21}}} \times \dfrac{\overset{1}{\cancel{7}}}{\underset{1}{\cancel{3}}} = \dfrac{1}{1} = 1$$

Example 12. Simplify $\dfrac{12xy}{a^2} \div \dfrac{3x}{2a^2}$

$$\dfrac{12xy}{a^2} \div \dfrac{3x}{2a^2} = \dfrac{\overset{4y}{\cancel{12xy}}}{\underset{1}{\cancel{a^2}}} \times \dfrac{\overset{2}{\cancel{2a^2}}}{\underset{1}{\cancel{3x}}}$$

$$= \dfrac{8y}{1} = 8y$$

Example 13. Simplify $\dfrac{9x^2}{(x+y)^2} \div \dfrac{6x}{x+y}$.

$$\frac{9x^2}{(x+y)^2} \div \frac{6x}{x+y} = \frac{\overset{3x}{\cancel{9x^2}}}{\underset{x+y}{\cancel{(x+y)^2}}} \times \frac{x+y}{\underset{2}{\cancel{6x}}}$$

$$= \frac{3x}{2(x+y)} = \frac{3x}{2x+2y}$$

Exercise 3

Simplify:

(1)　(a)　　　　(b)　　　　(c)　　　　(d)

$\dfrac{4}{9} \times \dfrac{15}{16}$　　$\dfrac{7}{8} \times 4$　　$\dfrac{3}{4} \times \dfrac{2a}{5}$　　$\dfrac{3x}{8} \times \dfrac{5}{9}$

(2)　(a)　　　　(b)　　　　(c)　　　　(d)

$\dfrac{3y}{8} \times 4$　　$\dfrac{7}{9} \times 3y$　　$\dfrac{2p}{3} \times 6q$　　$\dfrac{2a}{3b} \times \dfrac{3}{4}$

(3)　(a)　　　　(b)　　　　(c)　　　　(d)

$\dfrac{2x}{3y} \times \dfrac{y}{4}$　　$\dfrac{6a}{5b} \times \dfrac{2b}{3a}$　　$\dfrac{x^2}{3y} \times \dfrac{6z}{2x}$　　$\dfrac{3b^2}{2bc} \times \dfrac{4c^2}{b}$

(4)　(a)　　　　　(b)　　　　　(c)

$\dfrac{2x+3}{2x-3} \times \dfrac{2}{3}$　　$\dfrac{2}{a+3} \times \dfrac{a}{2}$　　$\dfrac{b-3}{3} \times \dfrac{6}{b+3}$

(5)　(a)　　　　　(b)　　　　　(c)

$\dfrac{1}{a^2b^2} \times \dfrac{2ab}{3}$　　$\dfrac{3cd}{4c-1} \times \dfrac{4c+1}{5d}$　　$\dfrac{2a^2-2a}{5} \times \dfrac{10}{a-2}$

(6)　(a)　　　　(b)　　　　(c)　　　　(d)

$\dfrac{4}{5} \div \dfrac{10}{16}$　　$\dfrac{11}{18} \div 3$　　$\dfrac{3a}{4} \div \dfrac{5}{8}$　　$\dfrac{3x}{5} \div \dfrac{9}{10}$

(7)　(a)　　　　(b)　　　　(c)　　　　(d)

$\dfrac{5x}{4y} \div \dfrac{x}{6}$　　$\dfrac{6r}{8s} \div \dfrac{2r}{4s}$　　$\dfrac{4x}{y} \div \dfrac{2x^2}{y^2}$　　$\dfrac{6p}{10q} \div \dfrac{4r^2}{6q^2}$

(8) (a) $\dfrac{4a^2}{(a+b)^2} \div \dfrac{8a}{a+b}$　　(b) $\dfrac{x-2y}{z^2} \div \dfrac{x+4y}{z}$

(c) $\dfrac{3ab}{a+b} \div \dfrac{2b}{a+b}$　　(d) $\dfrac{6r^3}{5^2} \div \dfrac{1}{2r^25^2}$

(9) (a) $\dfrac{2a-4}{b} \div \dfrac{2}{b^2}$ (b) $\dfrac{(6a-4b)^2}{a+b} \div \dfrac{6a-4b}{a}$

(c) $\dfrac{6b^2c}{3} \div 9bc^2$ (d) $\dfrac{2x}{x+y} \div \dfrac{4x^2}{(x+y)^2}$

(10) (a) $\dfrac{5bc}{2b^2} \div \dfrac{15cd}{4c^2}$ (b) $\dfrac{5x^2}{(x-2y)} \div \dfrac{10xy}{2(x-2y)}$

(c) $\dfrac{(a+b)(a-b)}{4ab} \div \dfrac{(a+b)^2}{6a^2}$

5*

15 Simple Equations

Solving an equation means finding the value of the unknown letter (usually x) which 'satisfies' the equation, that is, makes it 'work out'. Whenever an equation is solved the answer must be checked by substituting it in the original equation for x.

Example 1. Solve $x-9=23$.

Because $x-9$ is equal to 23 then 9 can be added to each side of the equation without unbalancing the equation. Therefore

$$x-9+9 = 23+9$$
so
$$x = 32$$

Check by substituting for x

$$x-9 = 23$$
$$32-9 = 23$$

Example 2. Solve $x+9=23$.

Because $x+9$ is equal to 23 then 9 can be subtracted from each side of the equation without unbalancing it. Therefore

$$x+9-9 = 23-9$$
so
$$x = 14$$

Check by substituting for x

$$x+9 = 23$$
$$14+9 = 23$$

Example 3. Solve $9x=36$.

Because $9x$ is equal to 36 each side of the equation can be divided by 9 without unbalancing it. Therefore

$$9x \div 9 = 36 \div 9$$
so
$$x = 4$$

Check

$$9x = 36$$
$$9 \times 4 = 36$$

128

Example 4. Solve $\frac{x}{4} = 7$.

Because $\frac{x}{4}$ is equal to 7 each side of the equation can be multiplied by 4 without unbalancing it. Therefore

$$\frac{x}{4} \times \frac{4}{1} = 7 \times 4$$

so
$$x = 28$$

Check

$$\frac{x}{4} = 7$$

$$\frac{28}{4} = 7$$

Any simple equation can be solved (worked out) by using one or more of these methods.

Briefly they can be stated as:

(i) *The same amount can be added to each side.*

(ii) *The same amount can be taken from each side.*

(iii) *Each side can be multiplied by the same amount.*

(iv) *Each side can be divided by the same amount.*

Example 5. Solve $5x - 13 = 27$.

This equation can be solved by adding 13 to each side

$$5x - 13 + 13 = 27 + 13$$

This removes -13 from the left side and puts $+13$ on the right side. If we go straight to this stage it gives us an easier method of working.

Solve
$$5x - 13 = 27$$

Change -13 over, where it becomes $+13$.

$$5x = 27 + 13$$
$$5x = 40$$
$$x = 40 \div 5 = 8$$

Check

$$5x - 13 = 27$$
$$5 \times 8 - 13 = 27$$

129

This shows that any term can be changed from one side of an equation to the other as long as its sign is changed.

Example 6. Solve $7x-5=2x+20$.

Change -5 to right-hand side and it becomes $+5$

$$7x = 2x+20+5$$

Change $2x$ to left-hand side and it becomes $-2x$

$$7x-2x = 20+5$$

Collect the terms

$$5x = 25$$

thus
$$x = 25 \div 5$$
$$= 5$$

The root (i.e. the solution) of an equation can be positive $(+)$ or negative $(-)$.

Example 7. Solve $6a+10=3a+1$.

Change 10 to the right-hand side, where it becomes -10, and change $3a$ to the left-hand side where it becomes $-3a$

$$6a-3a = 1-10$$

Collect the terms

$$3a = -9$$
$$\therefore a = -9 \div 3$$
$$= -3$$

Example 8. Solve $2b-8=9b+6$.

Change -8 to right-hand side where it becomes $+8$; change $9b$ to left-hand side where it becomes $-9b$

$$2b-9b = 6+8$$

Collect the terms

$$-7b = 14$$

thus
$$-b = 2$$

If $-b=2$, then
$$b = -2$$

It is usual to find the value of the unknown, not minus the unknown; thus in Example 8 the result is given as $b=-2$.

Exercise 1

(1) A class, told to solve the equation $\frac{5x}{6} - 10 = 10$ gives the following answers:

   (a) $x = 10$ (b) $x = 24$ (c) $x = 0$ (d) $x = -24$

By substituting find which is correct.

Solve the following equations:

(2)   (a)   (b)   (c)
$x - 7 = 18$ $x + 6 = 12$ $a - 17 = 2$

     (d)   (e)   (f)
$b + 8 = 11$ $c - 14 = 22$ $d + 9 = 16$

(3)   (a)   (b)   (c)
$8x = 48$ $7b = 42$ $4y = 36$

     (d)   (e)   (f)
$10c = 5$ $2x = 1$ $12b = 3$

(4)   (a)   (b)   (c)
$\frac{c}{5} = 5$ $\frac{x}{4} = 16$ $\frac{d}{8} = 4$

     (d)   (e)   (f)
$\frac{2a}{3} = 6$ $\frac{5x}{6} = 10$ $\frac{3b}{4} = 5\frac{1}{4}$

(5)   (a)   (b)   (c)
$5x + 3 = 18$ $4a - 2 = 14$ $3y + 9 = 27$

     (d)   (e)   (f)
$6a = 2a + 12$ $3c = 15 - 2c$ $7b = 16 - 3b$

(6)   (a)   (b)   (c)
$4x - 10 = 2x$ $4y - 11 = y + 1$ $4b = 21 - 3b$

     (d)   (e)   (f)
$3a - 10 = 15 - 2a$ $2r - 6 = r + 9$ $5c + 6 = 2c + 24$

(7)   (a)   (b)   (c)
$3x + 5 = 2x$ $5y + 9 = y - 7$ $12 + 4a = 7a - 21$

     (d)   (e)   (f)
$2z - 6 = 4z + 10$ $2c + 3 = 5c + 9$ $12 - 2b = 4b + 36$

(8)   (a)   (b)
$$5a-6+8 = 3a+10 \qquad 14+9x+4-2x = x-12$$

         (c)   (d)
$$4n-7+2n+3 = 2n+20 \qquad 3y-7y+14 = y-11$$

         (e)   (f)
$$11-r+4-2r = 2r-5 \qquad 3x-4+27-5x = 5-x$$

Simple equations with brackets

When the terms of an equation are bracketed together simply remove the brackets first and then solve the equation.

Note: Turn to page 107 if you want to revise the rules for removing brackets.

Example 9. Solve $6y-4(2+y)=16$.

Remove brackets

$$6y-8-4y = 16$$

Transfer -8, changing sign

$$6y-4y = 16+8$$
$$2y = 24$$
$$y = 12$$

Simple equations with fractions

If each side of an equation consists of a single fraction it can be solved by the method of cross multiplication.

Example 10. Solve $\dfrac{3x}{5}=\dfrac{4}{5}$.

Multiply in the direction of the arrows

$$\frac{3x}{5} \diagdown \diagup \frac{4}{5}$$

$$15x = 20$$

$$x = \frac{20}{15} = 1\tfrac{1}{3}$$

Example 11. Solve $\dfrac{3}{4} = \dfrac{y+3}{2y-6}$.

A numerator or denominator containing more than one term can be treated as a single term

$$\frac{3}{4} \times \frac{y+3}{2y-6}$$

$$3(2y-6) = 4(y+3)$$
$$6y-18 = 4y+12$$
$$6y-4y = 12+18$$
$$2y = 30$$
$$y = 15$$

If the equation has more than a single fraction on either side, the fractions must be removed by multiplying both sides by the common denominator, preferably the lowest common denominator.

Example 12. Solve $\frac{y+2}{4} - \frac{2y-8}{6} = \frac{y}{3}$.

The L.C.M. of 4, 6, 3 = 12. Multiply each side of the equation by 12. This is done by dividing each denominator into 12 and multiplying the numerator by the result, e.g.:

$$12 \times \frac{y+2}{4}, \qquad \text{4 into 12 gives 3,} \quad \therefore \; 3 \times (y+2)$$

$$12 \times -\frac{2y-8}{6}, \qquad \text{6 into 12 gives 2,} \quad \therefore \; 2 \times -(2y-8)$$

$$12 \times \frac{y}{3}, \qquad \text{3 into 12 gives 4,} \quad \therefore \; 4 \times y$$

Note: brackets must be put in when the fraction-bar disappears; for this bar acts as a bracket. This gives

$$3(y+2)-2(2y-8) = 4 \times y$$

Remove the brackets $\qquad 3y+6-4y+16 = 4y$

Collect terms $\qquad\qquad\quad 3y-4y+22 = 4y$

Transfer $+22$ and $4y$ $\qquad 3y-4y-4y = -22$

$$-5y = -22$$
$$-y = -4\tfrac{2}{5}$$

if $\qquad\qquad\qquad\qquad\qquad -y = -4\tfrac{2}{5}$

then $\qquad\qquad\qquad\qquad\quad +y = +4\tfrac{2}{5}$

Exercise 2

Solve the following equations:

(1)   (a)   (b)   (c)

$3(x+1) = 9$ $5(2a+3) = 25$ $3-(2-b) = 4$

      (d)   (e)   (f)

$5+(2x-3) = 6$ $5b-2(b+3) = 3$ $3(a+3)-4(a+4) = 0$

(2)   (a)   (b)

$6(b-2)+3(2b+1) = 3(b-9)$ $21 = 4(x+3)-2(6x+7)$

                (c)   (d)

$3x-3-2(4x-5) = -4(x+1)$ $2(2c-1)+3c+6 = 2(2c+5)-4c$

(3)   (a)   (b)   (c)   (d)

$\dfrac{3a}{4} = \dfrac{3}{2}$ $\dfrac{d}{3} = \dfrac{2}{5}$ $\dfrac{2x}{5} = \dfrac{5}{3}$ $\dfrac{P}{6} = \dfrac{4}{3}$

   (e)   (f)   (g)   (h)

$\dfrac{5}{a} = \dfrac{3}{6}$ $\dfrac{2 \cdot 1}{z} = \dfrac{2}{0 \cdot 8}$ $\dfrac{4}{7} = \dfrac{8}{y}$ $\dfrac{5}{2 \cdot 5} = \dfrac{x}{8}$

(4) (a) $\dfrac{2y+4}{3} = \dfrac{3y-2}{5}$ (d) $\dfrac{3b-5}{2} = \dfrac{2b+5}{3}$

    (b) $\dfrac{a+3}{2} = \dfrac{a-1}{3}$ (e) $\dfrac{3(2z-2)}{4} = \dfrac{z-3}{2}$

    (c) $\dfrac{3}{2x-4} = \dfrac{4}{x+3}$ (f) $\dfrac{5(x-3)}{4} = \dfrac{3x}{2}$

(5) (a) $\dfrac{2x}{5}-2 = 20$ (d) $\dfrac{a}{2}+\dfrac{a}{3}-\dfrac{a}{6} = 12$

    (b) $\dfrac{3a}{4}-6 = \dfrac{a}{4}+2$ (e) $\dfrac{n}{4}+\dfrac{n}{2} = 7-n$

    (c) $\dfrac{z}{3}+\dfrac{z}{4} = 7$ (f) $\dfrac{2x}{5}+\dfrac{3x}{5}+\dfrac{3x}{10} = \dfrac{7x}{10}+3$

(6) (a) $\dfrac{a+4}{8}+\dfrac{a-4}{2} = 1$ (d) $\dfrac{4b-3}{2}+1 = \dfrac{3b-5}{4}-\dfrac{3}{4}$

    (b) $\dfrac{2x-3}{3}-\dfrac{3x+2}{5} = 0$ (e) $\dfrac{2(a-3)}{3}-\dfrac{2(2a-2)}{2} = \dfrac{a+4}{3}+\dfrac{2}{3}$

    (c) $\dfrac{3c-5}{4}-\dfrac{2c-4}{3} = \dfrac{c}{3}$ (f) $\dfrac{3y+3}{4}-\dfrac{2y-5}{3}+\dfrac{7}{12} = \dfrac{-y}{6}$

Problems leading to simple equations

Many problems can be solved by using simple equations. The following examples show the general methods used.

Example 1. Three less than 5 times a number is the same as 9 added to 3 times the number. Find the number.

Let x represent the number, therefore

$$5 \text{ times the number} = 5x$$

$$3 \text{ less than } 5x = 5x - 3$$

This is the same as 3 times the number, i.e. $3x$, plus 9

$$= 3x + 9$$

so that $$5x - 3 = 3x + 9$$

Solve this equation,

$$5x - 3x = 9 + 3$$

$$2x = 12$$

$$x = 6$$

The number is 6.

Check: $$5 \times 6 - 3 = 27$$

$$3 \times 6 + 9 = 27$$

Example 2. The longest side of a rectangle is 3 times the shorter side. If the perimeter of the rectangle is 32 cm find the length of its sides.

Let x represent the length of the shorter side in centimetres. Therefore the length of the longer side $= 3x$ cm. Then the perimeter of the rectangle (see Fig. 35)

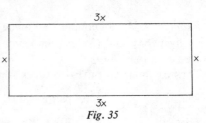

Fig. 35

$$= 3x + 3x + x + x$$

$$= 8x$$

$$\therefore 8x = 32 \text{ cm}$$

$$x = 4 \text{ cm}$$

and $$3x = 12 \text{ cm}$$

The size of the rectangle is 12 cm by 4 cm

Check: $$12 + 12 + 4 + 4 = 32$$

Example 3. A boy cycles for $2\frac{1}{2}$ h but has a puncture and has to finish his journey on foot, walking for a further 2 h. The total distance he covers is 48 km. If he cycles four times as fast as he walks, at what speed does he cycle?

Let x km/h be the speed at which the boy walks.

Since he walks for 2 h the distance he covers $= 2x$ km

Also the speed at which he cycles $= 4x$ km/h

Since he cycles for $2\frac{1}{2}$ h the distance he covers $= 4x \times 2\frac{1}{2}$
$$= 10x \text{ km}$$

Now distance walked + distance cycled $= $ total distance travelled

Thus
$$2x + 10x = 48 \text{ km}$$
$$12x = 48 \text{ km}$$
$$x = 4 \text{ km}$$

The boy walks at 4 km/h
Therefore he cycles at 4×4 km/h $= 16$ km/h

Check:
$$(2 \times 4) + (2\tfrac{1}{2} \times 16) = 48 \text{ km}$$
$$\downarrow \qquad \downarrow$$
Distance   Distance
walked   cycled

Example 4. A bag contains £6 made up of 5p and 10p coins, there are $6x$ fivepenny and $(3x-6)$ tenpenny pieces. Find the number of each type of coin.

Thus $6x$ times $5p + (3x-6)$ times $10p = £6$

And
$$30x \text{ pence} + (30x - 60) \text{ pence} = 600\text{p}$$

That is:
$$30x + 30x - 60 = 600$$
$$60x = 600 + 60$$
$$60x = 660$$
$$x = 11$$

So
number of 5p coins is $6 \times 11 = 66$
number of 10p coins is $33 - 6 = 27$

Check: $66 \times 5p = £3 \cdot 30$ and $27 \times 10p = £2 \cdot 70$
$$\text{Total} = £6$$

Exercise 3

(1) Find the number:

(a) when 7 times the number is four less than 67;
(b) when 28 is one more than $\frac{3}{4}$ of the number;
(c) when 5, plus 3 times the number, is 41.

(2) Two consecutive even numbers add up to 30. What are the numbers?

(3) Three consecutive odd numbers add up to 27. What are the numbers?

(4) Four times a number is 9 more than 3 times a smaller number. The sum of the two numbers is 11. Find both numbers.

(5) A rectangle is x m long and $(x-5)$ m wide. The perimeter of the rectangle is 38 m. Find its length and width.

(6) In $\triangle ABC$, $\angle A = (x-10)°$, $\angle B = 2x°$, $\angle C = (x+30)°$. Find the value of x and the size of $\angle A$, $\angle B$, and $\angle C$.

(7) Grade 1 petrol costs 33p for 5 litres and grade 2 petrol is 31p for 5 litres. How many litres of each grade are bought if £2·23 are paid for 35 litres?

(8) A man walks for 1 h and rides in a bus for a further $1\frac{1}{2}$ h. The average speed of the bus is 10 times the speed at which he walks. If he covers a total distance of 64 km, calculate (*a*) the speed at which he walks, and (*b*) the average speed at which the bus travels.

(9) A boy thinks of a number, multiplies by 5, subtracts 7 from this amount and then after dividing the result by 8 obtains 6 as an answer. What was the original number?

(10) In $\triangle XYZ$, YX is 3 cm longer than XZ, and 1 cm longer than YZ. The perimeter of the triangle is 14 cm. Find the length of the sides.

(11) £12 is divided between A, B, and C so that for every $7\frac{1}{2}$p received by A, B gets 10p and C gets $12\frac{1}{2}$p. How much money does each person receive?

(12) Two years ago a man's age was double what it was 15 years ago. What is his age now?

16 Formulae

Making formulae

One of the most useful things that algebra enables us to do is to make up our own formulae. When we have solved a particular problem we can often reduce the method of solving it to a set pattern and write down this pattern as a formula so that we can use it whenever we wish to solve a similar problem.

Example 1. Figure 36 represents the four walls of a room, spread out flat.

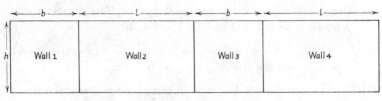

Fig. 36

We wish to find the area of the four walls.

From the diagram we can see that, laid out in this way, the walls can be represented as one large rectangle. The length of this large rectangle is made up of

$$1 \text{ breadth of the room} + 1 \text{ length} + 1 \text{ breadth} + 1 \text{ length}$$

or $\qquad b \qquad\qquad + \quad l \ + \quad b \ + \quad l$

or $\qquad\qquad 2b + 2l$

The width of the large rectangle is the height of the room, h. Thus the area of the rectangle, which is length × breadth, can be stated as $(2b + 2l) \times h$. So that the formula for the area of four walls of a room is,

$$\text{area of 4 walls} = (2b + 2l)h$$

In words, twice the breadth plus twice the length, multiplied by the height.

Exercise 1

(1) A rectangular sheet of metal is x cm long and y cm wide. Write a formula for (i) finding its area in cm², (ii) its weight in kilogrammes if 0·1 m² of the metal weighs 4 kg.

(2) A rectangular tank is *a* cm long, *b* cm wide, and *c* cm deep. Write an expression for the volume of this tank, and a formula that will give the capacity of the tank in litres.

(3) XYZ is a triangle. Write a formula that will give $\angle$X when $\angle$Y and $\angle$Z are known. (Remember that the sum of the angles of a triangle $= 180°$.)

(4) At a speed of *S* km/h how many kilometres are covered in (i) 2 hours, (ii) 7 hours, (iii) *t* hours?

(5) A boy cycles at the rate of *S* km/h. Write an expression that will convert this speed into (i) km per minute, (ii) metres per minute.

(6) Write an expression that will give the cost in pounds of *l* litres of petrol at (i) 7p per litre, (ii) *y* pence per litre.

(7) The cost of painting a square metre of wall is *p* pence. Write a formula that can be used to find the cost in pence of painting any area of wall, taking *l* for its length in metres and *h* for its height in metres. Find a second formula that gives the cost in pounds.

(8) The radius of the circle in Fig. 37 is *x* cm. Write an expression for (i) the area of the unshaded part of the circle, (ii) the area of the shaded part of the circle.

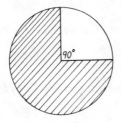

Fig. 37

(9) Write a formula for calculating the average number of km a car travels per litre of petrol when *k* is the number of km travelled and *l* is the number of litres of petrol used.

(10) Write a formula for calculating the perimeter of a rectangle *a* cm long and *b* cm wide. Construct a second formula that will give the perimeter in metres.

(11) Find in metres the perimeter of an equilateral triangle whose side is *d* cm. Write an expression for its area.

(12) Construct a formula for calculating the area of the shaded part of Fig. 38. The radius of the circle is r cm and the side of the square is a cm. (Area of circle $= \pi r^2$.)

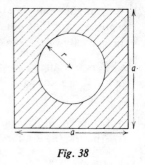

Fig. 38

Changing the subject of a formula

Frequently it is necessary to change a formula around. For example, the area of a rectangle can be stated as:

$$A = lb$$

If, however, we know the area and the length and wish to discover the breadth, we can change the subject of the formula to b.

Example 1. If $A = l \times b$, divide each side of the formula by l

$$\frac{A}{l} = \frac{l \times b}{l}$$

$$\therefore \frac{A}{l} = b \quad \text{or} \quad b = \frac{A}{l}$$

When changing the subject of a formula it is best to treat the formula as a simple equation.

Example 2. Change the subject of $p = 2(l + b)$ from p to l.

$$p = 2(1 + b)$$

Remove the bracket $\qquad p = 2l + 2b$

Change $2b$ to the other side of the equation

$$p - 2b = 2l$$

Divide each side by 2 $\qquad \dfrac{p - 2b}{2} = \dfrac{2l}{2}$

$$\therefore \frac{p}{2} - b = l \quad \text{and} \quad l = \frac{p}{2} - b$$

Example 3. If $\dfrac{x}{a} + \dfrac{y}{b} = 1$ change the formula to the form $y =$.

$$\frac{x}{a} + \frac{y}{b} = 1$$

Take $\dfrac{x}{a}$ to the other side of the equation

$$\frac{y}{b} = 1 - \frac{x}{a}$$

Multiply each side by b

$$y = b\left(1 - \frac{x}{a}\right)$$

$$= b - \frac{bx}{a}$$

Example 4. $V = \pi r^2 h$ is the formula that gives the volume of a cylinder. Change the subject of this formula from V to r.

$$V = \pi r^2 h$$

Divide each side by πh and cancel

$$\frac{V}{\pi h} = \frac{\pi r^2 \not h}{\not\pi \not h}$$

Thus $\qquad \dfrac{V}{\pi h} = r^2 \quad$ or $\quad r^2 = \dfrac{V}{\pi h}$

$\sqrt{r^2} = r$ so take sq. root of each side.

$$\therefore r = \sqrt{\frac{V}{\pi h}}$$

Example 5. Change the subject of $S = C + \dfrac{PC}{100}$ from S to C.

$$S = C + \frac{PC}{100}$$

Multiply each side by 100
$$100S = 100C + PC$$

To obtain a single C factorise $100C + PC$
$$100S = C(100 + P)$$

Divide each side by $100 + P$.

$$\frac{100S}{100 + P} = C$$

$$\therefore C = \frac{100S}{100 + P}$$

Note: to cancel the 100 would be wrong 'partial cancelling'.

Exercise 2

(1) The area of a parallelogram is found from the formula $A=bh$ where b is the base and h is the perpendicular height of the parallelogram.

    (*a*) Find A when $b=12·7$ cm and $h=6·35$ cm.

    (*b*) If both sides of the formula (i.e. equation) are divided by b, then the subject of the formula becomes h. Do this and then calculate the value of h when $A=58$ cm^2 and $b=5$ cm.

(2) The formula $V=lbh$ gives the volume of a rectangular tank, where l, b, and h are the length, breadth, and height of the tank.

    (i) Change the subject of the formula so that it is in the form $h=$.

    (ii) If $V=12$ m^3, $l=4$ m, and $b=2$ m, find the value of h.

(3) Change the subject of $C=\pi d$ to the form $d=$.

(4) From Boyle's Law the formula $P=\dfrac{k}{V}$ is obtained. Change its subject to $V=$.

(5) Change the subject of $2S=U+V$ to the form $V=$.

(6) Change the subject of $V=u+at$, (i) from V to u, (ii) from V to t.

(7) Change the formula $\dfrac{P}{3}+\dfrac{q}{4}=5$ to the form $P=$.

(8) $A=\pi(R^2-r^2)$. Change the subject of this formula from A to r.

(9) Use the formula $u=\sqrt{32R}$ to express R in terms of u. Find R when $u=40$.

(10) The formula for finding simple interest is

$$I = \frac{PRT}{100}$$

    (i) Make P the subject of the formula;

    (ii) Make R the subject of the formula;

    (iii) Make T the subject of the formula.

(11) Using the formulae constructed in Question 10, find,

    (i) P when $I=£16$, $R=4\%$, and $T=2$ yr.

    (ii) T when $I=£21$, $P=£150$, and $R=3\frac{1}{2}\%$.

17 Simultaneous and Quadratic Equations

Simultaneous equations

In the simple equations that we have solved, so far, we have been concerned with finding the value of one unknown. The next stage is to solve equations with two unknowns; instead of solving only for x, we solve for x and y. To do this, however, we must start from two equations since we use one of them to help us solve the other.

Substitution method

Example 1. Solve:

$$3x - 2y = 10 \quad \text{(i)}$$
$$x + y = 5 \quad \text{(ii)}$$

Take equation (ii) $\qquad x + y = 5$

Changing x over we get y in terms of x

$$y = 5 - x$$

Substitute this value for y in equation (i). Thus

$$3x - 2y = 10$$

Substituting for y $\qquad 3x - 2(5 - x) = 10$

$$3x - 10 + 2x = 10$$

Then $\qquad\qquad\qquad 5x = 10 + 10$

$$5x = 20$$
$$x = 4$$

Take the easiest of the original equations, i.e. (ii):

$$x + y = 5$$

Substituting for $x = 4$ we get

$$4 + y = 5$$
$$y = 5 - 4 = 1$$

Thus $\qquad\qquad\qquad x = 4, \quad y = 1$

Check this result by substituting in the original equations.

This method of solving simultaneous equations is known as the substitution method.

Some equations can be solved by eliminating (getting rid of) one unknown instead of substituting a value for it.

Example 2. Solve:

$$3x+y = 14 \quad \text{(i)}$$
$$x-y = 2 \quad \text{(ii)}$$

Add the equations together, thus eliminating y and getting

$$4x = 16$$
$$\therefore x = 4$$

Substitute in equation (ii) (simplest)

$$x-y = 2$$
$$4-y = 2$$
$$-y = -4+2$$
$$-y = -2$$
$$\therefore y = 2$$

Thus $\qquad x = 4, \quad y = 2$

Check this result by substitution.

Example 3. Solve:

$$2x-2y = 8 \quad \text{(i)}$$
$$x-2y = 1 \quad \text{(ii)}$$

Adding will not eliminate either x or y, so subtract (ii) from (i) (change signs and add)

$$x = 7$$

Substitute in (ii)

$$x-2y = 1$$
$$7-2y = 1$$
$$-2y = 1-7$$
$$-2y = -6$$
$$y = 3$$

Sometimes, before an unknown can be eliminated it is necessary to adjust one or both of the equations.

Example 4. Solve:

$$3s-4t = 10 \quad \text{(i)}$$
$$s+t = 8 \quad \text{(ii)}$$

Multiply each side of equation (ii) by 4 (remember that this does not change the balance of the equation)

$$4s+4t = 32$$

The pair of equations for solution are now

$$3s-4t = 10$$
$$4s+4t = 32$$

add
$$7s \quad = 42$$
$$s = 6$$

Substitute in original equation (ii)

$$6+t = 8$$
$$t = 8-6$$
$$t = 2$$

Thus $\qquad s = 6$, and $t = 2$.

Example 5. Solve:

$$\frac{a}{3}+\frac{b}{4} = \frac{3}{2} \quad \text{(i)}$$
$$3a-2b = 5 \quad \text{(ii)}$$

Multiply (i) by 12 (L.C.M. of 3, 4, 2). This gives

$$4a+3b = 18$$

The equations to be solved are now

$$4a+3b = 18 \quad \text{(iii)}$$
$$3a-2b = 5 \quad \text{(ii)}$$

Multiply (iii) by 2 and (ii) by 3 to obtain the same coefficients for y in each equation.

This gives
$$8a+6b = 36$$
$$9a-6b = 15$$

Add the equations
$$17a \quad = 51$$
$$\therefore \quad a \quad = 51 \div 17 = 3$$

145

Substitute in (ii) for b

$$3 \times 3 - 2b = 5$$
$$-2b = 5 - 9$$
$$-b = -2$$
$$\therefore b = 2$$

Exercise 1

Solve the following pairs of simultaneous equations by using the substitution method (i.e. Example 1):

(1) $y = x + 2$
$x + 2y = 16$

(2) $y - 2x = 4$
$2x + y = 12$

(3) $2x + y = 10$
$x - 2y = 0$

(4) $3a - 4b = 5$
$a = 2b - 3$

(5) $a - 2b = -6$
$2a - 5b = 0$

(6) $4a - 2y = -6$
$3a - y = 5$

(7) $b + c = 6$
$b - c = 14$

(8) $4x + 4y = 12$
$5x - y = 9$

Solve the following simultaneous equations by adding or subtracting to eliminate one unknown:

(9) $x + 2y = 9$
$x - 2y = 5$

(10) $2x - 5y = 2$
$x + 5y = 16$

(11) $4x - y = 4$
$2x - y = 0$

(12) $3x - 5y = 4$
$3x - 3y = 6$

(13) $5a + 3b = 19\frac{1}{2}$
$5a - b = 13\frac{1}{2}$

(14) $5a - 2b = 26$
$2a - 2b = 14$

The following simultaneous equations must be 'adjusted' before they can be solved by the elimination method:

(15) $3x + 2y = 8$
$2x - y = 3$

(16) $4x - 3y = 6$
$2x - y = 4$

(17) $x - 3y = -4$
$3x + y = 8$

(18) $4a - 5b = 3$
$7a - 10b = 5$

(19) $4x - y = 6$
$3x - \frac{y}{2} = 6$

(20) $a + \frac{3y}{4} = 11$
$2a - 5y = 9$

Choose what you consider to be the best method to solve the following simultaneous equations:

(21) $3x-2y = 11$
$\quad\ x+y = 7$

(22) $4x-y = 5$
$\quad\ 2x-2y = -2$

(23) $5a+2b = -8$
$\quad\ 4b-a = 6$

(24) $5p-2q = 7$
$\quad\ p+q = 3\frac{1}{2}$

(25) $b+3c = 21$
$\quad\ b-5 = c$

(26) $3m-4n = 0$
$\quad\ m = 5-2n$

(27) $\dfrac{a}{2}+\dfrac{b}{3} = 6$

$\quad\ \dfrac{a}{3}-\dfrac{b}{3} = 0$

(28) $2a-5b = 8$

$\quad\ a+\dfrac{3b}{3} = -3$

(29) $\dfrac{3a}{2}+\dfrac{b}{3} = 7$

$\quad\ a-1 = b$

(30) $\dfrac{P}{2}+3q = 15$

$\quad\ \dfrac{P}{3}-q = 4$

Quadratic equations

In the earlier section on the factorising of trinomials we became acquainted with expressions of the type, y^2-2y-8, $3x^2-10x+8$, x^2-9^2, etc.

An expression which contains a square as the highest power of any letter (x^2, y^2, etc.) is called a quadratic. If we say that such an expression is altogether equal to some value, then the resulting equation is known as a quadratic equation, or an equation of the second degree, i.e. the highest power of any quantity or letter is 2.

Before we attempt to solve a quadratic equation the following facts should be remembered:

(a) If any thing is multiplied by 0 (nought) the result is 0 (nought).

(b) If two numbers or expressions are multiplied together and give 0 (nought) then one of them must be 0 (nought).

147

Example 1.

$$14 \times 0 = 0$$
$$x \times 0 = 0$$
$$37 \times 0 \times 5x = 0$$

Example 2. If $(x+3) \times (2x-4) = 0$.

Then either $\qquad\qquad x+3 = 0$

or $\qquad\qquad 2x-4 = 0$

Example 3. Solve $(x-6)(x-1)=0$.

Since $\qquad\qquad (x-6) \times (x-1) = 0$

Then either $\qquad\qquad x-6 = 0$

or $\qquad\qquad x-1 = 0$

If $\qquad\qquad x-6 = 0$

then $\qquad\qquad x = 6$

If $\qquad\qquad x-1 = 0$

then $\qquad\qquad x = 1$

This result is a typical solution to a quadratic equation. The question is often set in a slightly different manner.

Example 4. Solve $x^2 - 5x + 6 = 0$.

Factorising we get $\qquad\qquad (x-2)(x-3) = 0$

Therefore either $\qquad\qquad x-2 = 0$

So $\qquad\qquad x = 2$

or $\qquad\qquad x-3 = 0$

So $\qquad\qquad x = 3$

$$\therefore x = 2 \quad \text{or} \quad 3$$

These values for x are the **roots** of the equation. If either is substituted into the left-hand side of the original equation, the value becomes the same as the right-hand side, zero. This is the usual method of checking the answer.

148

Example 5. Solve $4y^2 + 11y = 3$.

Change the equation so that it equals 0. If

$$4y^2 + 11y = 3$$

bring the 3 over

Then $\qquad\qquad\quad 4y^2 + 11y - 3 = 0$

Factorise $\qquad\qquad\quad (4y-1)(y+3) = 0$

Therefore either $\qquad\qquad 4y - 1 = 0$

$$4y = 1$$

$$\underline{y = \tfrac{1}{4}}$$

or $\qquad\qquad\qquad\qquad y + 3 = 0$

$$y = -3$$

$$\therefore\ y = \tfrac{1}{4}\ \text{ or }\ -3$$

Quadratic equations can appear in the form $3x^2 - 6x = 0$.

Example 6. Solve $3x^2 - 6x = 0$.

Factorise $\qquad\qquad\qquad 3x(x-2) = 0$

Therefore either $\qquad\qquad\quad 3x = 0$

$$x = 0$$

or $\qquad\qquad\qquad\qquad x - 2 = 0$

$$x = 2$$

$$\therefore\ x = 0\ \text{ or }\ 2$$

Exercise 2

Solve the following equations:

(1) $(x-5)(x-2) = 0$

(2) $(x-9)(x+7) = 0$

(3) $(x+2)(x-3) = 0$

(4) $(a-4)(a-4) = 0$

(5) $(b+5)(b+2) = 0$

(6) $(4x+1)(x-1) = 0$

(7) $(2a-6)(a+3) = 0$

(8) $(3z-9)(2z-4) = 0$

Solve the following equations:

(9) $x^2 - x - 6 = 0$

(10) $x^2 + 3x - 4 = 0$

(11) $x^2 - 2x - 8 = 0$

(12) $x^2 - 7x + 12 = 0$

(13) $2x^2 + x - 6 = 0$

(14) $12x^2 - 12x - 24 = 0$

(15) $6x^2 - 5x = 6$

(16) $4c^2 + 4c = 24$

(17) $z^2 = 3z - 2$

(18) $2x^2 - 5x = 0$

(19) $4a^2 - 9 = 0$

(20) $5x^2 - 15x = 0$

18 Charts and Diagrams

Facts and figures are often easier to understand if they are presented in the form of a chart or diagram. In newspapers and on television, charts and diagrams are used a great deal to illustrate a trend or to enable us to compare two sets of figures.

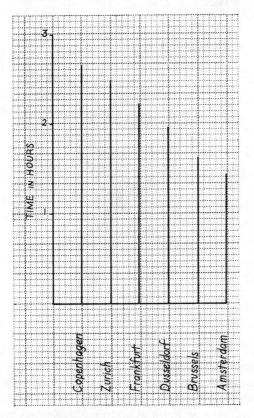

Fig. 39

Figure 39 is a very simple form of diagram that illustrates the flying times from Manchester to various cities in Europe. Basically it is a number of straight lines drawn to scale.

151

The diagram in Fig. 39 can be drawn as a **block diagram**, the method is the same but instead of a single line, a block is used. The diagram of flying times, as a block diagram, would appear like this (Fig. 40); it is drawn to the same scale as Fig. 39.

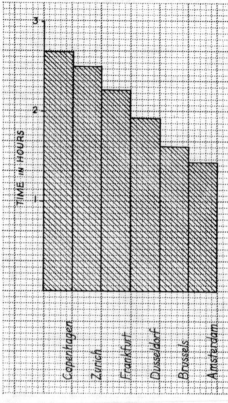

Fig. 40

The circular or pie diagram

In this diagram each quantity is expressed as a fraction of the whole amount being dealt with, and each fraction is represented in diagrammatic form as a segment of the circle. Thus Fig. 41 illustrates what part of each £1, collected as Rates, is spent on the various public services. One third of each £1 is spent on education so the segment that represents this amount is one third of the whole circle. The angle that the arc of the segment subtends at the centre of the circle is 120°.

152

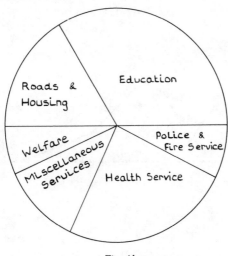

Fig. 41

Charts

Information that has to be recorded at regular intervals and be readily available for comparison, such as weather records, or a patient's temperature in a hospital, is most conveniently presented on a chart in the form of a graph.

Figure 42 is such a record of a patient's temperature kept as a graph.

Note

When you draw a chart or diagram the scale used is important, since too small a scale leads to inaccurate work. Further, the proportions, that is the ratio of height to width of the diagram, should be carefully thought out so that the information is clearly presented. A suitable scale for Fig. 42 would be

Time Scale: 1 day to 1 cm
Temperature Scale: 1° C to 1 cm

Use Fig. 42 to answer these questions:

(a) What is the significance of the broken line on the graph?
(b) When do you think that the patient was most ill?
(c) Why does the temperature scale start at 33° C?
(d) A temperature is given as 38° C. What does the C stand for?

153

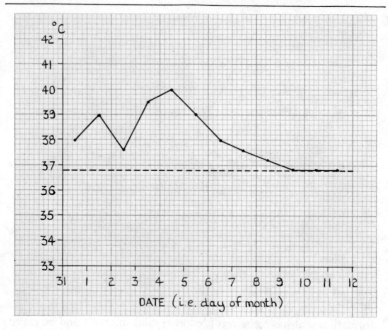

Fig. 42

Exercise 1

(1) (*a*) By measuring the diagram in Fig. 39 estimate the scale used.
 (*b*) Using an average speed of 400 km/h calculate the distances from Manchester to each European city.
 (*c*) Convert Fig. 39 to a block diagram, using a scale of 5 cm = 1 h.

(2) The marks obtained by a group of boys in an examination are as follows:

Marks out of 100	No. of boys
0 to 10	0
10 to 20	2
20 to 30	5
30 to 40	7
40 to 50	15
50 to 60	8
60 to 70	6
70 to 80	4
80 to 90	2
90 to 100	1

Illustrate these results by means of a block diagram. In what group of marks will the average mark fall?

(3) The litter left by visitors in four London parks on the Late Summer Holiday is as follows:

	Left in bins (*tonnes*)	Left on ground (*tonnes*)
Hyde Park	3	1·1
Kensington Gardens	0·85	0·4
Regent's Park	3·25	1·65
Hampton Court	0·9	0·45

Illustrate this information by means of two circular diagrams, one for litter left in bins, and the other for litter left on the ground. In each case use a circle of radius not less than 5 cm.

(4)

Average weekly expenses of a family

Food	£5·25
Rent	£1·75
Clothes	£2·25
Fuel and Light	£1·00
Other items	£3·75
Total	£14·00

Illustrate these figures by means of a circular diagram.
(5) The table shows the average maximum and minimum temperatures in degrees Celsius for each month in a particular year.

	Jan.	Feb.	Mar.	Apl.	May	June	July	Aug.	Sept.	Oct.	Nov.	Dec.
Max.	6°	7°	11°	13°	17°	20°	23°	23°	20°	15°	9°	6°
Min.	2°	3°	2°	4°	8°	11°	12°	13°	10°	7°	4°	3°

Record both these sets of figures as separate graphs on the same chart. From your chart answer the following questions:

(*a*) Which month has the widest range of temperature?
(*b*) Which month has the smallest range of temperature?
(*c*) You will see that no average minimum falls below 2° C. Does this mean that the temperature did not fall below this figure during this particular year?

Straight line graphs

The graphs that you have drawn so far have been concerned with quantities or measurements that were independent of each other, so that they were plotted separately and when they were joined together the result was a jagged line. If, however, two quantities which are related to each other so that they are in direct proportion are plotted against each other, the resulting graph is a straight line.

Example 1. Given that £1 = $2·40, draw a graph to convert amounts up to £50 to dollars.

Since the ratio of pounds to dollars is 1:2·40 for all amounts the graph will be a straight line, and only three points will be required to 'fix' it.

The following table gives us the position of 3 points, A, B, and C along the graph.

	A	B	C
Pounds	£5	£25	£50
Dollars	$12	$60	$120

A convenient scale to use will be 1 cm = $10 and 1 cm = £5.

The first point, 0, is where the two axes meet. Dollars are measured along the vertical axis since this is the greater available length; this leaves the horizontal axis for the pounds.

The position of point A is fixed at the point where a perpendicular from £1 on the pounds axis meets a line drawn horizontally from the $2·40 mark on the dollar axis. Mark this position with a small cross. The positions of points B and C are fixed in a similar way. A straight line drawn through A, B, and C is the required graph (see Fig. 43).

To convert, say £35 to dollars, find the point where a perpendicular from £35 on the pounds axis meets the graph, draw a line (or use a ruler) parallel to the pounds axis to meet the dollar axis. Read off the number of dollars, i.e. $84. To convert dollars to pounds, merely reverse this process.

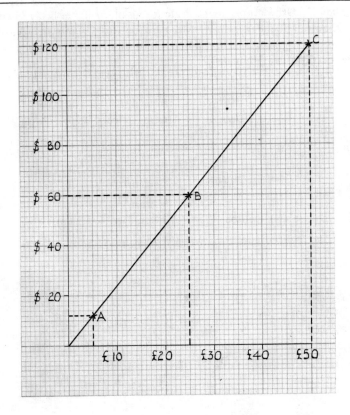

Fig. 43

Travel graphs

The graph of a constant **average** speed is always a straight line, because it is the result of plotting Time against Distance, and

$$\frac{\text{Distance}}{\text{Time}} = \text{Average Speed}$$

i.e. Distance and Time are in direct proportion.

157

Example 2. Draw graphs to illustrate speeds of (*a*) 40 km/h, (*b*) 75 km/h.

If the straight lines are drawn with care, only two points are needed to position each graph. The first point will be '0' in each case, since in 'no time, no distance' is covered.

(*a*)

Time	0	60 min
Distance	0	40 km

(*b*)

Time	0	60 min
Distance	0	75 km

A convenient scale will be 12 cm = 1 hour, 1 cm = 7·5 km.

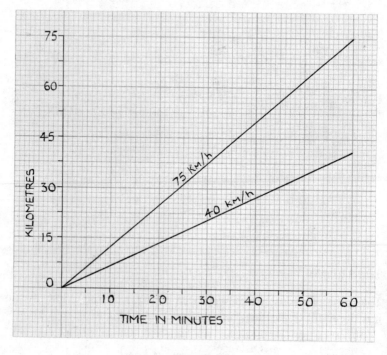

Fig. 44a

Note the change in the slope of the graph as the speed increases.

158

The slope of a graph is measured by its gradient. A point moving along the slope of a graph will rise vertically as it moves along horizontally. The gradient of the slope is the ratio of the vertical rise to the distance moved horizontally.

In Fig. 44b the 75 km/h graph has been redrawn.

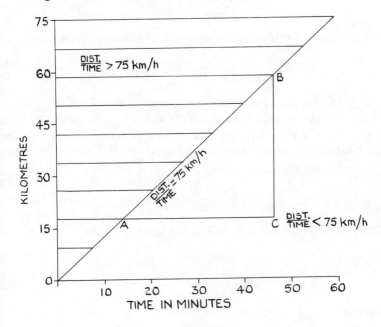

Fig. 44b

A right-angled triangle, ABC, has been drawn on the graph using part of the graph, AB, as the hypotenuse. A point moving along the graph from A to B will rise vertically a distance equivalent to CB, at the same time moving horizontally a distance equivalent to AC. The gradient of AB is given by the ratio

$$\frac{\text{Length of CB}}{\text{Length of AC}}$$

where CB is measured along the vertical scale (km) and AC along the horizontal scale (time). This is the gradient for the whole of the graph, since the triangle can be drawn anywhere along the line of the graph and to any convenient size.

6*

Copy Fig. 44a and by drawing and measuring find the gradients of the 75 km/h and 40 km/h lines. Give your results as a decimal fraction.

When we compare the lengths CB and AC we are comparing distance with time and

$$\frac{\text{Distance}}{\text{Time}} = \text{Velocity}$$

In Figs. 44a and 44b we have drawn the graph of the equation:

$$\frac{\text{Distance}}{\text{Time}} = \text{a Velocity of 75 km/h}$$

This particular equation is true only along the line of the graph itself, where we have a constant ratio that represents 75 km/h. Any space–time graph drawn in the shaded part, i.e. above the 75 km/h line, will be the resultant of a ratio that represents a velocity greater than 75 km/h, so that distance/time is greater than 75 km/h,

$$\text{i.e. } \frac{\text{Distance}}{\text{Time}} > 75 \text{ km/h}$$

Below the line distance/time will be less than 75 km/h,

$$\text{i.e. } \frac{\text{Distance}}{\text{Time}} < 75 \text{ km/h}$$

Exercise 2

(1) Use the graph in Fig. 43 to change:

    (*a*) £10, £22·50, £43, £65·50 to dollars.

    (*b*) $15, $25, $50·5, $70 to pounds.

(2) Given that £1 = 13·40 fc, draw a graph that can be used to convert pounds to francs, for amounts up to £5. Use your graph to convert:

    (*a*) £4·50, 50p, £3·75, £50 to francs.

    (*b*) 9·50 fc, 55 fc, 17·25 fc, 42·50 fc to pounds.

(3) Given that 1 km/h = 0·278 metres per second, draw a graph that will convert km/h to m/s with reasonable accuracy. Do not go beyond 30 km/h.

    Use your graph to find:

    (*a*) 10 km/h, 15 km/h, 25 km/h in m/s, and (*b*) 3 m/s, 6·5 m/s, 5·25 m/s in km/h.

(4) Use Fig. 44a to find:

    (*a*) the distance travelled in 35 min at
        (i) 75 km/h   (ii) 40 km/h

    (*b*) the distance travelled in 9 min at
        (i) 75 km/h   (ii) 40 km/h

    (*c*) the time taken to travel 17 km at
        (i) 75 km/h   (ii) 40 km/h

(5) Draw a graph to show the simple interest at $2\frac{1}{2}\%$ that will be earned after 1 year by sums of money up to £100. From your graph find the interest earned by (i) £5, (ii) £27·50, (iii) £85.

(6) Using the formula Circumference $= \pi \times$ Diameter, draw a graph to show this relationship for circles with diameters up to 25 cm. From your graph find:

    (*a*) the Diameter when the Circumference is (i) 33 cm, (ii) 12 cm

    (*b*) the Circumference when the Diameter is (i) 7 cm, (ii) 5·6 cm.

(7) Draw a graph to illustrate a flight from London to Geneva via Paris, given the following information:

    Distance: London to Paris, 340 km
              Paris to Geneva, 420 km
    Average speed for both legs of flight, 400 km/h
    Take-off time London, 08·00 hours, and there is a stop for 30 min in Paris. From your graph find the time of arrival in Geneva.

(8) Figure 45 illustrates as graphs the journeys made by Smith and Jones. Smith sets out from town 'A' at mid-day; at the same time Jones sets out from town 'B'. Smith is riding a bicycle and Jones is using a car. From the graph answer the following questions:

    (*a*) What distance is A from B?

    (*b*) How far has each man travelled by 5 p.m.?

    (*c*) Calculate the overall average speeds for the distances covered by each man.

    (*d*) What are the gradients of the sections of the graphs BP and AX? Express these gradients as a velocity in km/h.

    (*e*) What are the gradients of the sections PQ and XY?

    (*f*) What lengths of time do the sections PQ and XY represent on the graph? What was happening during these times?

    (*g*) At what distance from 'A' will the travellers meet?

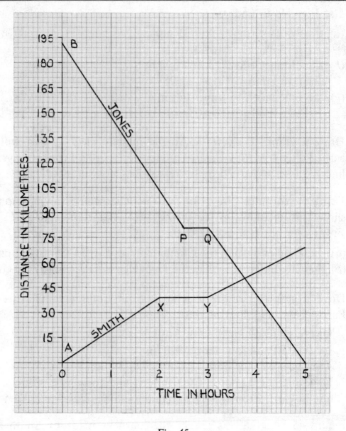

Fig. 45

19 Graphs with Positive and Negative Values

So far the graphs we have drawn have been concerned only with positive values. When we wish to plot negative values we need to extend the axes in the way shown in Fig. 46.

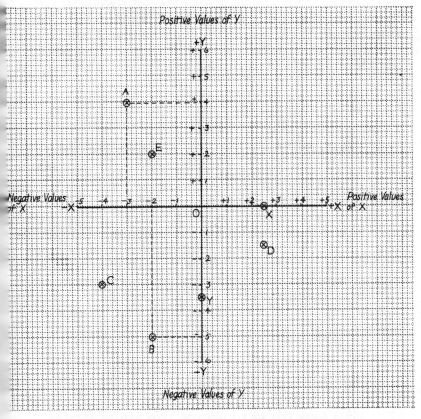

Fig. 46

This is the standard form of layout and you should become familiar with it. The axes divide the 'plane' into four quadrants and the point O where they meet is called the 'origin'. The vertical axis is the '*y*' axis and the horizontal axis is the 'x' axis. Positive values for y are measured upwards from point O and negative values downward from point O on the y axis.

Positive values for x are measured to the right of 'O' and negative values to the left. Working with positive values you will have realised that we have been using only the first quadrant.

Points are plotted as before, for example the values for point A in Fig. 46 are $x = -3$, $y = +4$; and for point B, $x = -2$, $y = -5$.

These values of x and y are the co-ordinates of the points A and B that enable us to fix their positions. However, it is rather clumsy to have to refer to a point, A for instance, as $x = -3$ and $y = 4$, so we usually simply refer to it by its co-ordinates. Thus point A is the point $(-3, 4)$. You will notice that the x value is given first and that the co-ordinates are bracketed together as a pair. Similarly the point B where $x = -2$ and $y = -5$ is the point $(-2, -5)$.

Graphs of linear equations

Take the equation $y = 2x + 3$. This is an equation of the **first degree** because it contains no powers of x or y greater than one. Remember when we write x we mean x to the power of one, or x^1. Equations of this kind are called **linear equations**.

The numerical value of the expression $2x + 3$ can always be found if the value of x is known, so the expression $2x + 3$ is said to be a **function** of x.

In fact since x is to the power of one, $2x + 3$ is a *first degree function of x* or *a linear function of x*.

Further, since the value of y in the equation $y = 2x + 3$ depends directly on the value of x, then, as we would expect, the graph of this equation will be a straight line, hence the word 'linear'.

Example 1. Draw the graph of $y = \dfrac{3x}{2} - 1$ for values of x from -3 to $+4$.

You will notice that we are given limits to work between; -3 and $+4$ are the values we are interested in at the moment, but other limits could apply just as well.

Since the graph will be a straight line only two points need be plotted with possibly a third to act as a check.

164

The table of values needs careful calculation since any mistake in he table will make the graph wrong. Enter the values of x first, using he limits we have to work between and select an intermediate value to ict as a check.

x	-3	0	$+4$
$\frac{3x}{2} - 1$	$-5\frac{1}{2}$	-1	$+5$
y	$-5\frac{1}{2}$	-1	$+5$

By substituting in the original equation, three values for y can be obtained, thus:

$$y = \frac{3x}{2} - 1 \qquad\qquad y = \frac{3x}{2} - 1 \qquad\qquad y = \frac{3x}{2} - 1$$

when $x = -3$ $\qquad$ when $x = 0$ $\qquad$ when $x = +4$

$$y = -\frac{9}{2} - 1 \qquad\qquad y = 0 - 1 \qquad\qquad y = \frac{12}{2} - 1$$

$$y = -5\frac{1}{2} \qquad\qquad y = -1 \qquad\qquad y = +5$$

Remember that any point on this graph (Fig. 47) will have an x and y that will satisfy the equation $y = \frac{3x}{2} - 1$.

The solution of simultaneous equations graphically

To solve simultaneous equations graphically, draw the graphs of both equations on the same axes. The co-ordinates (values) of x and y of the point where the lines intersect will satisfy both equations.

Example 2. Solve graphically these simultaneous equations:

$$4x - 2y = 7$$
$$x + 3y = 7$$

If we assume 0 and 5 as values for x, then in $4x - 2y = 7$

by substituting $x = 0$ $\quad$ and $\quad$ substituting $x = 5$
$\qquad 4 \times 0 - 2y = 7 \qquad\qquad 4 \times 5 - 2y = 7$
$\qquad\qquad -2y = 7 \qquad\qquad\qquad -2y = 7 - 20$
$\qquad\qquad\quad y = -3\frac{1}{2} \qquad\qquad\qquad\quad y = 6\frac{1}{2}$

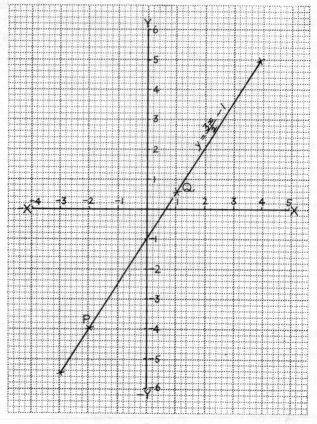

Fig. 47

and in $x+3y=7$

by substituting $x = 0$ and   substituting $x = 5$

$$0+3y = 7 \qquad\qquad 5+3y = 7$$
$$3y = 7 \qquad\qquad 3y = 7-5$$
$$y = 2\tfrac{1}{3} \qquad\qquad y = \tfrac{2}{3}$$

Thus the tables of values will be:

$4x-2y = 7$

x	0	5
y	$-3\tfrac{1}{2}$	$6\tfrac{1}{2}$

$x+3y = 7$

x	0	5
y	$2\tfrac{1}{3}$	$\tfrac{2}{3}$

These values are plotted as two straight line graphs in Fig. 48.

166

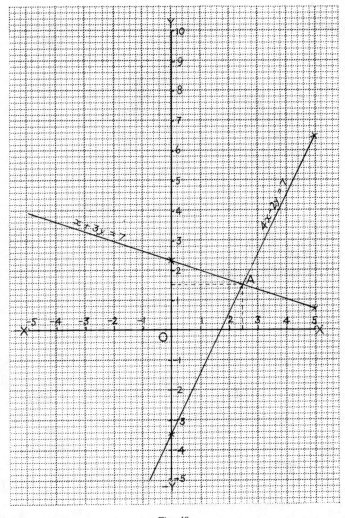

Fig. 48

From the graph we see that point A is the point of intersection and at this point $x = 2\frac{1}{2}$, $y = 1\frac{1}{2}$. These values satisfy the original equations.

Graphs

Exercise 1

(1) From the graph in Fig. 47 find the x values that correspond to $y = -2$, 0, 3·5, $-4·2$, and the y values that correspond to $x = 3$, 0, $-1·5$, $-0·6$.

(2) (a) Give the co-ordinates of points C, D, E, X, and Y in Fig. 46.
(b) What are the values for x and y of points P and Q on the graph in Fig. 47?

(3) For the graph $y = 3x - 1$ complete the following table of values:

x	-2	-1	0	1	2	3
y						

Using a scale of 1 cm for the y axis and 2 cm on the x axis draw this graph. From the graph find the value of x when $y = 4·5$ and the value of y when $x = -1·5$; find x when $y = 1·2$, find y when $x = 2·4$, and find y when $x = 0·75$.

(4) Draw x and y axes as in Fig. 46, for $x = \pm 5$ and $y = \pm 6$. Plot these points: $(2·5, 3·75)$, $(-1, 6)$, $(-4·5, -3·5)$, $(0, 0)$, $(1·5, -3·5)$, $(-5, -5)$.

(5) Draw the graph of $y = \dfrac{2x}{4} - 1$ for values of x from -2 to $+4$. Read off the values of x and y for any point on the graph and substitute in the original equation to check the accuracy of the graph.

(6) Complete the tables of values for these equations

$$x + 2y = 8 \quad \text{and} \quad x + 4y = 2$$

x	-10	$+10$
y		

x	-10	$+10$
y		

Plot the graph of each equation on the same axes and from the point where they intersect find the values of x and y that satisfy both equations.

(7) Use a graph to solve the following pair of equations,

$$2x - y = 6$$
$$x + 3y = 10$$

(8) Solve the following pair of equations graphically,

$$y - 5x = 11$$
$$2y + 4x = 1$$

Check your answers by substitution.

(9) Use graphs to solve the following pair of equations

$$\frac{x}{2} + 3y = 15$$

$$\frac{x}{3} - y = 4$$

Check the accuracy of your work by solving the equations by any other method that you know.

20 Curved Graphs

The graphs of quantities that do not vary in direct proportion are usually in the form of a curve.

For example, the stopping distances of a car travelling at various speeds are given in the following table.

Speed in km/h	0	32	48	64	80	96
Stopping distance in metres	0	12	22·5	36	52·5	72

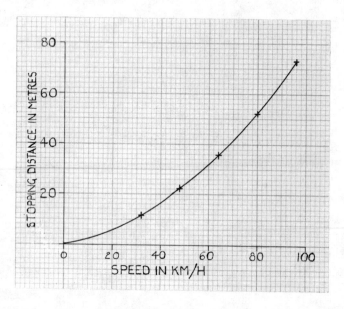

Fig. 49

In Fig. 49 these values are plotted giving a curved graph. Obviously the two points sufficient for a straight line are not enough for a curve

170

and to obtain an accurate graph as many points as possible should be plotted along the curve. Further when the curve is drawn it should be made as smooth as possible so that accurate readings can be made for intermediate values.

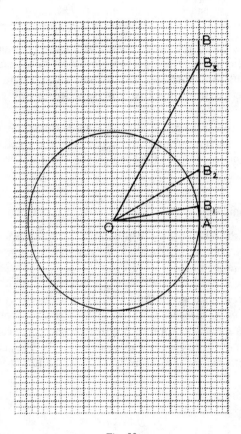

Fig. 50

The Graph of the tangent

In the diagram (Fig. 50) O is the centre of the circle and AB is a tangent so that OA is a radius. At O $\angle AOB_1 = 10°$, $\angle AOB_2 = 30°$, and $\angle AOB_3 = 60°$ are drawn. The lengths AB_1, AB_2, and AB_3 are the tangents 'cut off' by $\angle AOB_1$, $\angle AÓB_2$, and $\angle AOB_3$. By measuring the diagram the following table of values is obtained for these angles and their corresponding tangents:

Angle	10°	30°	60°
Length of tangent in mm	4·2	13·8	41·5

If plotted as a graph the result would be a curve. (Values are *not* in direct proportion.) From this curve it would be possible to obtain the size of ∠AOB that corresponded to any given length of AB and conversely the length of AB that corresponded to any given size for ∠AOB.

In practice, since the graph is a curve, more than three points would be needed to draw it accurately. Remember that the greater the number of points plotted on a curve then the greater the degree of accuracy to which it can be drawn.

Graphs of formulae

It is useful to be able to draw the graph of a formula since from a graph it is possible to obtain intermediate values without repeatedly having to work out the formula.

The formula $S=\frac{1}{2}at^2$ enables us to calculate how far a car will travel, from rest, in a given time at a particular rate of acceleration.

Acceleration means gain in speed. If we say that, from a standing start a car has an acceleration of 5 m per second per second, we mean that at the end of the first second its velocity will be 5 m per second, and at the end of the second second its velocity will be 10 m per second, and so on.

In the formula

$$S = \frac{1}{2}at^2$$

S = distance covered in metres

a = acceleration in metres per second per second

t = time in seconds

Example 1. Using the formula $S=\frac{1}{2}at^2$, draw a graph to show the relationship between time and distance covered when a car accelerates at 5 m per second per second starting from rest.

Taking the first 9 seconds of the car's journey, from the formula $S = \frac{1}{2}at^2$ the following table of values can be worked out.

t = time in seconds	1	2	3	4	5	6	7	8	9
S = dist. in metres	$2\frac{1}{2}$	10	$22\frac{1}{2}$	40	$62\frac{1}{2}$	90	$122\frac{1}{2}$	160	$202\frac{1}{2}$

In Fig. 51 these points have been plotted and the curve drawn.

Values can be read off the graph in the usual way; for example, the car travels approximately 50 m in 4·5 s and in 8·5 s it will have travelled approximately 180 m.

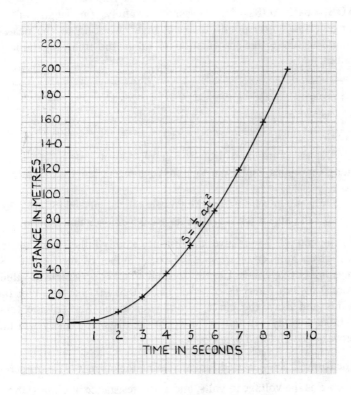

Fig. 51

173

Exercise 1

(1) The following is a table of times of sunrise at intervals of a week.

Oct. 7	Oct. 14	Oct. 21	Oct. 28	Nov. 4	Nov. 11	Nov. 18	Nov. 25	Dec. 2	Dec. 9	Dec. 16	Dec. 23	Dec. 30
06·09	06·21	06·33	06·46	06·58	07·10	07·22	07·34	07·44	07·53	07·59	08·04	08·05

Plot these times on a graph and join the points with a smooth curve. Use the graph to estimate the time of sunrise on (*a*) 17 October (*b*) 17 November (*c*) on Christmas Day.

(2) Copy Fig. 50, drawing a circle of radius = 3·75 cm; draw in radius OA and tangent AB. Use a protractor to draw angles $AOB_1 = 10°$, $AOB_2 = 22°$, $AOB_3 = 31°$, $AOB_4 = 39°$, $AOB_5 = 45°$, $AOB_6 = 58°$, $AOB_7 = 64°$, $AOB_8 = 76°$. Measure, carefully, the length of the tangent that corresponds to each angle, working to the nearest millimetre. Use this information to fill in the following table of values.

Angle	10°	22°	31°	39°	45°	58°	64°	76°
Length of Tangent								

Plot the points and draw the graph. Use a scale of 10° = 1 cm along the *x* axis, and 1 cm to 1 cm for tangent lengths along the *y* axis.

From the graph find (*a*) the tangents for angles of 15°, 25°, 35°, 72°; (*b*) the angles whose tangents are 0·5 cm, 0·9 cm, 2·5 cm.

(3) The formula $D = 4·9t^2$ gives the distance a body falls from a height, in a given number of seconds. $D =$ the number of metres and $t =$ the number of seconds. Use this formula to make up a table of values from 0 to 3 at intervals of 0·5 s, i.e. 0, 0·5, 1·0, 1·5, etc. Plot the points and draw the curve. From your graph find (*a*) the total distance a body will fall in 2·5 s; (*b*) the distance a body will fall between the 2nd and 3rd seconds.

(4) The formula $I = \dfrac{E}{R}$ is used for calculating the current (I) in amperes, when E is the voltage in volts, and R the resistance in ohms (Ohm's Law).

Plot a graph of I against E for values of E from 0 to 10 volts, when R is a constant at 4 ohms. From the graph find the current when the voltage is $4\frac{1}{2}$ volts, and the voltage that will give a current of $2\frac{1}{2}$ amps.

(5) Draw a graph to show the relationship between the area of a circle and its radius. Use the formula $A = \pi r^2$, taking $\pi = 3 \cdot 1$ and values of r from 0 to 7·5 cm. From your graph find the areas of circles with radii of 1·8 cm, 7·5 cm, 2·5 cm.

21 Lines and Angles

It must be stressed that although this section is devoted to geometry no branch of mathematics should be regarded as standing on its own. The different techniques must be thought of as parts of a whole; just as a craftsman uses different tools to do a single piece of work so we must be prepared to use, in turn, all the tools of mathematics to solve a problem. The skills learnt in geometry are very valuable tools that we can use not only to solve problems in mathematics, but in our everyday lives.

Angles at a point

When a straight line meets another straight line, the adjacent angles so formed together make two right angles.

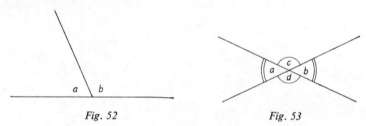

Fig. 52   *Fig. 53*

In Fig. 52 $\angle a + \angle b = 2$ right angles $= 180°$. The angles are said to be supplementary.

When two straight lines intersect (cut each other) the vertically opposite angles are equal. The four angles formed are together equal to 4 right angles.

In Fig. 53 angles a and b are equal and vertically opposite; angles c and d are equal and vertically opposite; and angles $a + b + c + d = 4$ right angles $= 360°$.

Parallels

Parallel straight lines are lines drawn in the same plane (on the same surface) that will not meet however far they are produced (made longer).

A straight line drawn across a set of two or more parallel straight lines is called a **transversal**.

In Fig. 54 AB and CD are parallel straight lines, marked with an

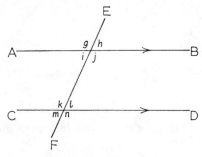

Fig. 54

arrow to show that they are parallel thus →—. EF is the transversal.
Again in Fig. 54 angles *j* and *k* are alternate angles and angles *i* and *l*
are also alternate angles.

*When two parallel straight lines are cut by a transversal, the alternate
angles are equal, i.e.* $\angle j = \angle k$ *and* $\angle i = \angle l$.

Angles *h* and *l* are a pair of corresponding angles, as are angles *g* and
k, *h* and *j*, *m* and *i*.

*When two or more parallel straight lines are cut by a transversal the
corresponding angles are equal, i.e.* $\angle h = \angle l$, $\angle g = \angle k$, $\angle n = \angle j$ *and*
$\angle m = \angle i$.

Exercise 1

(1) In Fig. 55 find the size of $\angle a$, $\angle b$, and $\angle c$.

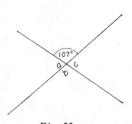

Fig. 55

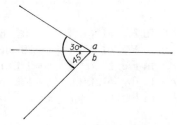

Fig. 56

(2) In Fig. 56 find $\angle a$ and $\angle b$.
(3) In Fig. 57 find $\angle a$ if $\angle b = 67°$.

177

(4) In Fig. 57 find the size of ∠b if,

    (i) ∠a=2∠b
    (ii) ∠a=4∠b
    (iii) ∠a=5∠b
    (iv) ∠a=3∠b

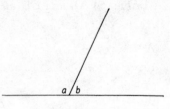

Fig. 57

(5) In Fig. 58 find the value of ∠x and the size of angles *a* and *b*.

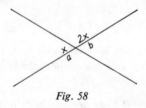

Fig. 58

(6) In Fig. 59 find the value of x and the size of angles *a* and *b*.

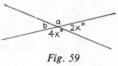

Fig. 59

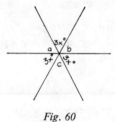

(7) In Fig. 60 find the value of x and the size of angles *a*, *b*, and *c*.

Fig. 60

(8) In Fig. 61, (*a*) if ∠s=60° find ∠t.
(9) In Fig. 61, (*b*) if ∠v=70° find ∠u.
(10) In Fig. 61, (*c*) if ∠w=110° find ∠p.
(11) In Fig. 61, (*d*) if ∠p=100° find ∠t.
(12) In Fig. 61, (*e*) if ∠u=75° find ∠q.

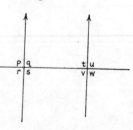

Fig. 61

In Numbers 13, 14, 15, and 16 say if the lines PQ and RS are parallel; give a reason for your answer.

(13)

(14)

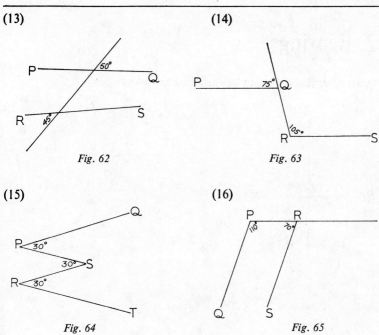

Fig. 62

Fig. 63

(15)

(16)

Fig. 64

Fig. 65

22 Bearings

A bearing or direction can be stated in two ways:

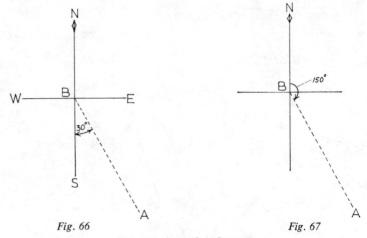

Fig. 66   Fig. 67

The bearing of A from B

1 *As a Quadrant Bearing: S 30° E* (Fig. 66). Read as 30° East of South. In this method directions are always measured either from North or South, never from East and West, and the angle is confined to one quadrant of the compass, that is, the angle is less than 90°, i.e.

> 40° East of North (N 40° E)
> 30° West of South (S 30° W)

2 *As a Three-figure Bearing* (Fig. 67). In this method the angle is measured in a clockwise direction starting from North. Thus the bearing of A from B is given as 150°. Three figures are always given, e.g. 025° instead of 25°

Exercise 1

(1) Use a protractor to measure the necessary angles in Fig. 68 and express the directions of A, B, C, D, E, F, G, H, from O as both quadrant and three-figure bearings.
(2) Convert these quadrant bearings to three-figure bearings:
> N 25° W, S 10° E, N 26° E, S 76° W

180

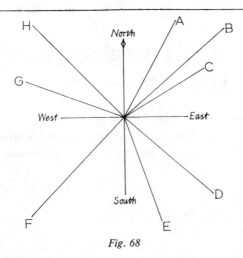

Fig. 68

(3) Convert these three-figure bearings to quadrant bearings:
    005°, 276°, 090°, 193°

(4) From the information given in Fig. 69 give:
    (i) the bearings of C and D from B
    (ii) the bearings of C and D from A
    From the results obtained what fact can you deduce about the lines
    BC and AD?

(5) An aircraft leaves G and flies due North for 60 km to point P. At
    point P it changes course to due West, and flies a further 80 km
    to point R. Draw a diagram to illustrate the flight using a scale of
    2·5 cm to 20 km. Use this diagram to find the bearing and distance
    of point R from point G.

(6) A boat leaves A and sails for
    4 km on a course of 080° to
    point B, then changes course
    to 025° and sails for 8 km
    to point C. At point C it
    changes course to due South
    and sails 9·6 km to point D.
    Using a scale of 1 km to
    1 cm, draw an accurate plot
    (diagram) of the course sailed
    and by measurement find the
    bearing and distance of point
    A from point D.

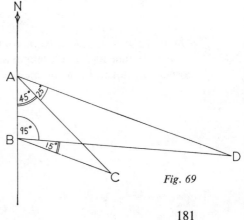

Fig. 69

181

23 Angles of Triangles, Quadrilaterals, and Polygons

Angles of triangles and quadrilaterals

A plane figure formed by 3 straight lines is called a **triangle**. A plane figure formed by 4 straight lines is called a **quadrilateral**. (See Fig. 70.)

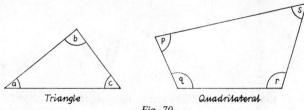

Triangle   Quadrilateral

Fig. 70

The angles a, b, c; p, q, r, s, marked inside the figures are called **interior angles**.

If the sides of these figures are produced, angles are formed outside the figures as in Fig. 71.

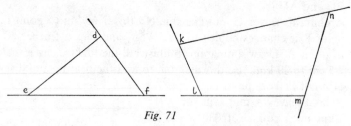

Fig. 71

These angles d, e, f; k, l, m, n, are called **exterior angles**.

If a triangle and quadrilateral are cut out of paper or card, and the corners are torn off, in the manner shown in Fig. 72, the torn corners

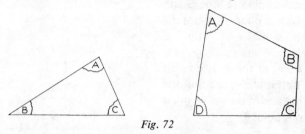

Fig. 72

of each figure can be placed together in the way shown in Fig. 73 and thus it can be seen that the interior angles of a triangle are together equal to 180°; and the interior angles of a quadrilateral are together equal to 360°.

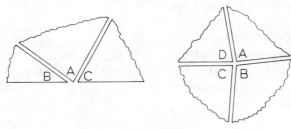

Fig. 73

The exterior angle of a triangle is equal to the sum of the two interior opposite angles. That is to say, in Fig. 74 $\angle E = \angle C + \angle B$.

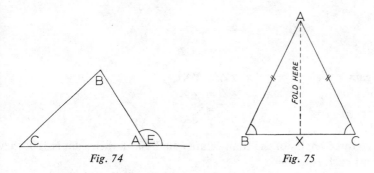

Fig. 74   *Fig. 75*

This can be proved or shown to be true in this way:

$$\angle A + \angle E = 180°$$
$$\angle A + (\angle B + \angle C) = 180°$$

Therefore

$$\angle E = \angle B + \angle C$$

The isosceles triangle

A triangle with two sides equal is called an **isosceles triangle**.

In Fig. 75 triangle ABC is isosceles, i.e.

$$AB = AC$$

183

Take point X, this is the middle point of the base BC. Join AX. If this triangle is cut out and folded along the line AX the two halves will exactly match each other. Thus the angle at B = the angle at C.

Therefore in an isosceles triangle two sides are equal and the angles at the base of these sides are also equal.

The equilateral triangle

An **equilateral triangle** is a triangle with all sides equal.
In the triangle XYZ (Fig. 76), because XY = XZ, then $\angle Z = \angle Y$ (see isosceles triangle above).

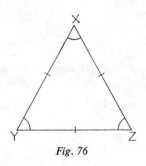

Fig. 76

Again	YZ = YX
therefore	$\angle Z = \angle X$
but	$\angle Z = \angle Y$
then	$\angle Z = \angle X = \angle Y$

The three angles of the triangle are equal. Since their sum is 180° they must each equal 60°.

In an equilateral triangle all side are equal and all angles are equal and each angle equals 60°.

Angles of a polygon

A plane figure made up or bounded by 5 or more straight lines is called a **polygon**. Certain polygons have special names, e.g.:

	A	5 sided polygon is called a Pentagon
	A	6 ,, ,, ,, ,, ,, Hexagon
	An	8 ,, ,, ,, ,, ,, Octagon
	A	10 ,, ,, ,, ,, ,, Decagon

If a pentagon is drawn and its sides are produced to form five exterior angles, as in Fig. 77, and if these exterior angles are cut out and placed together, as was done for the angles of a quadrilateral, the result will be as in Fig. 78, that is, the exterior angles are together equal to 360°. The same result will be obtained for a polygon of any number of sides.

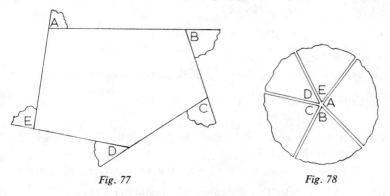

| Fig. 77 | Fig. 78 |

Thus the sum of the exterior angles of a polygon is 360°.

If the sides of a polygon are all the same length it is called a regular polygon and not only are its sides equal, but all its interior angles are equal to each other, and in consequence all its exterior angles are equal to each other.

Note on angles

When a particular angle has to be named it is best done by three letters, thus ∠ABC. The sign ∠ is used instead of the word angle, and the middle letter is always the letter at the vertex or point of the angle. If there is no possibility of confusion, as in Fig. 76, the middle letter can be used alone thus: ∠A.

Example 1. In Fig. 79 find the size of the angle marked *a*.

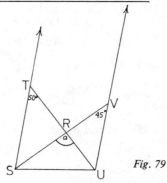

Fig. 79

185

Because ST∥UV (parallel to) and SV is a transversal, then

$$\angle RVU = \angle RST \text{ (alternate angles)}$$

But $\qquad\qquad \angle RVU = 45°$

So $\qquad\qquad\quad \angle RST = 45°$

In triangle TRS,
$\angle a$ (exterior angle) $= \angle RST + \angle STR$ (sum of interior and opposite)

Therefore $\qquad \angle a = 45° + 50°$
$$= 95°$$

A shorter way of writing the answer to this problem is as follows:
Using Fig. 79, in △TRS,
$\quad \angle a$ (exterior angle) $= \angle RST + 50°$ (sum of interior and opposite)

But $\qquad\qquad \angle RST = 45°$ (alternate angles, ST∥UV)

Therefore $\qquad \angle a = 45° + 50°$
$$= 95°$$

Example 2. Find the value of x and the size of $\angle a$ (Fig. 80).

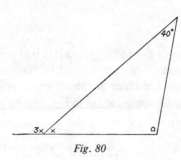

Fig. 80

$$3x + x = 180°$$

Therefore $\qquad\qquad 4x = 180°$
$$x = 180° \div 4$$
$$= 45°$$

and $\qquad\qquad\qquad 3x = 45° \times 3$
$$= 135°$$

But $\qquad 135° \text{ (exterior angle)} = a + 40°$

so $\qquad\qquad\qquad a = 135° - 40°$
$$= 95°$$

186

Example 3. Find the size of each interior angle of a regular hexagon (i.e. a regular polygon with 6 sides and 6 exterior angles all equal).

Sum of the exterior angles of a polygon = 360°
Then each exterior angle = 360° ÷ 6 = 60°

But each interior angle is supplementary to its exterior angle

(i.e. exterior + interior = 180°)
Then each interior angle = 180° − 60
= 120°

Exercise 1

(1) Calculate the sizes of the angles (Fig. 81) marked by letters:

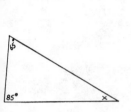

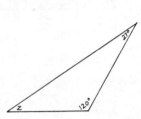

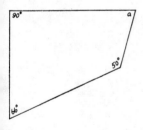
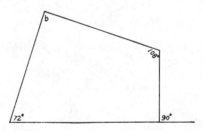

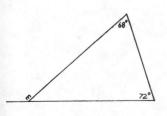
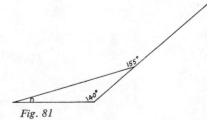

Fig. 81

(2) Calculate the sizes of the angles marked by letters in Fig. 82.

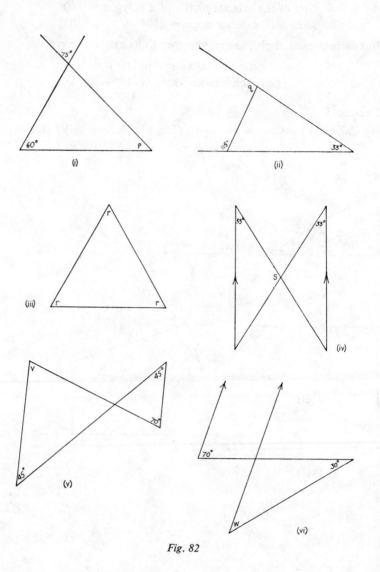

Fig. 82

3) Calculate the sizes of the angles marked by letters in Fig. 83. O and P
are the centres of the circles. Remember that radii of the same circle
are equal.

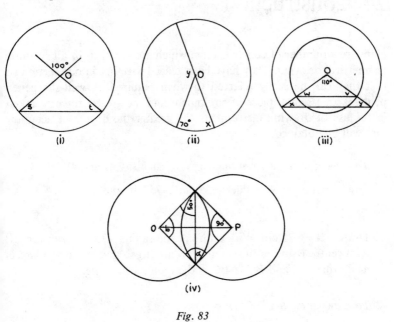

(i)   (ii)   (iii)

(iv)

Fig. 83

24 Constructions

Here are a number of constructions, which are the basis of all accurate geometrical drawing. They have been placed together in one section so that they can be easily referred to when required. A well-sharpened pencil is an essential piece of equipment and the greater the care taken in the use of drawing instruments the greater the degree of accuracy that will be obtained.

1 *To draw a triangle given the length of each side* (Fig. 84).

Draw a triangle with sides 6·25 cm, 3·75 cm, and 3 cm.

Method

Draw AB = 6·25 cm. With centre A and radius 3·75 cm draw arc (i); with centre B and radius 3 cm draw arc (ii) so that the arcs intersect at C. Join AC and BC. ABC is the required triangle.

2 *To draw an angle of 60°* (Fig. 85).

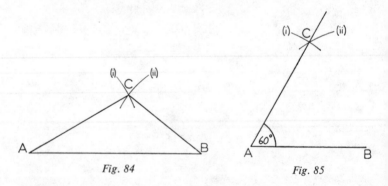

Fig. 84   Fig. 85

Method

Draw a straight line AB, of any convenient length. With centre A and radius AB draw arc (i); with centre B and the same radius, draw arc (ii) cutting arc (i) at C. Join AC. Then CAB = 60° (because △CAB is equilateral).

3 *To bisect an angle* (Fig. 86).

Method

Given any angle ABC, with centre B and any convenient radius draw arcs (i) and (ii) cutting BA at D and BC at E. With centres D and E and equal radii draw arcs (iii) and (iv) cutting at F. Join BF. BF bisects the angle ABC.

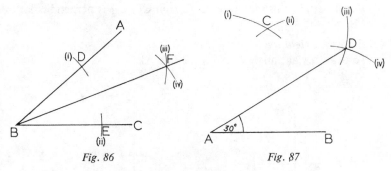

Fig. 86   Fig. 87

4 *To draw an angle of 30°* (Fig. 87).

Method

Draw AB, find point C with arcs (i) and (ii) as in Method 2. With centres C and B and any convenient radii draw arcs (iii) and (iv) cutting at D. As will be seen in Method 3 the additional construction halves a 60° angle, giving 30°.

5 *To bisect a straight line* (Fig. 88).

Method

AB is a straight line. With centre A and radius greater than a half of AB draw arcs (i) and (ii) above and below the line. With centre B and the same radius draw arcs (iii) and (iv) to cut arcs (i) and (ii) at C and D. Join CD which is the perpendicular bisector of AB.

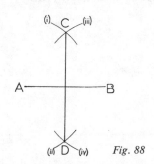

Fig. 88

7*

6 *To draw a perpendicular to a straight line from a point outside it* (Fig. 89).

To draw a perpendicular from C to AB.

Method

With centre C and a convenient radius draw arcs (i) and (ii) to cut AB at D and E, and with centres D and E and equal radii draw arcs (iii) and (iv) to intersect at F. Join CF. CF is perpendicular to AB.

7 *To draw a right angle* (*90°*). (Fig. 90.)

To draw a right angle at A on the line AB.

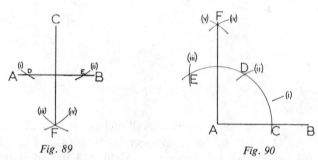

Fig. 89   Fig. 90

Method

With centre A and a convenient radius draw arc (i) to cut AB at C. With centre C and the same radius draw arc (ii) to cut arc (i) at D. With centre D and the same radius draw arc (iii) to cut arc (i) at E. With centres D and E and equal radii draw arcs (iv) and (v) cutting at F. Join FA. ∠FAB=90°.

8 *To draw an angle equal to a given angle* (Fig. 91).

Draw an angle equal to angle ABC.

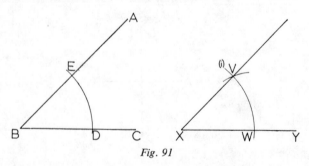

Fig. 91

Method

Draw a straight line XY. With centre B and any convenient radius draw an arc cutting BC at D and BA at E. With the same radius and centre X draw an arc (i) cutting XY at W. With centre W and radius equal to DE draw an arc cutting arc (i) at V. Join XV. Then ∠ABC = ∠VXY.

9 *To draw a straight line parallel to a given straight line to pass through a given point* (Fig. 92).

To draw a line parallel to AB passing through C.

Method

Take any point D in AB. Join DC. With centre D and a convenient radius draw arc (i) to cut DC at E, and AB at F. With the same radius and centre C draw arc (ii) cutting DC at G. With centre G and radius FE draw an arc cutting arc (ii) at H. Join CH and produce to J. Then JC is parallel to AB.

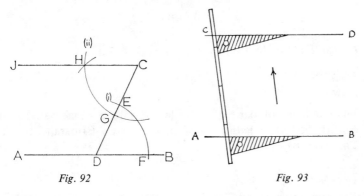

Fig. 92   Fig. 93

10 Although construction 9 is an accurate method of drawing parallels a simpler method using ruler and set-square is often used (see Fig. 93). As in all constructions its accuracy depends on the care taken. To draw a line parallel to AB through point C.

Method

 (i) Place the longest side of a 60° set-square along line AB.

 (ii) Holding the set-square firmly in position place a ruler along the shortest side of the set square.

 (iii) Holding both instruments firmly on the paper, slide the set-square along the edge of the ruler until it reaches point C. Draw a line CD through point C. Then CD is parallel to AB.

11 *To divide any straight line into any number of equal parts* (Fig. 94).
To divide AB into 5 equal parts.

Method

Draw AC at any convenient angle to AB. Step off 5 equal distances
along AC (use a pair of compasses for this). Letter them D, E, F, G,
and H. Join HB. Using ruler and set square draw parallels to HB
through G, F, E, and D to cut AB, which will be divided into 5
equal parts.

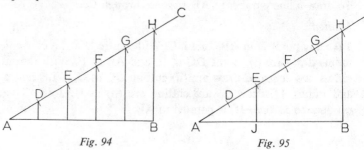

Fig. 94   Fig. 95

12 *To divide a straight line in a given ratio* (Fig. 95).

To divide AB in the ratio of 2:3.

Method

Total number of parts=5. Divide AB into 5 equal parts as in
construction 11. E is the second point so draw EJ parallel to HB.
Then AJ:JB=2:3.

13 *To construct a rectangle to a given size* (Fig. 96).

To draw rectangle ABCD with AB=6 cm and BC=3 cm.

Method

Draw AB=6 cm. At A draw a perpendicular (Cons. 7). With
centre A mark off, along the perpendicular AD=3 cm. With centre
B and radius=3 cm. draw arc (i), with centre D and radius=6 cm.
draw arc (ii) to cut arc (i) at C. Join BC and DC. Then ABCD is the
required rectangle.

14 *To draw the circumcircle of a triangle* (Fig. 97).

The circumcircle of a triangle is the circle drawn around the triangle
passing through each vertex (angle) of the triangle.

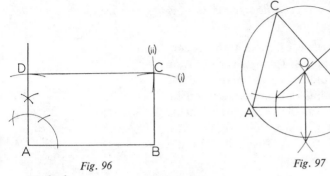

Fig. 96   *Fig. 97*

Method

To draw the circumcircle of triangle ABC, bisect any two sides (use Cons. 6) and produce the bisectors to meet at point O. With centre O and radius OA, or OB, or OC, draw a circle. This circle is the circumcircle of triangle ABC.

15 *To draw the inscribed circle of a triangle* (Fig. 98).

The inscribed circle of a triangle is the circle drawn inside the triangle so that it touches the three sides.

Method

To draw the inscribed circle of triangle ABC bisect any two angles (use Cons. 3) and produce the bisectors to meet at O. With centre O and radius equal to the perpendicular distance of O from AB, or AC, or BC, draw the inscribed circle of triangle ABC.

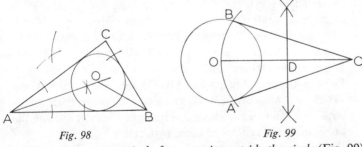

Fig. 98   *Fig. 99*

16 *To draw a tangent to a circle from a point outside the circle* (Fig. 99).

Method

Given a circle AOB with centre O, draw a tangent to AOB from point C which lies outside the circle. Join OC. Bisect OC (use Cons. 6) at point D. With centre D and radius DO draw an arc cutting the circle at A and B. Join CA and CB. Each line is a tangent from C to the circle AOB.

17 *To draw a regular hexagon* (6 *sided polygon*) (Fig. 100).

Method
Draw a circle, centre O, with any convenient radius. Taking any point A on
the circumference as centre and the
same radius as the circle, step off six
arcs around the circumference at A,
B, C, D, E, and F. Join AB, BC, CD,
DE, EF, and FA. Then ABCDEF is a
regular hexagon.

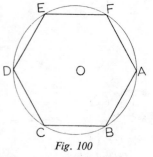
Fig. 100

Note: each side is equal in length to the radius of the circle. So
if you wish to draw a regular hexagon of side 3 cm, you draw your
circle with radius 3 cm.

Exercise 1

(1) Construct a triangle XYZ with XY = 7·5 cm, $\angle$X = 30°, and $\angle$Y
= 90°. Measure the sides XZ and ZY and the size of $\angle$Z.

(2) Construct a triangle ABC with AB = 8 cm, AC = 5 cm, and $\angle$A
= 45°. Measure the side CB and the size of $\angle$C and $\angle$B.

(3) Construct a square with a side of 55 mm.

(4) Draw a triangle PQR so that PQ = 6 cm, QR = 9 cm, and $\angle$Q =
50°. Construct a triangle PQS on PQ so that S is on the opposite
side of PQ to R, with PQ = PS = SQ. Drop a perpendicular from S
to meet RQ produced at T. Measure TQ.

(5) Draw a triangle DEF with DE = 5 cm, DF = 3 cm, EF = 4·5 cm.
Through F draw FG parallel to DE, through E draw EG parallel
to DF to meet FG at G. Join GD. GD cuts FE at H. Measure
FH and HE, GH and HD.

(6) Draw a triangle ABC, with AB = 75 mm, BC = 100 mm, and AC
= 125 mm. Measure $\angle$B. Working carefully, construct the circumcircle and inscribed circle of this triangle. Measure the length of the
line joining the centres of these two circles.

(7) Draw a circle with centre O and radius 3 cm. Take any point P
outside the circle and construct the two tangents from P to touch
the circle at A and B. Measure PA and PB. Construct a perpendicular
from A and B respectively towards O. If the drawing is accurate
the perpendiculars should meet at O.

25 Congruent Triangles

If two triangles are exact copies of each other, the same size and shape, so that if one is placed on the other it will match it exactly, then the triangles are congruent.

The symbol ≡ is used to show that two figures are congruent.
If the three triangles in Fig. 101 are drawn accurately on tracing paper

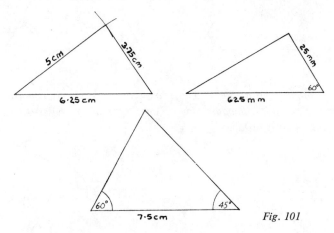

Fig. 101

using only the measurements given, then in each case the trace will fit exactly over the original diagram. No other result can be obtained if the drawing is well done. In other words the trace and original in each case represents a pair of congruent triangles.

The measurements given for each triangle then are conditions under which two triangles can be congruent.

These general conditions for congruency should be memorised; they are:

1 *If three sides of one triangle are respectively equal to three sides of another triangle the triangles are congruent* (see Fig. 102).

Fig. 102

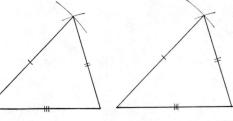

197

2 *If two sides and the included angle of one triangle are respectively equal to two sides and the included angle of another triangle, the triangles are congruent* (see Fig. 103).

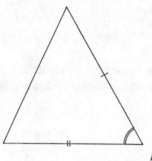 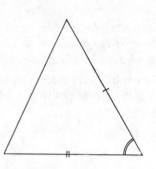

Fig. 103

3 *If two angles and a side of one triangle are respectively equal to two angles and the corresponding side of another triangle the triangles are congruent* (see Fig. 104).

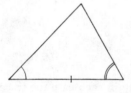 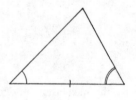

Fig. 104

The case of the right-angled triangle

In Fig. 105, ABC is a right-angled triangle with A = a right angle. The

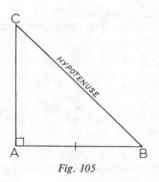

Fig. 105

side opposite the right angle is called the **hypotenuse**. To copy this triangle only two measurements are needed, the length of the hypotenuse and the length of any other side. If the triangle in the figure is drawn using these two measurements and a right angle the result will be an exact copy of the original triangle.

This is a fourth condition of congruency. It can be stated in this way:

4 *If the hypotenuses of two right-angled triangles are equal and one side of one triangle is equal to one side of the other triangle, the triangles are congruent* (see Fig. 106).

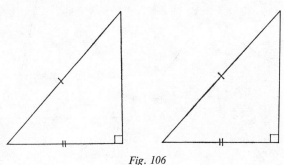

Fig. 106

Exercise 1

(1) State which of the following pairs of triangles (Figs. 107–111) are congruent, and give, briefly, the condition of congruency that they satisfy.

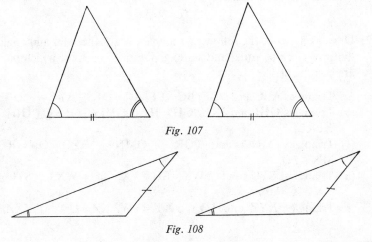

Fig. 107

Fig. 108

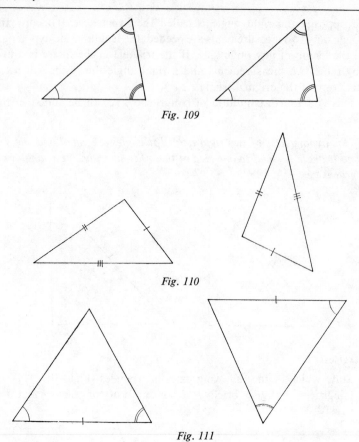

Fig. 109

Fig. 110

Fig. 111

(2) Draw sketches of the following triangles. Mark the sides and angles that are given as equal and state, giving brief reasons, which pairs are congruent.

(*a*) Triangles ABC and DEF; BC=EF, AC=DF, ∠ABC=∠DFE.

(*b*) Triangles GHI and JKL; GH=JL, ∠GHI=∠JLK, ∠GIH=∠JKL.

(*c*) Triangles MNO and PQR; ∠OMN=∠RPQ, ON=RQ, MN=PQ.

(*d*) Triangles STU and VWX; SU=VX, TU=WX, ∠STU=∠VWX=90°.

(*e*) Triangles XYZ and UVW; XY=VW, XZ=UW, ∠YXZ=∠WUV.

Example 1. In Fig. 112 PQRS is a quadrilateral with PS=QR and PR=QS. Prove that ∠PSR=∠QRS.

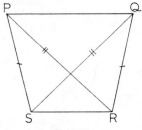

Fig. 112

In the △'s PSR and QRS (this means consider the triangles PSR and QRS)

    (i) PS=QR (given this in question)
    (ii) PR=QS (given this in question)
    (iii) SR=SR (side that is common to both △'s)

Therefore △PSR≡△QRS (3 sides equal or S.S.S)

    So ∠PSR = ∠QRS (corresponding parts of congruent △'s).

Example 2. In Fig. 113, prove that PQ=SR. Given that PT=ST and QT=RT.

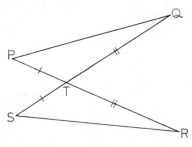

Fig. 113

In the △'s PQT and SRT

    (i)   PT=ST (given)
    (ii)   QT=RT (given)
    (iii) ∠PTQ=∠STR (vertically opposite angles)

Therefore △PQT≡△RST (S.A.S.).

So   PQ=SR (corresponding sides).

201

Example 3. In Fig. 114, given that O is the centre of the circle and DE and CF are perpendicular to AB, prove that (i) DE = CF; (ii) AE = FB.

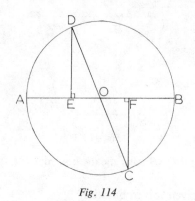

Fig. 114

In the triangles OED an OFC,

   (i)   OD = OC (radii of circle)
  (ii)   ∠DOE = ∠COF (vertically opposite)
 (iii)   ∠DEO = ∠CFO (both right angles)

Therefore △OED ≡ △OFC
(Reason A.S.A.—if two angles are equal then third angles of the triangles must also be equal.)

So   DE = FC   (i)

Also   OE = OF

But   OA = OB (radii)

and   OA − OE = AE

also   OB − OF = FB

                       ∴ AE = FB   (ii)

Exercise 2

(1) In Fig. 115, given that ∠ADB = ∠BDC, and ∠ABD = ∠CBD, use congruent triangles to prove that AB = BC.

(2) Given that O is the centre of the circle in Fig. 116, prove that ST = QR.

202

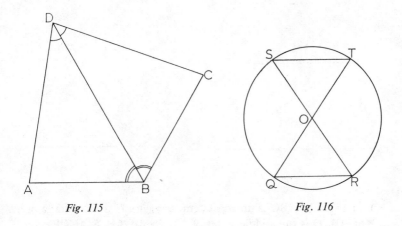

Fig. 115   Fig. 116

(3) In Fig. 117, AB bisects ∠CBD. ∠ACB = ∠ADB = rt. angle. Prove that AC = AD.

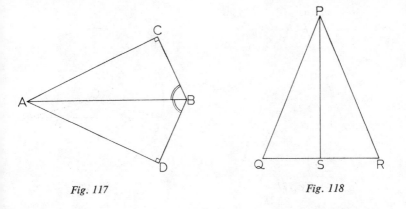

Fig. 117   Fig. 118

(4) In Fig. 118, PQR is an isosceles triangle and SP bisects ∠P. Prove that S is the middle point of QR (i.e. QS = SR). If ∠QPS = 35° what is the size of ∠PQS?

(5) In Fig. 119 ABCD is a parallelogram with BD a diagonal and AD parallel to BC and AB parallel to DC. Prove that △ABD is congruent to △CDB.

203

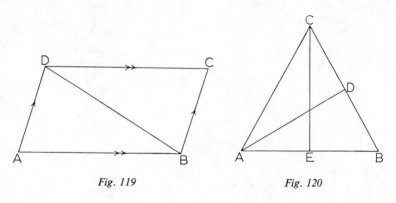

Fig. 119   Fig. 120

(6) In Fig. 120 ABC is an equilateral triangle. E is the middle point of AB, D is the middle point of CB. Prove that AD = CE.

(7) In Fig. 121 AF = DB, EB = AD. If △ABC is an isosceles triangle (i.e. AC = BC) prove that DF = DE.

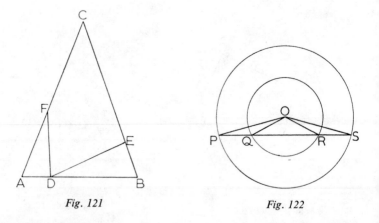

Fig. 121   Fig. 122

(8) Given two concentric circles with centre O (Fig. 122), cut by the straight line PQRS, prove that (i) PQ = RS, and (ii) PR = QS.

(9) In Fig. 123, given that AC = BC, and AD = BD, prove that ∠CAD = ∠CBD.

(10) Given that O is the centre of the circle in Fig. 124 and OZ is perpendicular to XY (i.e. ∠OZX and ∠OZY are right angles), prove that XZ = ZY.

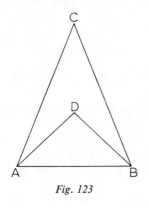

Fig. 123

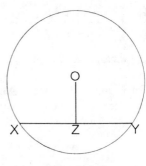

Fig. 124

(11) In Fig. 125, given that PZ is parallel to RY, RQ=XZ, and ∠RPQ=∠XYZ=right angle, prove that PQ=XY.

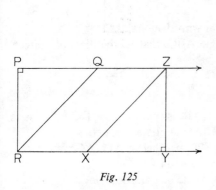

Fig. 125

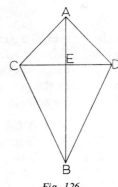

Fig. 126

(12) In Fig. 126, AB bisects CD at right angles. Prove: (i) BC=BD, (ii) △ACB≡ADB.

(13) Using ruler and compasses only bisect any straight line. Use congruent triangles to prove that your construction does bisect the line.

(14) ABC is a triangle. D is the middle point of the side AB. DE is perpendicular to AC, and DF is perpendicular to BC. If DE=DF, prove that AC=BC.

205

26 Parallelograms

A parallelogram is formed by the intersection of two pairs of parallel lines.

1 Given a parallelogram ABCD with diagonal AC, prove that the triangles so formed are congruent (Fig. 127).

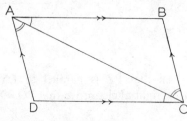

Fig. 127

Given   ABCD a parallelogram with diagonal AC.

To prove Triangle ADC≡triangle ABC, that is, the diagonal bisects the parallelogram.

Proof   In the △'s ADC, ABC
            Because:

   (i) ∠DCA=∠CAB (AB is parallel to DC, AC is a transversal, alternate angles are equal)
   (ii) ∠DAC=∠BCA (BC parallel to AD, AC transversal, alternate angles are equal)
   (iii) AC=AC (common side of both triangles)

   Therefore
$$△ADC \equiv △ABC$$

Thus the diagonal AC bisects the parallelogram ABCD.

Further, since △ADC≡△ABC, then

   AD = BC and AB = DC (opposite sides of a parallelogram are equal)
   also
   ∠ABC = ∠ADC (opposite angles equal)

Again,   because ∠ADC = ∠ABC and ∠DAC=∠BCA then
   ∠DAB = ∠DCB (opposite angles equal)

206

2 Given a parallelogram ABCD with diagonals AC and BD prove that the diagonals bisect each other (Fig. 128).

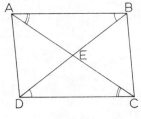

Fig. 128

Given   A parallelogram ABCD with diagonals AC and BD intersecting at E.

To prove Diagonals AC and BD bisect each other, that is AE = EC and BE = ED.

Proof   In △'s AEB and DEC
Because:

  (i) AB = DC (opposite sides of parallelogram are equal)
  (ii) ∠ABE = ∠EDC (alternate angles)
  (iii) ∠BAE = ∠ECD (alternate angles)

Therefore

$$△AEB \equiv △DEC$$

Thus

$$AE = EC \quad and \quad BE = ED$$

Hence the diagonals AC and BD bisect each other.

These 'properties' of a parallelogram can be stated as follows:

  (i) *Each diagonal of a parallelogram divides the parallelogram into two equal parts.*
  (ii) *The opposite sides of a parallelogram are equal.*
  (iii) *The opposite angles of a parallelogram are equal.*
  (iv) *The diagonals of a parallelogram bisect each other.*

Remember that the diagonals of a parallelogram do **not** bisect the angles.

The rectangle

The rectangle can be regarded as a 'special' parallelogram in which the angles are right angles.

The rhombus and square

The rhombus and the square are also special forms of the parallelogram (see Fig. 129).

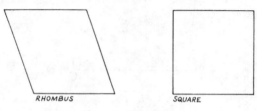

Fig. 129

A rhombus is a parallelogram in which the sides are all equal.

A square is a parallelogram with angles of 90° and all sides equal. Alternatively, the square can be regarded as a 'special' rhombus. In both rhombus and square the diagonals bisect the angles and also bisect each other at right angles.

Using these properties of the parallelogram and also what you know about parallel lines, and the properties of triangles, try to solve the problems in Exercise 1.

If at first you cannot see the way in which to solve a problem, try working backwards.

For example, you have to prove that two triangles are congruent. Ask yourself the question, 'If these triangles *are* congruent what do I know about their sides and angles?' Examine your diagram closely looking for angles and sides that can be shown to be equal. Make a positive attack on the problem; sometimes viewing the diagram from a different angle can make the solution easier to see. Whatever you do, don't just sit and stare. Remember that all these problems can be solved, but they require some knowledge, some intelligence, and a good deal of determination.

Here are some examples that illustrate the method used to solve this type of problem.

Example 1. In Fig. 130, PQRS is a parallelogram with diagonals PR and QS cutting at T. UTV is a straight line through T cutting PQ at V and SR at U. Prove that VQ = SU.

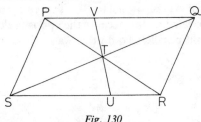

Fig. 130

Given   that PQRS is a parallelogram.

To prove   that VQ=SU (to do this △'s VTQ and STU must be proved congruent)

Proof   In △'s VTQ and STU

Because:

  (i) TQ=TS (QS is a diagonal, diagonals bisect each other, thus T is the mid point of QS)

  (ii) ∠TSU=∠TQV (PQ parallel to SR, alternate angles)

  (iii) ∠STU=∠QTV (vertically opposite angles)

Therefore   △VTQ ≡ △STU

Then   VQ = US (corresponding sides)

Example 2. In Fig. 131, D is the middle point of AC, F is the middle point of CB; BE is parallel to AC. Prove that ABED is a parallelogram.

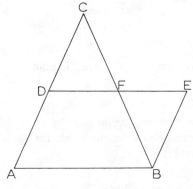

Fig. 131

Given   D mid-point of AC, F mid-point of BC, AD is parallel to BE.

To prove   that ABED is a parallelogram.

We are told that AD is parallel to BE; if we can prove that AD = BE then ABED is a parallelogram, because the opposite sides of a parallelogram are equal and parallel. To do this we start by proving △DFC ≡ △BFE.

Proof   In the △'s DFC and BFE,

Because:

  (i) FC = FB (F is middle of CB)

 (ii) ∠EBF = ∠FCD (BE is parallel to AC, ∠EBF and ∠FCD are alternate angles)

(iii) ∠EFB = ∠CFD (vertically opposite angles)

Therefore   △DFC ≡ △BFE

Thus   CD = BE (corresponding sides)

But   CD = AD (D is middle of CA)

Therefore   AD = BE

So AD is equal and parallel to BE

Thus ABED is a parallelogram.

Note

In geometry symbols are sometimes used. Here are some that may be useful.

$$\therefore \quad \text{means therefore}$$
$$\because \quad \text{,,} \quad \text{because}$$
$$AB \parallel DC \quad \text{,,} \quad AB \text{ is parallel to DC}$$
$$\parallel \text{gram} \quad \text{,,} \quad \text{parallelogram}$$

Exercise 1

(1) Draw a parallelogram, rectangle, rhombus, and square to any convenient scale. Draw the diagonals for each figure. Name the figures that have,

  (i) equal diagonals

 (ii) diagonals that bisect each other at right angles.

(2) In Fig. 132, ABCD is a parallelogram, DM = MC, ∠C = 70°, AB = 15 cm, and BC = 7·5 cm. Find, with reasons, the length of AD, the length of DM, angle D, and angle DMA.

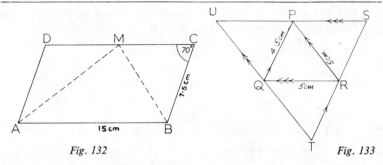

Fig. 132   Fig. 133

(3) In Fig. 133, △PQR has sides of 5 cm, 4·5 cm, and 5 cm. △STU is drawn with sides parallel to the sides of △PQR. Calculate the lengths of US, UT, and ST. (Write the lengths of the sides of △PQR on your diagram.)

(4) In Fig. 134, ABCD is a parallelogram and AF and CE are perpendicular (at right angles) to DB. Prove that AF=CE.

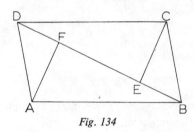

Fig. 134

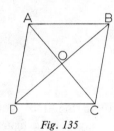

Fig. 135

(5) In Fig. 135, ABCD is a rhombus with diagonals bisecting at O. Prove that the diagonals bisect at right angles.

(6) In Fig. 136, two equal circles, with centres O and P, cut at Q and R. Prove that OQPR is a rhombus.

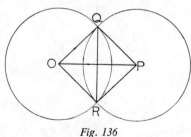

Fig. 136

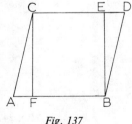

Fig. 137

(7) In Fig. 137, ABDC is a rhombus, CF is at right angles to AB, BE is at right angles to CD. Prove FB=CE.

211

(8) In Fig. 138, A is the centre of the circle. ABCD is a parallelogram. Prove (i) ∠ADE = ∠EAB; (ii) ∠EAB = ∠ABC.

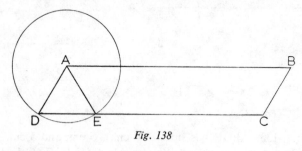

Fig. 138

(9) In Fig. 139, ABDE and BCDE are parallelograms. Prove (i) AB = BC, (ii) △AEB ≡ △EBD ≡ △BDC.

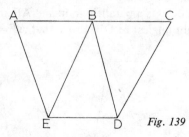

Fig. 139

(10) In Fig. 140, ABCD is a parallelogram. From the information given in the figure calculate the angles of ABCD.

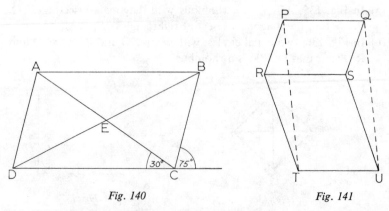

Fig. 140   *Fig. 141*

(11) In Fig. 141, PQSR and RSUT are parallelograms. Prove that PQUT is a parallelogram.

(12) In Fig. 142, PQR is any triangle. ST is parallel to QR, SU is parallel to PR, TU is parallel to PQ. Prove that P is the middle point of ST, Q is the middle point of SU and R is the middle point of TU.

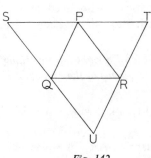

Fig. 142

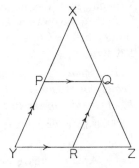

Fig. 143

(13) In the △XYZ in Fig. 143, P is the middle point of XY, Q is the middle point of XZ. QR is parallel to XY, PQ is parallel to YZ. Prove (i) △XPQ ≡ △QRZ, (ii) PQ = ½YZ.

(14) In Fig. 144, PQRS is a parallelogram with diagonals cutting at O. UT is a straight line drawn through O. Prove that OT = OU.

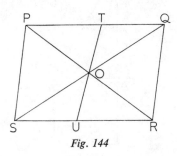

Fig. 144

213

27 Pythagoras' Theorem

A fundamental fact in geometry is called a **theorem**.

Pythagoras was a Greek mathematician who lived in the sixth century before Christ. He gave his name to a basic geometrical fact that states:

If a square is drawn on the hypotenuse of a right-angled triangle the area of this square is equal to the combined areas of the squares drawn on the other sides of the triangle.

That is to say, in the △ABC (see Fig. 145), with ∠A = right angle then,

Area of square 1 = Area of Square 2 + Area of Square 3.

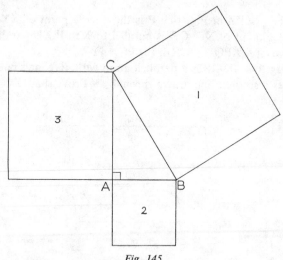

Fig. 145

(Remember that in a right-angled triangle the side opposite the right angle is called the **hypotenuse**.)

We have seen that the area of a square is given by the formula

$$\text{Area} = s^2$$

where s is the length of the side of the square. Given a right-angled triangle (as in Fig. 146) with side a (hypotenuse) = 5 cm, side b = 4 cm,

214

side $c = 3$ cm. If a square is constructed on side a then its area will be:

$$a \times a = a^2 = 5^2 = 25 \text{ cm}^2$$

The area of the square on side b will be

$$b \times b = b^2 = 4^2 = 16 \text{ cm}^2$$

The area of the square on side c will be

$$c \times c = c^2 = 3^2 = 9 \text{ cm}^2$$

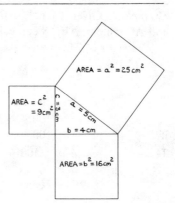

Fig. 146

Using Pythagoras' theorem:

Area of square on a = Area of square on b + Area of square on c

$\parallel$		$\parallel$		$\parallel$
25 cm²	=	16 cm²	+	9 cm²
$\parallel$		$\parallel$		$\parallel$
a^2	=	b^2	+	c^2

This last result, $a^2 = b^2 + c^2$ is the neatest way of expressing Pythagoras' theorem, and it is the way we shall use in the future.

The example used, a triangle with sides of 3, 4, and 5 units, is something of a special case of Pythagoras' theorem because a triangle drawn with sides in this ratio is always right-angled. Nevertheless the truth of the theorem can be demonstrated by constructing any right-angled

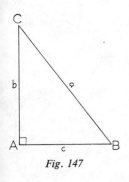

Fig. 147

triangle, measuring the sides and repeating the above calculation. Egyptian surveyors made use of the fact that a 3, 4, 5 triangle always gives a right angle, when building the Great Pyramid.

The following notation is used in most calculations that use Pythagoras' theorem: if the triangle ABC has $\angle A$ = right angle then the side opposite $\angle A$ is called a, the side opposite $\angle B$ is called b, and the side opposite $\angle C$ is called c (see Fig. 147).

215

Example 1. Given triangle ABC (see Fig. 148) with $\angle A$=right angle and $AC=6$ cm, $AB=8$ cm, calculate the length of BC.

Pythagoras' Theorem states,

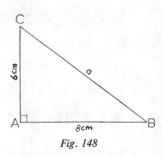

$$a^2 = b^2+c^2$$
$$\therefore\ a^2 = 6^2+8^2$$
$$a^2 = 36+64$$
$$a^2 = 100$$
if $\quad a\times a = 100$
Then $\quad\quad a = \sqrt{100} = 10$
$$a = 10 \text{ cm}$$
$$BC = 10 \text{ cm}$$

Fig. 148

Example 2. Given $\triangle$XYZ with $\angle X$=right angle, $XZ=12$ cm, and $XY=5$ cm, calculate the length of ZY. With the notation in Fig. 149,

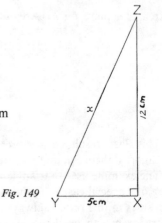

$$x^2 = y^2+z^2$$
$$\therefore\ x^2 = 12^2+5^2$$
$$x^2 = 144+25$$
$$x^2 = 169$$
Then $\quad\quad x = \sqrt{169} = 13 \text{ cm}$
$$ZY = 13 \text{ cm}$$

Fig. 149

Example 3. Given $\triangle$PQR with $\angle Q=$ right angle, $PQ=23$ m, and $QR=35$ m, find the length of PR. Using the notation in Fig. 150,

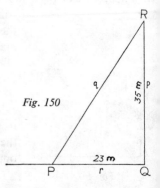

$$q^2 = p^2+r^2$$
$$q^2 = 35^2+23^2$$
$$q^2 = 1225+529$$
$$\therefore\ q^2 = 1754$$
$$q = \sqrt{1754} = 42 \text{ m (approx.)}$$
$$PR = 42 \text{ m}$$

Fig. 150

The next examples show how Pythagoras' theorem can be used to calculate the length of sides other than the hypotenuse. The calculation is based on the method used for solving simple equations.

Example 4. Given triangle ABC with $\angle B$=right angle, AC=15 cm, and BC=12 cm, find the length of AB. With the notation in Fig. 151,

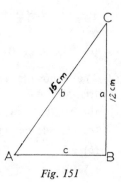

$$b^2 = a^2 + c^2$$

Substitute $\qquad 15^2 = 12^2 + c^2$

$$225 = 144 + c^2$$

Thus $\qquad 225 - 144 = c^2$

or $\qquad c^2 = 225 - 144$

$$\therefore c^2 = 81$$

$$c = \sqrt{81} = 9$$

$$AB = 9 \text{ cm}$$

Fig. 151

Example 5. In Fig. 152, if BC=64 cm and AD=81 cm, how much longer is CD than AB?

Draw AX parallel to BC. Then in $\triangle AXD$, $\angle X$=right angle and AX=BC=64 cm. Also

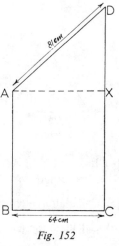

$$x^2 = a^2 + d^2$$

$$\therefore a^2 = x^2 - d^2$$

$$a^2 = 81^2 - 64^2$$

$$a^2 = 6561 - 4096$$

$$a^2 = 2465$$

Then $\qquad a = \sqrt{2465} = 49\cdot6 \text{ cm}.$

CD is 49·6 cm longer than AB.

Note: The calculation of $81^2 - 64^2$ can be done using factors.

Fig. 152

Since the factors of $\qquad a^2 - b^2 = (a+b)(a-b)$

Then the factors of $\quad 81^2 - 64^2 = (81 + 64)(81 - 64)$

$$= (145)(17)$$

$$= 2465$$

217

Exercise 1

(1) Without accurate drawing, say which of these triangles are right-angled, and name the right angle in each case.

    (*a*) AB = 4 cm, AC = 3 cm, BC = 5 cm

    (*b*) BC = 15 cm, AC = 9 cm, AB = 12 cm

    (*c*) XY = 130 mm, XZ = 40 mm, ZY = 120 mm

    (*d*) XY = 7·5 cm, XZ = 6 cm, ZY = 4·5 cm

    (*e*) RQ = 4 m, RP = 2·4 m, PQ = 3·2 m

(2) The following examples refer to the triangle in Fig. 153. In each case find the length of the missing side.

    (*a*) PQ = 15 cm, QR = 8 cm

    (*b*) PR = 1·3 m, QR = 0·5 m

    (*c*) PR = 37 cm, QR = 12 cm

    (*d*) QR = 20 m, PQ = 21 m

(3) Find the length of side *a* in Fig. 154.

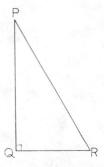

Fig. 153

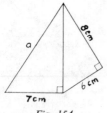

Fig. 154

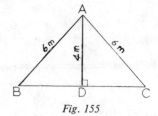

Fig. 155

(4) In Fig. 155, if AB = AC = 6 m, AD = 4 m, and ∠ADC = 90°, what is the length of BC?

(5) Calculate the length of a diagonal of a square of side 50 mm.

(6) Calculate the length of side *x* in Fig. 156.

(7) In Fig. 157, ABCD is a rhombus. AC = 9 cm, DB = 6 cm. Calculate the length of the sides of the rhombus.

(8) Given that AC = 45 m, BC = 28 m, ∠ACD = 18° and ∠DCB = 72°, calculate the length of AB, in Fig. 158.

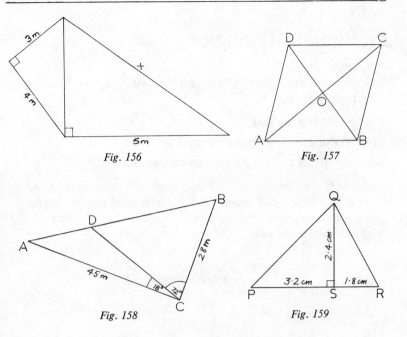

Fig. 156

Fig. 157

Fig. 158

Fig. 159

(9) In the triangle PQR (Fig. 159), QS is perpendicular to PR, PS = 3·2 cm, SR = 1·8 cm, QS = 2·4 cm. Prove that PQR = right angle.

(10) The inside measurements of a box are 120 mm wide, 160 mm long, and 150 mm high. What is the length of its longest diagonal?

28 Similar Triangles

Earlier in this Part (p. 197) it was shown that two triangles are congruent if, for both of them,

   (i) three sides are equal;

   (ii) two sides and the included angle are equal;

   (iii) two angles and the corresponding side are equal.

If, however, the three angles of one triangle are respectively equal to three angles of the other triangle the triangles need not be congruent.

Fig. 160 shows two triangles, whose respective angles are equal, but which are unequal in size.

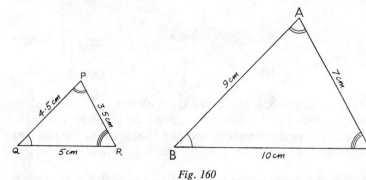

Fig. 160

They are of the same shape but not the same size. In fact △PQR is similar to △ABC, and this can be written as

$$\triangle PQR \parallel\mid \triangle ABC$$

Again in the △'s PQR and ABC, QR is half BC, PQ is half AB, PR is half AC. Expressed another way

$$\frac{QR}{BC} = \frac{5}{10} = \frac{1}{2}$$

also

$$\frac{PR}{AC} = \frac{3 \cdot 5}{7} = \frac{1}{2}$$

and

$$\frac{PQ}{AB} = \frac{4 \cdot 5}{9} = \frac{1}{2}$$

220

Thus, if two triangles are similar their corresponding sides are in the same ratio (i.e. proportional to one another). Also, if the corresponding angles of two triangles are equal (i.e. equiangular) then they are similar triangles.

This can be applied to any geometrical shape, plane or solid, and is the basis of work that depends on the scaling down of an original. A map is similar to the country it is drawn from, a model ship is similar to the original vessel, an architect's model is similar to the finished building. The principal of similarity will be worked out through triangles, in the main, because it is easier to do this and because a number of useful applications of the principle of similarity are based on similar triangles.

Example 1. At mid-day a vertical pole 120 cm high casts a shadow that is 90 cm long. At the same time a flagpole casts a shadow 7·2 metres long. What is the height of the flagpole?

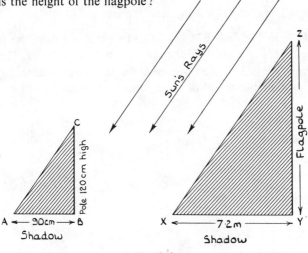

Fig. 161

From Fig. 161 it can be seen that the length of the shadow of the pole is three-quarters of the height of the pole, thus the length of the shadow of the flagpole (7·2 m) will be three-quarters of the length of the flagpole.

If $\quad\quad\quad \dfrac{3}{4}$ of length of the flagpole $= 7\cdot2$ m

then $\quad\quad\quad \dfrac{4}{4}$ of length of the flagpole $= 7\cdot2 \times \dfrac{4}{3}$ m

$$= 9\cdot6 \text{ metres}$$

221

The height of the flagpole can be found in another way.

In △'s ABC and XYZ

(i) $\angle A = \angle X$ (angle between sun's rays and ground)

(ii) $\angle B = \angle Y$ (rt. angles)

$$\therefore \triangle ABC \parallel\!\parallel \triangle XYZ \text{ (equiangular)}$$

Thus $\dfrac{BC}{BA} = \dfrac{YZ}{YX}$ (remember—corresponding sides are those opposite to equal angles)

So
$$\frac{4}{3} = \frac{YZ}{7 \cdot 2}$$
$$3YZ = 28 \cdot 8 \text{ (cross multiplied)}$$
$$YZ = 9 \cdot 6$$

Thus height of flagpole $= 9 \cdot 6$ metres

Example 2. In Fig. 162, BM is a line of sight taken from the top of a pylon to the top of a pole and then to a point on the ground. The length of the pole AP is 3 m, the distance MP $= 5$ m, and the distance MY $= 50$ m. Calculate the height of the pylon.

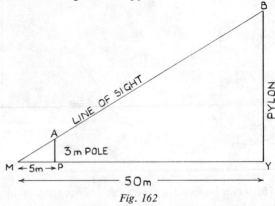

Fig. 162

In △'s MPA and MYB

(i) $\angle M = \angle M$ (common to both △'s)

(ii) $\angle P = \angle Y$ (rt. angles)

$$\therefore \triangle MPA \parallel\!\parallel \triangle MYB$$

Thus
$$\frac{PA}{PM} = \frac{YB}{YM} \text{ (corresponding sides)}$$

so
$$\frac{3}{5} = \frac{YB}{50}$$

$$5YB = 150 \text{ (cross multiplied)}$$

$$YB = 30 \text{ m}$$

Height of pylon $= 30$ metres

Example 3. In Fig. 163, ABC is a triangle with $\angle C =$ right angle and the ratio of $\frac{AB}{AC} = \frac{3}{2}$. If AB is produced to D so that AD $= 15$ cm, and AC is produced to E so that $\angle AED =$ right angle, find the length of AE.

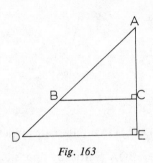

Fig. 163

In $\triangle$'s ABC and ADE

Because (i) $\angle ACB = \angle AED =$ right angle

(ii) $\angle BAC = \angle DAE$ (common to both triangles)

$\therefore$ Third angles must be equal

$\therefore$ $\triangle$'s ABC and ADE are equiangular

So $\triangle ABC \, ||| \, \triangle ADE$ (are similar)

and $$\frac{AB}{AD} = \frac{AC}{AE}$$

but $$\frac{AB}{AC} = \frac{3}{2} \quad \text{and} \quad AD = 15 \text{ cm}$$

Substitute in $$\frac{AB}{AD} = \frac{AC}{AE}$$

$$\frac{3}{15} \times \frac{2}{AE}$$

Cross multiply $$3AE = 30$$

$$AE = 10 \text{ cm}$$

8*

Example 4. From Fig. 164, in which AB ∥ DC prove that

$$\triangle BOA \parallel\!\!\!\mid \triangle DOC$$

If OA = 8 m, OB = 14 m, AB = 12 m, DC = 9 m, calculate the length of OD and OC.

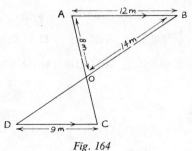

Fig. 164

In △'s BOA and DOC

Because (i) ∠OCD = ∠OAB (alternate angles)

    (ii) ∠DOC = ∠BOA (vertically opposite angles)

$$\therefore \triangle BOA \parallel\!\!\!\mid \triangle DOC \quad \text{and} \quad \frac{AB}{DC} = \frac{OB}{OD} = \frac{OA}{OC}$$

Substitute

$$\frac{12}{9} = \frac{14}{OD} = \frac{8}{OC}$$

Since

$$\frac{12}{9} \times \frac{14}{OD} \quad \text{(cross multiply)}$$

$$12OD = 126$$

$$OD = 10 \cdot 5 \text{ m}$$

Since

$$\frac{12}{9} \times \frac{8}{OC} \quad \text{(cross multiply)}$$

$$12OC = 72$$

$$OC = 6 \text{ m}$$

Exercise 1

(1) In each of the pairs of similar triangles (Fig. 165) find the length of sides x and y.

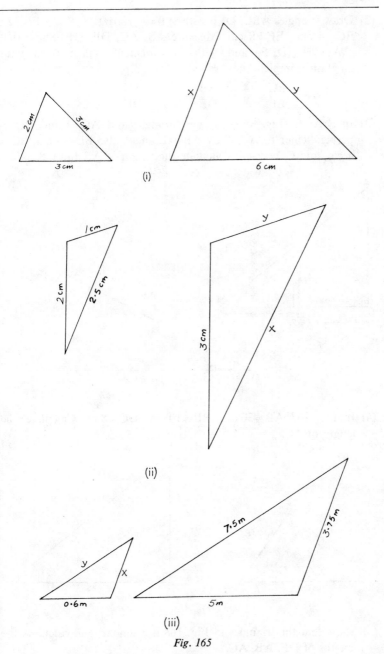

(i)

(ii)

(iii)

Fig. 165

225

(2) Draw triangles ABC, DEF with $\angle B = \angle E = 60°$; $\angle C = \angle F = 72°$, BC=4 cm., EF=8 cm. Measure AB, AC, DE, DF. Show that $\triangle ABC \parallel\!\parallel\!\parallel \triangle DEF$, and with measurements taken from your diagram, complete these ratios:

$$\frac{BC}{EF} = \frac{4}{8} \qquad \frac{AB}{DE} = - \qquad \frac{AC}{DF} = -$$

(3) In $\triangle ACE$ (Fig. 166), $\angle A$=rt. angle and AC=8 cm. BD is perpendicular to AC, thus $\angle B$=rt. angle, also BD=3 cm, BC= 4 cm, and CD=5 cm. Calculate the length of AE and CE.

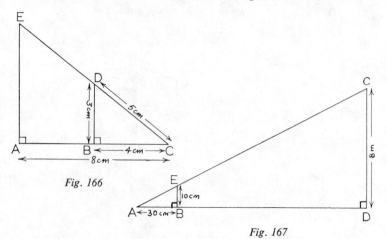

Fig. 166

Fig. 167

(4) In Fig. 167 AB=30 cm, BE=10 cm, DC=8 m. Calculate the length of AC.

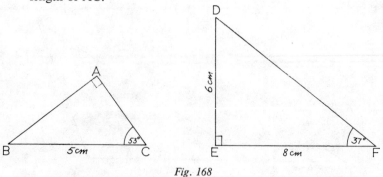

Fig. 168

(5) Show that the triangles in Fig. 168 are similar, and calculate the lengths of DF, AB, AC.

(6) Draw triangle XYZ, with XY = 40 mm, $\angle X = 45°$, $\angle Y = 75°$. Draw triangle PQR, with PQ = 70 mm, $\angle P = 45°$, $\angle Q = 75°$. Measure the sides and express these ratios as decimal fractions:

(i) $\dfrac{XZ}{XY}$ $\dfrac{XY}{YZ}$ $\dfrac{YZ}{XZ}$

(ii) $\dfrac{PR}{PQ}$ $\dfrac{PQ}{QR}$ $\dfrac{QR}{PR}$

(7) In Fig. 169, RP is parallel to TS, $\angle R = \angle P$, $\angle T = \angle S$. PQ = 1 m and QT = 3 m. Express the ratio $\dfrac{RP}{TS}$ as a vulgar fraction. If RP = 0·8 m what is the length of TS?

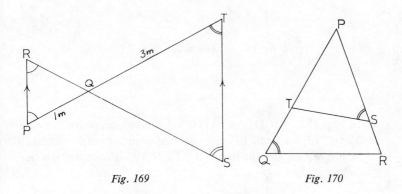

Fig. 169   *Fig. 170*

(8) In Fig. 170, if $\angle PST = \angle TQR$, show that $\triangle PRQ \parallel\parallel \triangle PTS$. Given that PS = 3 cm, PR = 4 cm, PQ = 5 cm and QR = 8 cm, calculate the lengths of PT and of TS.

(9) In Fig. 171 there are two triangles similar to $\triangle AOE$. By looking for equal angles, find these triangles. Give the reasons. If AO = 50 m, OE = 30 m, BO = 20 m, BD = 16 m, calculate the lengths of AE and OD.

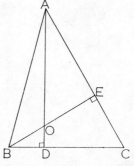

Fig. 171

227

(10) A man 1·80 m tall casts a shadow 1·20 m long; at the same time, a nearby building casts a shadow 8 m long. Calculate

  (i) the height of the building;
  (ii) the length of the shadow cast at this time by a tree 6 m high.

(11) In Fig. 172, given that PQ is parallel to ST, PR = 7·5 cm, QR = 6 cm, PQ = 9 cm, ST = 12 cm, prove that triangle PQR is similar to triangle STR. Calculate the lengths of RS and RT.

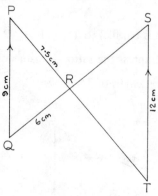

Fig. 172

(12) In Fig. 173, ABCD and EFGH are similar rectangles with AB = 15 cm, BC = 10 cm, EF = 30 cm. Use similar triangles to find the length of FG. Use the fact that △EFG is a right-angled triangle to calculate the length of EG.

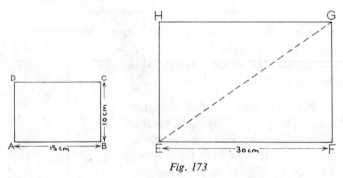

Fig. 173

29 The Circle

Figure 174 is a reminder of the names given to the different parts of a circle.

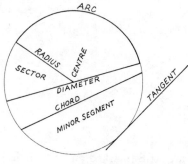

Fig. 174

If AB (see Fig. 175) is a chord in any circle with centre O, and the angle ACB is drawn on the chord as shown, then the chord AB is said to subtend the angle ACB at the circumference of the circle. The arc

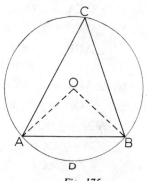

Fig. 175

ADB also subtends the angle ACB. If A and B are joined to O, the centre of the circle, then the chord AB and the arc ADB subtend the angle AOB at the centre of the circle.

Theorem

The angle subtended by an arc or chord at the centre of the circle is twice the angle subtended at the circumference by the same arc or chord. In Fig. 176.

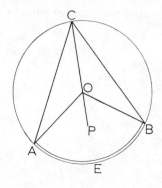 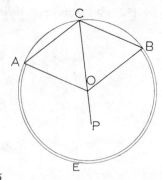

Fig. 176

Given   The arc AEB (marked on both circles) subtends ∠AOB at O the centre of each circle, and ∠ACB at the circumference of each circle.

To prove   ∠AOB = 2∠ACB

Construction Join CO and produce it to any point P.

Proof   In   △OAC, OC = OA (radii of same circle)

           ∴ ∠OCA = ∠OAC

and   ∠OCA + ∠OAC = 2∠OCA

but   ∠AOP = ∠OCA + ∠OAC
                     (exterior angle)

        ∴ ∠AOP = 2∠OCA

Similarly it can be proved that ∠BOP = 2∠OCB.

But   ∠AOP + ∠BOP = ∠AOB

and   ∠OCA + ∠OCB = ∠ACB

        ∴ ∠AOB = 2∠ACB

This basic fact enables us to discover other facts about angles in a circle.

In Fig. 177, ABDC is a circle with centre O, ∠ACB and ∠ADB are angles in the same segment of the circle, subtended by the same arc AB.

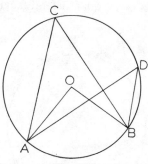

Fig. 177

To prove $\angle C = \angle D$

Construction   Join AO and BO.

Proof   From the above theorem it follows that

$$\angle O = 2\angle C$$

and $$\angle O = 2\angle D$$

$$\therefore \ \angle C = \angle D$$

In Fig. 178, AB is the diameter of the circle ABC with centre O. $\angle ACB$ is any angle drawn in the semi-circle.

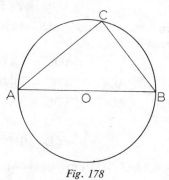

Fig. 178

To prove $\angle ACB$ = a right angle (90°)

Proof $\angle AOB$, angle at the centre = $2\angle ACB$, angle at the circumference.

But AOB is a straight line.

$$\therefore \ \angle AOB = 180°$$

Hence $\angle ACB = 90° =$ a right angle.

In Fig. 179, ABCD is a cyclic quadrilateral (angles lie on the circumference of the circle).

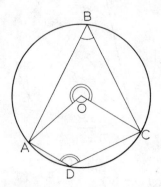

Fig. 179

| *To prove* | The opposite angles of the quadrilateral are supplementary, i.e. |

$$\angle B + \angle D = 180° \quad \text{and} \quad \angle A + \angle C = 180°$$

Construction Join AO and OC where O is the centre of the circle.

Proof The arc ADC subtends $\angle AOC$ at the centre O, and $\angle B$ at the circumference.

$$\therefore \ \angle AOC = 2\angle B$$

The arc ABC subtends $\angle AOC$ at the centre and $\angle D$ at the circumference,

$$\therefore \ \angle AOC = 2\angle D$$

Thus $\angle AOC + \angle AOC = 2\angle B + 2\angle D$

But $\angle AOC + \angle AOC = 360°$

So $2\angle B + 2\angle D = 360°$

$$\therefore \ \angle B + \angle D = 180°$$

Similarly, by joining BO and OD, it can be shown that,

$$\angle A + \angle C = 180°$$

Thus the opposite angles of a cyclic quadrilateral are supplementary.

In Fig. 180, ABCD is a cyclic quadrilateral with the side DC produced to E.

To prove Exterior $\angle e$ = interior opposite $\angle a$.

Proof $\angle d + \angle e = 180°$ (DCE is a straight line)

232

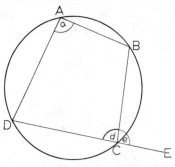

Fig. 180

But $\angle d + \angle a = 180°$ (opposite angles of a cyclic quadrilateral)

$\therefore \angle d + \angle e = \angle d + \angle a$

Take $\angle d$ from each side. Then $\angle e = \angle a$.

Summary of facts

1 *The angle subtended by an arc or a chord at the centre of a circle is twice the angle subtended by the arc or chord at the circumference of the circle.*

2 *All angles in the same segment are equal.*

3 *The angle in a semi-circle is a right angle.*

4 *The opposite angles of a cyclic quadrilateral are supplementary.*

5 *The exterior angle of a cyclic quadrilateral is equal to the interior and opposite angle.*

Exercise 1

(1) In Fig. 181 (i) On what arc do $\angle ADE$, $\angle ABE$ stand?

(ii) What angles are subtended, at the circumference, by the chord DE?

(iii) If $\angle CAD = 20°$ name another angle which is also $20°$.

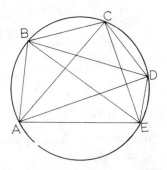

Fig. 181

233

(2) In each of the diagrams in Fig. 182 calculate, in each case, the angle marked x. O is the centre of the circle.

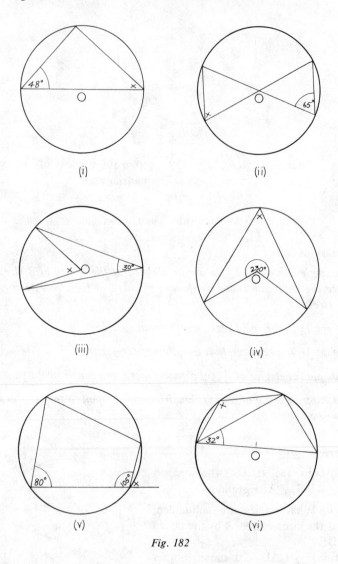

Fig. 182

(3) In each of the diagrams in Fig. 183 find the size of the angle marked a.

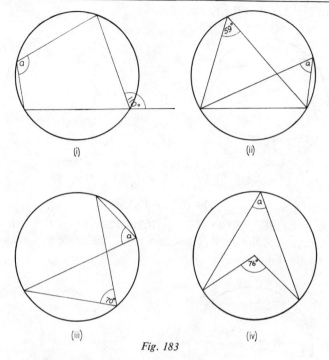

Fig. 183

(4) In a circle two chords AB and CD intersect at right angles, ∠BAC=40°. Find the size of ∠ABD.

(5) ABCD is a cyclic quadrilateral, ∠DAC=50°, ∠ADC=70°. Find ∠ABD.

(6) In Fig. 184, calculate the size of angle *x*.

(7) In Fig. 185, ABCD is a circle with centre O, ∠ABC=65°. Calculate the size of ∠CDB.

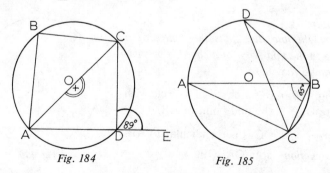

Fig. 184   *Fig. 185*

(8) In Fig. 186 find the size of ∠*x* and ∠*y*.

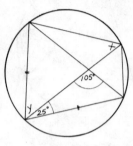

Fig. 186

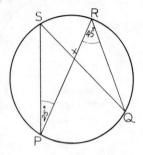

Fig. 187

(9) In Fig. 187 calculate the size of ∠SXP.

(10) In Fig. 188, ∠ACD = 30°, ∠DCB = 120°. Show that AB is the diameter of the circle. (Remember that the angle in a semi-circle is a right angle.)

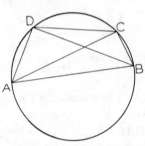

Fig. 188

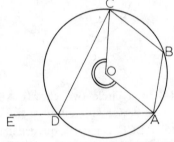

Fig. 189

(11) In Fig. 189, O is the centre of the circle. Prove that the marked ∠COA = ∠2CDE.

Theorem

A straight line that joins the centre of a circle to the mid-point of a chord is perpendicular to the chord.

In Fig. 190, AB is a chord of a circle with centre O. C is the mid-point of AB.

To prove   OC is perpendicular to AB.

Construction   Join OA, OB.

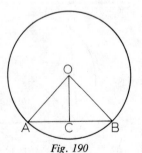

Fig. 190

236

Proof   In △'s AOC, BOC

∵ (i)   AO = OB (radii)

(ii)   OC = OC (common)

(iii)   AC = BC (Given. C is mid-point of AB)

∴ △AOC ≡ △BOC (S.S.S)

∴ ∠OCA = ∠OCB,

these are equal adjacent angles so

∠OCA = ∠OCB = right angle.

Conversely, a perpendicular from the centre of a circle to a chord bisects it.

In Fig. 191, AB is a chord of a circle with centre O, OC is perpendicular to AB.

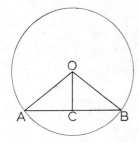

Fig. 191

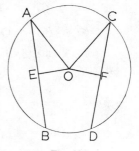

Fig. 192

To prove   OC bisects AB at C

Construction   Join AO, OC.

Proof   In △'s AOC, BOC

∵ (i)   OA = OB (radii)

(ii)   OC = OC (common)

(iii) ∠OCA = ∠OCB = right angle

∴ △AOC ≡ △BOC (R.H.S.)

∴ AC = CB or C is the mid-point of AB.

These basic facts enable us to discover further information about the chord and tangent properties of the circle.

In Fig. 192, AB and CD are equal chords in the circle ABDC with centre O.

237

To prove	AB and CD are equidistant from centre O.
Construction	Join OA, and OC. Draw OE perpendicular to AB, and OF perpendicular to CD.
Proof	Because E and F are the mid-points of AB and CD, OE is at right angles to AB, and OF is at right angles to CD (theorem). In the △'s OAE and OCF

  ∵ (i)   OA = OC (radii)

    (ii) ∠OEA = ∠OFC = right angle

    (iii)   AE = CF (perpendicular from centre of circle to chord bisects chord)

      ∴ △OAE ≡ △OCF (R.H.S.)
       ∴ OE = OF

Conversely, if OE = OF, then in △'s AOE and COF

    ∵ (i)   OE = OF

     (ii)   OA = OC (radii)

     (iii) ∠OEA = ∠OFC = right angle

      ∴ △AOE ≡ △COF

and   AE = CF

But   AE = ½AB and CF = ½CD

Thus   AB = CD

Theorem

The tangent drawn at any point on a circle is perpendicular to the radius drawn through the point of contact.

Given   AB is a tangent at point A to the circle, centre O (Fig. 193)

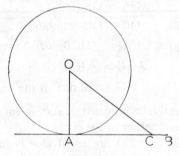

Fig. 193

To prove   OA is perpendicular to AB

Construction   Take any point C in AB. Join OC.

Proof   Since AB is a tangent then every point on it except A is outside the circle.

          ∴ OC must be longer than the radius OA. This is true for any point on AB except A.

          Thus OA must be the shortest distance from O to AB, so OA must be perpendicular to AB.

Note: Because there can be only one perpendicular from O to AB then only *one tangent* can be drawn to a circle from any one point on the circumference.

Since the radius is perpendicular to the tangent, then the perpendicular must pass through the centre of the circle. The radius, also, passes through the point of contact of the tangent and the circle.

Theorem

If two tangents are drawn to a circle from a point outside the circle:
    (i) *the tangents are equal,* (ii) *the tangents subtend equal angles at the centre,* (iii) *the line joining the centre to the point outside the circle, bisects the angle between the tangents.*

Given   In Fig. 194, AB and AC are tangents from A to the circle centre O.

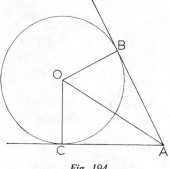

Fig. 194

To prove (i)   AC = AB

         (ii) ∠BOA = ∠COA

         (iii) ∠BAO = ∠CAO

Proof   In the △'s ABO, ACO

     ∵ (i)   OB = OC (radii)

       (ii)   ∠OBA = ∠OCA = right angle (tangent is perpendicular to the radius drawn through point of contact.)

       (iii) OA = OA (common)

             ∴ △ABO ≡ △ACO (R.H.S)

∴ (i) AC = AB, (ii) ∠BOA = ∠COA, (iii) ∠BAO = ∠CAO

239

Example 1. In Fig. 195 a chord 5·6 cm long is 1·4 cm from the centre of a circle. Calculate the radius of the circle.

In Fig. 195, B is the mid point of AC (perpendicular from centre to chord)

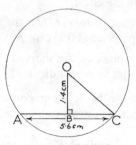

Fig. 195

∴ BC = 2·8 cm

In the △OBC,

$$\angle OBC = \text{right angle (perpendicular from centre to chord)}$$
$$\therefore OC^2 = OB^2 + BC^2 \text{ (Pythagoras)}$$
$$OC^2 = 1\cdot4^2 + 2\cdot8^2$$
$$OC^2 = 1\cdot96 + 7\cdot84$$
$$OC^2 = 9\cdot8$$
$$\therefore OC = \sqrt{9\cdot8} = 3\cdot13 \text{ cm}$$
$$\text{Radius} = 3\cdot13 \text{ cm}$$

Exercise 2

(1) In Fig. 196, OA = 10 cm, C is the mid-point of AB so that AC = CB = 8 cm. Calculate the length of OC.

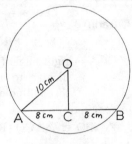

Fig. 196

(2) The radius of a circle is 5 cm. A chord in the same circle is 8 cm long. How far is the centre of the chord from the centre of the circle?

(3) The radius of a circle is 4 cm, a chord is 1·5 cm from the centre. Find the length of the chord.

(4) In a circle of radius 12·5 cm there are two parallel chords on opposite sides of the centre of lengths 15 cm and 10 cm. Calculate the distance between the chords.

(5) In Fig. 197, O is the centre of both circles. Prove that AB=CD.

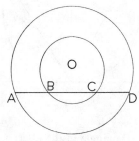

Fig. 197

(6) A bowl is the shape of a hemisphere, it has an internal diameter of 30 cm. It is partly filled with water to within 10 cm of the top of the bowl. Find the diameter of the water surface.

Alternate segment

The segment DEB of the circle in Fig. 198 is described as being the alternate segment to the angle CBD. Again, the segment DFB is the alternate segment to the angle ABD.

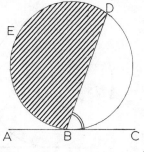

Fig. 198

241

Theorem

The angle between a tangent to a circle and a chord drawn through the point of contact is equal to any angle drawn in the alternate segment.

Given Circle BED with ABC a tangent and DB a chord (Fig. 199).

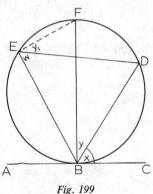

Fig. 199

To prove ∠DBC = the angle in the alternate segment ∠DEB

Construction Draw the diameter BF. Join FE.

Proof
$$\angle y = \angle y_1 \text{ (angles in same segment)}$$
$$\angle y + \angle x = 90° \text{ (tangent and radius)}$$
$$\angle y_1 + \angle w = 90° \text{ (angle in semi-circle)}$$
$$\therefore \angle x = \angle w$$

that is

$$\angle DBC = \angle DEB$$

Similarly it can be shown that any angle drawn in the segment to the right of the chord BD will be equal to ∠ABD.

Exercise 3

(1) In Fig. 200, if ∠x = 70° find ∠y.

(2) In Fig. 200, if ∠y = 60° find ∠x.

(3) In Fig. 200, if ∠x = 75°, ∠z = 30° find ∠w.

(4) In Fig. 200, if ∠y = 60°, ∠z = 40°, find ∠w.

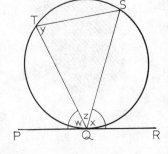

Fig. 200

(5) In Fig. 201, ∠DCB = 80°. Calculate the size of ∠DEC.

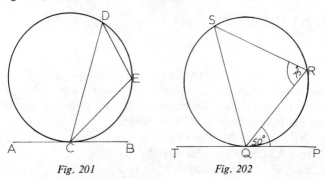

Fig. 201   *Fig. 202*

(6) In Fig. 202, given that ∠SRQ = 75° and ∠RQP = 50°, calculate the size of ∠SQR.

(7) In Fig. 203, ABC is a tangent to the circle at B.

    (i) If ∠ABD = 60°, ∠DBE = 85°, calculate ∠CBE.

    (ii) If ∠BDE = 35°, ∠DBC = 125°, calculate ∠DBE.

    (iii) If DE is a diameter and ∠BDE = 30°, find ∠ABD.

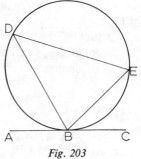

Fig. 203

(8) In Fig. 204, if:

    (i) ∠QTS = 35°, ∠QRS = 60° find ∠TQS.

    (ii) ∠QTS = 35°, ∠QST = 95° find ∠SRQ.

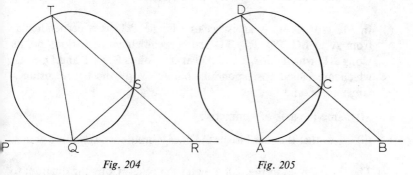

Fig. 204   *Fig. 205*

(9) In Fig. 205 prove that ∠ACB = ∠DAB.

30 Symmetry

If a circle, cut out of a sheet of paper, is folded along its diameter, the two halves of the circle will coincide exactly. Because it can be folded into exactly equal halves the circle can be said to be **symmetrical**.

Again, if a square ABCD is folded along the diagonal AC the two triangles ADC and ABC will coincide exactly (see Fig. 206). Thus the square ABCD is a symmetrical figure and the diagonal is its axis of symmetry, just as the diameter of the circle would be the axis of symmetry of the circle.

Further, if the square is folded along the diagonal DB, this line will also be an axis of symmetry.

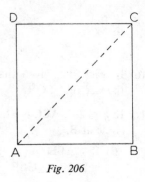

Fig. 206

Practical work

(1) Draw (i) a square, (ii) a rectangle, (iii) an isosceles triangle, (iv) an equilateral triangle, (v) a rhombus, (vi) a trapezium. Which of these figures are symmetrical? Draw in the axes of symmetry where possible.

(2) How many axes of symmetry has a circle?

(3) In Fig. 207, ABC is an isosceles triangle. AD is a perpendicular from A to BC. PQ, RS, TU are perpendiculars at various points along AD which cut AB and AC at the points P, R, T and Q, S, U, which are called corresponding points. Copy the figure, using a larger scale, and

  (i) name the axis of symmetry,

  (ii) show that this axis bisects the lines joining corresponding points.

(4) The three circles in Fig. 208 touch each other. Copy the diagram to any convenient scale and draw its axis of symmetry.

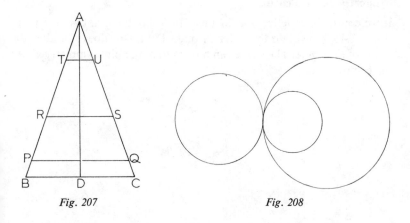

Fig. 207   Fig. 208

(5) In Fig. 209 AB is the axis of symmetry for each of the three figures.
Draw each figure as it would appear in its completed form.

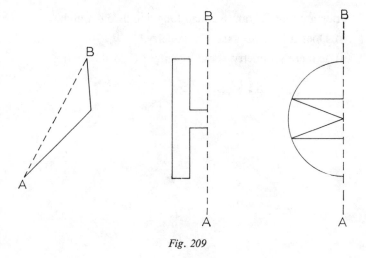

Fig. 209

The plane of symmetry

If a cube is cut into exactly equal halves then the plane of the cut is the
plane of symmetry of the cube.

245

Symmetry about a centre

If we consider the letter S as in Fig. 210, using the point A as a pivot it is possible to rotate the letter through 180°. This does not alter the shape of the figure. The shape can be said to have point symmetry about the centre A.

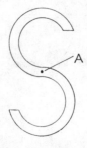

Fig. 210

Practical work

(1) Draw 3 capital letters which have point symmetry.

(2) Draw a parallelogram 6·25 cm long and 3·75 cm high.

   (i) Does it have an axis of symmetry?

   (ii) Is there symmetry about a centre? Find the centre.

31 Loci

The locus of a point is the path traced by that point when it moves in accordance with a given law.

The tip of the second hand of a watch takes up a number of separate positions as it ticks around the dial in the course of a minute; these positions taken all together result in a circle. This circle is the path traced out by the tip of the second hand, and is thus the **locus** of the tip.

Example 1. If O is any point, then the locus of a point 5 cm from O is the circumference of a circle with centre O and radius 5 cm (Fig. 211).

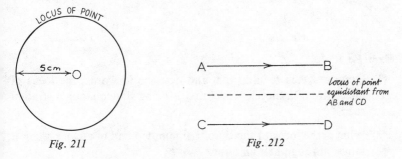

Fig. 211   Fig. 212

Example 2. In Fig. 212, AB and CD are parallel straight lines. The locus of a point that will be always the same distance from both AB and CD will be a line drawn between AB and CD parallel to them and equidistant from them.

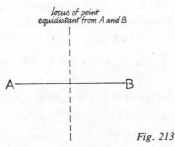

Fig. 213

Example 3. The locus of a point equidistant from points A and B will be the perpendicular bisector of the line joining the two points (see Fig. 213).

247

Example 4. Two straight lines AC and BC meet at C. The locus of a point equidistant from AC and BC is the bisector of the angle formed by the two lines. In Fig. 214 the locus of a point equidistant from AC and BC is the line CL.

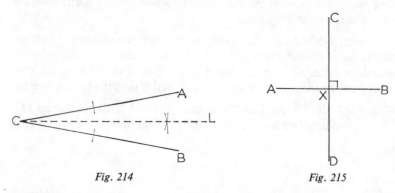

Fig. 214   Fig. 215

Exercise 1

(1) Draw a sketch to illustrate, and describe in words, the locus of the centre of a bicycle wheel that is being ridden along a straight road.

(2) What is the locus of the tip of the minute hand of a clock when it moves through half an hour?

(3) A pendulum 1 metre long swings through an arc 30° on each side of the vertical. Draw a diagram to illustrate the locus of the tip of the pendulum.

(4) A wheel of diameter 5 cm rolls around the outside of a larger wheel of diameter 30 cm. Draw a diagram of the locus of the centre of the small wheel.

(5) In Fig. 215, CD is perpendicular to AB. Using a separate diagram in each case:
   (i) Draw the locus of a point 50 mm from X.
   (ii) Draw the locus of a point 3 cm from AB.
   (iii) Draw the locus of a point equidistant from CX and XB.

(6) In Fig. 216, ABCD is a 5 cm cube. It is rolled along a flat surface, in the direction of the arrow, until the point B again rests on the surface. Draw a diagram showing the path followed by point B.

(7) In Fig. 217, ABCD is a rectangular piece of wood. It is rolled along a table top, in the direction of the arrow, until point C touches the table. Draw a diagram to show the path followed by point C.

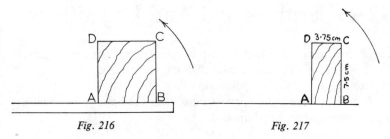

Fig. 216   Fig. 217

(8) In Fig. 218, AB is a piece of card, 15 cm long. It is pinned to a table at a point which is 5 cm from A. The card is rotated through 360°. Draw a diagram to show the locus of point A and point B.

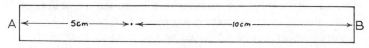

Fig. 218

(9) Construct a triangle with sides of 8 cm, 6·5 cm, and 5 cm. Find a point that is equidistant from each vertex of the triangle.

(10) In Fig. 219, PQ is a fishing rod 6 m long, QR is a length of line 4 m long. When the rod is lowered what is the locus of Q? When the rod is lowered what path will be traced by point R?

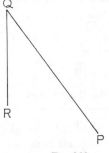

Fig. 219

32 Logarithms and Anti-Logarithms

Logarithms are used to take the drudgery out of mechanical arithmetic. By their use, multiplication and division, the raising to powers, and the extraction of roots are all made easier.

Logarithms are indices, and to use them the basic rules of indices must be remembered and applied.

Since $$10 = 10^1$$
and $$100 = 10^2$$

100×10 can be expressed as $10^2 \times 10^1 = 10^{2+1} = 10^3 = 1,000$. Again $100 \times 1000 = 10^2 \times 10^3 = 10^{2+3} = 10^5 = 100,000$. When 100 is written as 10^2 and 1000 as 10^3 the numbers are expressed as powers of 10; in other words they are expressed as powers to a base of 10.

Any number can be expressed as a power to a base of 10,

$$10 = 10^1$$
$$100 = 10^2$$

are easily expressed in this form. It is not so easy, however, to express a number such as 5 to the base 10. To do this we use *logarithm tables* which give us the index or power to which 10 has to be raised to obtain a particular number.

Here is an extract from a table of logarithms. You will notice that the index only is given since the whole table is calculated to a base of 10.

	0	1	2	3	4	5	6	7	8	9	Mean Differences								
											1	2	3	4	5	6	7	8	9
50	·6990	6998	7007	7016	7024	7033	7042	7050	7059	7067	1	2	3	3	4	5	6	7	8
51	·7076	7084	7093	7101	7110	7118	7126	7135	7143	7152	1	2	3	3	4	5	6	7	8
52	·7160	7168	7177	7185	7193	7202	7210	7218	7226	7235	1	2	2	3	4	5	6	7	7
53	·7243	7251	7259	7267	7275	7284	7292	7300	7308	7316	1	2	2	3	4	5	6	6	7
54	·7324	7332	7340	7348	7356	7364	7372	7380	7388	7396	1	2	2	3	4	5	6	6	7

To express 5 as a power of ten, the table is used in the following way. Find 5 (in fact 50) in the left-hand column, move to the right to the column headed 0 and the number here is the required index, i.e. 0·6990. Thus

$$\text{5 as a power of 10 is } 10^{0 \cdot 6990}$$

A difficulty at this stage is that the same result will be obtained if we look up 5, 50, or 500 in the tables.

However, since

$$10^0 = 1 \quad \text{and} \quad 10^1 = 10$$

any number between 1 and 10 (such as 5) will, when expressed to the base 10, have an index that lies between 0 and 1. Further, 50 lies in the range 10 to 100, i.e. 10^1 to 10^2, and 500 in the range 100 to 1000, i.e. 10^2 to 10^3. Using this information the values obtained from the table can be adjusted to make allowance for this variation in size. Thus

5 as a power of 10 is $10^{0 \cdot 6990}$ (i.e. between 10^0 and 10^1)

50 ,, ,, ,, ,, 10 ,, $10^{1 \cdot 6990}$ (,,   ,, 10^1 ,, 10^2)

500 ,, ,, ,, ,, 10 ,, $10^{2 \cdot 6990}$ (,,   ,, 10^2 ,, 10^3)

When a number is fully expressed as a power of 10 the index carried by the 10 is the logarithm of that number, i.e. $50 = 10^{1 \cdot 6990}$ and so the logarithm of 50 is 1·6990.

The tables we are using are calculated to base 10 and give only the index. The logarithm of 50 is written as log $50 = 1 \cdot 6990$; similarly log $5 = 0 \cdot 6990$ and log $500 = 2 \cdot 6990$.

Taking log $50 = 1 \cdot 6990$ you will notice that the logarithm is made up of two parts, a whole number that is not obtained from the tables and a decimal fraction that the table supplies.

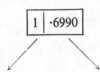

The whole number is called the **characteristic**. Its value depends on the size of the original number. It can be positive (+) or, as you will see later, negative (−).

The decimal fraction is called the **mantissa**. It is obtained from the tables and is always positive (+).

Until you are more skilled in the use of logarithms the following table may help you decide on the characteristic for the logarithm of a number.

251

For a number between

1 and 10	i.e. 10^0–10^1 characteristic is 0			
10 „ 100	„ 10^1–10^2	„	„ 1	
100 „ 1000	„ 10^2–10^3	„	„ 2	
1000 „ 10,000	„ 10^3–10^4	„	„ 3	
10,000 „ 100,000	„ 10^4–10^5	„	„ 4	

and so on.

Example 1. Use the extract from the tables to find log 526·7.

 (i) Find 52 (the first two figures of the number) in the left-hand column.

 (ii) Move along the row of 4 figure columns until the column headed 6 (third figure of original number) is reached. Note this figure, i.e. 0·7210.

(iii) Move to the right again to the part of the tables made up of single figures. Note the figure that appears in the column headed 7 (the fourth of the original number) in this case 6.

(iv) Add this 6 to the result obtained in (ii) in this way:

$$\begin{array}{r} 0\cdot7210 \\ 6 \\ \hline 0\cdot7216 \end{array}$$

0·7216 is the mantissa we require and the characteristic can be found by seeing which group our original number falls into.

Thus 526·7 is between 100 and 1,000 i.e. 10^2–10^3 and so has a characteristic of 2.

$$\therefore \ \log 526\cdot7 = 2\cdot7216$$

Summary of terms

Remember

Any number can be expressed as a power of 10, e.g. $51 = 10^{1\cdot7076}$. In this, 10 is the base, and 1·7076 the index or logarithm. This logarithm has two parts as explained on page 251.

Exercise 1

(1) Use the extract from the tables given on page 250 to express the following numbers as 'powers of 10':

52, 5·25, 546, 53·67, 5,345, 51,240, 5·026

(2) Use the extract from the tables on page 250 to find the logarithms of the following numbers:

    (*a*) 5·146, 51·46, 514·6, 5,146

    (*b*) 53·78, 5·219, 5·041, 546

    (*c*) 52,360, 5·082, 547·7, 51·39

(3) Given that log 83 is 1·9191 give the log of

    (*a*) 8·3   (*b*) 830   (*c*) 8,300

(4) Given that log 1·745 is 0·2417 give the log of

    (*a*) 17·45   (*b*) 1,745   (*c*) 174·5

Anti-logarithms

To convert logarithms back to numbers we make use of tables of anti-logarithms. As their name suggests these tables convert a number expressed as a power of 10 back to an ordinary number.

Here is an extract from anti-logarithm tables.

	0	1	2	3	4	5	6	7	8	9	1	2	3	4	5	6	7	8	9
														Mean Differences					
·60	3981	3990	3999	4009	4018	4027	4036	4046	4055	4064	1	2	3	4	5	6	6	7	8
·61	4074	4083	4093	4102	4111	4121	4130	4140	4150	4159	1	2	3	4	5	6	7	8	9
·62	4169	4178	4188	4198	4207	4217	4227	4236	4246	4256	1	2	3	4	5	6	7	8	9
·63	4266	4276	4285	4295	4305	4315	4325	4335	4345	4355	1	2	3	4	5	6	7	8	9
·64	4365	4375	4385	4395	4406	4416	4426	4436	4446	4457	1	2	3	4	5	6	7	8	9

They are used in the following way:

Example 2. Find the number of which 1·6143 is the log.

  (i) Ignore the characteristic for the time being. Find ·61 (first two figures of the mantissa) in the left-hand column of the table.

 (ii) Move to the right along the row of four figure numbers to the column headed 4. Note this number, i.e. 4111.

(iii) Continue along the row to the single number section of the table, note the figure that appears in the column headed 3 (fourth figure in original number), i.e. 3.

(iv) Add this 3 to the result obtained in (ii) in this way:

$$
\begin{array}{r}
4111 \\
+ \quad 3 \\
\hline
4114
\end{array}
$$

The characteristic of the original log is 1, therefore our result must lie in the range 10^1–10^2, that is 10 to 100. The decimal point is placed by inspection thus 41·14 as this is the only position that allows the result to lie in the range 10 to 100.

$$\therefore \ 1\cdot6143 \text{ is the logarithm of } 41\cdot14$$

Note

The following are different ways of saying the same thing:

(i) 1·6143 is the logarithm of 41·14.

(ii) Log 41·14 = 1·6143.

(iii) 41·14 = $10^{1\cdot6143}$.

(iv) 41·14 is the anti-logarithm of 1·6143.

(v) 41·14 is the number whose logarithm is 1·6143.

(vi) Antilog 1·6143 = 41·14.

Exercise 2

Use the extract from the anti-logarithm tables to find the numbers for which the following are logs.

(1) 1·6243, 1·6407, 0·6328, 0·6333.

(2) 3·6351, 2·6001, 0·6479, 2·6477.

(3) If anti-log 0·4673 is 2·933, write down the numbers of which the following are logs:

(a) 3·4673   (b) 1·4673   (c) 2·4673.

For the remainder of this exercise use the complete tables of logarithms and anti-logarithms at the end of the book.

(4) Find the log of each of these numbers:

(a) 7·460	(d) 557·5	(g) 89·98
(b) 41·33	(e) 6,000	(h) 342·6
(c) 8·004	(f) 227·6	(i) 250,000

(5) Use anti-log tables to find the numbers of which the following are the logs:

(a) 1·3465   (d) 3·7459   (g) 4·5173

(b) 0·0703   (e) 2·398   (h) 1·2698

(c) 2·2546   (f) 0·9578   (i) 3·3171

33 More Work with Logarithms

Logarithms with negative characteristics

So far in our work on logarithms we have been concerned with numbers greater than 1.

You will remember that

$$\frac{1}{10} = 0.1 \quad \text{can be written as } 10^{-1}$$

$$\frac{1}{100} = 0.01 \quad \text{,, \quad ,, \quad ,, \quad ,, } 10^{-2}$$

$$\frac{1}{1000} = 0.001 \quad \text{,, \quad ,, \quad ,, \quad ,, } 10^{-3}$$

and so on.

The characteristic of the logarithms of 0·1, 0·5, or 0·7 is -1, written as $\bar{1}$ and read as 'bar one'.

Similarly the characteristic of log 0·01, log 0·04, and log 0·08 is $\bar{2}$, and the characteristic of log 0·001, log 0·003, and log 0·009 is $\bar{3}$.

Remember

Negative (minus) characteristics apply to the logs of numbers *less than one*.

Even if the characteristic is negative ($-$) the mantissa is always positive ($+$).

It may help in the early stages if you remember the following rule for the logarithms of numbers less than one: *The negative characteristic is one more than the number of noughts after the decimal point.*

Thus the characteristic of log 0·07 is $\bar{2}$ ($1+1=2$), and the characteristic of log 0·3 is $\bar{1}$ ($0+1=1$).

Example 1. From the tables find log 0·0326. The mantissa is found in the usual way (find 32 and then move along the row to the column headed 6)

$$0.5132$$

The characteristic is one more than the number of noughts after the decimal point and is negative, that is, $\bar{2}$

$$\therefore \ \log 0.0326 = \bar{2}.5132$$

Example 2. Find the number of which $\bar{2}{\cdot}9678$ is the logarithm. Use anti-log tables to convert the mantissa; this gives

9285

Place the decimal point by inspection. Since the characteristic is $\bar{2}$ there will be one nought after the point, thus

0·09285

So log 0·09285 = $\bar{2}{\cdot}9678$

Exercise 1

(1) Use tables to find the logarithms of the following numbers:

(*a*) 0·275	(*d*) 0·00014	(*g*) 0·2625
(*b*) 0·00683	(*e*) 0·4562	(*h*) 0·00435
(*c*) 0·0307	(*f*) 0·3768	(*i*) 0·08374

(2) Find the numbers of which these are the logs:

(*a*) $\bar{1}{\cdot}6342$	(*d*) $\bar{3}{\cdot}8163$	(*g*) $\bar{1}{\cdot}2004$
(*b*) $\bar{2}{\cdot}3941$	(*e*) $\bar{4}{\cdot}1128$	(*h*) $\bar{3}{\cdot}5655$
(*c*) $\bar{1}{\cdot}6342$	(*f*) $\bar{2}{\cdot}7845$	(*i*) $\bar{4}{\cdot}4763$

When powers of the same base are multiplied together, the rule $x^m \times x^n = x^{m+n}$ may be expressed as 'add the indices'. Since logarithms are simply indices, with base 10, any two numbers may be multiplied together by expressing them as powers of 10, and 'adding the logarithms'.

Thus: (i) $100 \times 1{,}000 = 10^2 \times 10^3$

$$= 10^{2+3}$$

$$= 10^5 = 100{,}000.$$

(ii) $50{\cdot}54 \times 7{\cdot}341 = 10^{1{\cdot}7036} \times 10^{0{\cdot}8658}$ (from tables)

$$= 10^{2{\cdot}5694} \text{ (add the logs)}$$

$$= 317{\cdot}0 \text{ (take the anti-log)}$$

Layout

It is convenient to set out sums like (ii) as in Example 3.

Example 3. Use logs to evaluate 50.54×7.341.

No.	Log
50·54	1·7036
7·341	0·8658
371·0	2·5694

Place point by inspection after using anti-logs to convert logs.

Obtain logs from tables. Add the mantissae. Carry 1 across point to the characteristic.

Ans. = 371

When numbers smaller than one are multiplied, difficulty may occur in the manipulation of the negative or minus characteristic.

Remember

Although the characteristic may be negative the mantissa is *always* positive.

Example 4. Use logs to evaluate 3.14×0.07357.

No.	Log
3·14	0·4969
0·07357	$\bar{2}$·8667
0·2310	$\bar{1}$·3636

Place point by inspection after using anti-logs to convert logs.

Obtain logs from tables. Add mantissae, remember the mantissae are positive (+) so +1 is carried over the point, so $-2+1 = -1$

Ans. = 0·231

Division using logarithms

When indices are divided the rule is

$$x^m \div x^n = x^{m-n}$$

To divide numbers using logs, the rule is the same, the logarithms are subtracted one from the other.

Remember that even if the characteristic is negative the mantissa is always positive.

Example 5. Use logs to find the value of $26.35 \div 7.25$.

No.	Log
26·35	1·4208
7·25	0·8603
3·635	0·5605

Place point by inspection after using anti-logs to convert logs.

Obtain logs from tables. Subtract mantissae. Carry 1 across the point and subtract characteristics.

Ans. = 3·635

The mantissae of logarithms with negative characteristics are subtracted in the usual way. The subtraction of the characteristics obeys the ordinary rule for subtracting signed numbers—change the sign and add.

Example 6. Use logs to evaluate $0.3824 \div 0.0731$.

No.	Log
0·3824	$\bar{1}$·5826
0·0731	$\bar{2}$·8639
5·232	0·7187

Use anti-logs and place point by inspection.

Subtract the mantissae in the usual way. Carry $+1$ across the point, this gives $\bar{1}$ as the lower characteristic. Follow the rule for subtraction—change sign and add.

Ans. = 5·232

Example 7. Use logs to evaluate $\dfrac{8.37 \times 0.0867}{0.0911}$.

No.	Log
8·37	1·9227
0·0867	$\bar{2}$·9380
	0·8607
·0911	$\bar{2}$·9595
7·966	1·9012

Perform multiplication by adding logs, $+1$ is carried across point.

Perform division by subtracting logs. Carry $+1$ across the point, adjust the lower characteristic, change the sign and add.

Ans. = 7·966

Exercise 2

Use logs to evaluate the following:

(1) 4.63×2.465

(2) 17.98×7.364

(3) 124.7×5.637

(4) 0.763×4.672

(5) 0.0432×0.693

(6) 9.68×0.00583

(7) $9.816 \times 1.829 \times 0.3145$

(8) $17.95 \div 3.19$

(9) $5.684 \div 2.84$

(10) $3.14 \div 0.92$

(11) $4.723 \div 0.06783$

(12) $0.0427 \div 7.93$

(13) $0.04622 \div 0.0046$

(14) $\dfrac{5.62 \times 3.714}{6.891}$

(15) $\dfrac{0.56 \times 17.54}{0.02481}$

(16) $\dfrac{150}{6.6 \times 9.41 \times 2.813}$

(17) $\dfrac{51.2 \times 4.351}{0.6731 \times 127}$

259

Powers using logarithms

You will remember that $x \times x \times x = x^3$ is raising x to the power of 3. To raise a number to a power, using logs, multiply the log of the number by the power, that is

$$\log x^n = n \times \log x$$

Remember that the mantissa is always positive.

Example 8. Use logs to evaluate $(9 \cdot 346)^3$

No.	Log
9·346	0·9706
(9·346)³	2·9118
816·2	2·9118

Multiply by 3. Two is carried across the point.

Ans. = 816·2

Example 9. Use logs to evaluate $(0 \cdot 342)^2$

No.	Log
0·342	$\bar{1}$·5340
(0·342)²	$\bar{1}$·0680
0·1169	$\bar{1}$·0680

Multiply by 2, +1 is carried over the point so $\bar{2}+1 = \bar{1}$.

Ans. = 0·1169

Roots using logarithms

To find the root of a number, using logs, divide the log of the number by the index of the root, that is

$$\log \sqrt[n]{x} = \log x \div n$$

Example 10. Use logs to find $\sqrt[4]{468}$.

No.	Log
468	2·6702÷4
4·650	0·6675

Divide by 4 to obtain log of root.
The division is carried out in this way,

$$4 \mid \underline{2 \cdot 6702}$$
$$0 \cdot 6675$$

and is quite straight-forward.

Ans. = 4·65

Example 11. Use logs to evaluate $\sqrt[3]{0.00563}$.

No.	Log
0.00563	$\bar{3}.7505 \div 3$
0.1779	$\bar{1}.2502$

Divide by 3 to obtain log of root.

Division is carried out in this way

$$3 \mid \frac{\bar{3}.7505}{\bar{1}.2502}$$

Ans. = 0.1779

Example 12. Use logs to find $\sqrt[4]{0.2568}$.

In this case difficulty can arise. Notice how the division of the log is carried out.

In order to divide by 4 the characteristic must be changed to $\bar{4}$. To compensate for the -3 added to the characteristic $+3$ is added to the mantissa thus

No.	Log
0.2568	$\bar{1}.4096 \div 4$ to obtain root
0.7119	$\bar{1}.8524$

$$\bar{1}.4096$$
becomes $\qquad \bar{1} + 3 + 3 + 0.4096$
that is $\qquad \bar{4} + 3.4096$
Dividing by 4 $\mid \dfrac{\bar{4} + 3.4096}{\bar{1}.8524}$

Ans. = 0.7119

Example 13. Use logs to find the value of $\sqrt{\dfrac{3.187 \times 0.1508}{215}}$.

No.	Log
3.187	0.5034
0.1508	$\bar{1}.1783$
	$\bar{1}.6817$
215	2.3324
$\sqrt{}$	$\bar{3}.3493$
0.04728	$\bar{2}.6746$

Add to perform multiplication

Subtract to perform division. (Change sign and add.)

$\div 2$ to find root, in this way:

$$\bar{3} + \bar{1} + 1 + 0.3493$$
$$2 \mid \frac{\bar{4} + 1.3493}{\bar{2}.6746}$$

Ans. = 0.04728

Exercise 3

Use logs to find the value of the following:

(1) $(5.32)^2$ (2) $(8.625)^3$

(3) $(3.72)^4$ (4) $(30.07)^2$

(5) $(0.81)^2$ (6) $(0.0685)^3$

(7) $(0·7)^5$

(8) $(0·0287)^3$

(9) $(0·326)^4$

(10) $\sqrt{9·64}$

(11) $\sqrt{96·4}$

(12) $\sqrt[3]{64·9}$

(13) $\sqrt[4]{2376}$

(14) $\sqrt{0·732}$

(15) $\sqrt{0·05146}$

(16) $\sqrt{0·806}$

(17) $\sqrt[3]{0·05146}$

(18) $\sqrt[5]{0·02128}$

(19) $\sqrt{\dfrac{2·45 \times 6·3}{4·231}}$

(20) $\dfrac{\sqrt[3]{16·39 \times 9·81}}{4·5}$

(21) $\sqrt[4]{\dfrac{36}{0·964}}$

(22) $\dfrac{2004 \times 0·56}{\sqrt[3]{69·15}}$

Four figure logarithms are inaccurate as far as the fourth figure is concerned, and results found by logs are usually given correct to three significant figures.

Logarithms in formulae

Logarithms are useful when working with formulae.

Example 14. The radius of a sphere can be found from the surface area by using the formula

$$r = \sqrt{\frac{S}{4\pi}}$$

Find r when $S = 785$ and $\pi = 3·14$. If

$$r = \sqrt{\frac{S}{4\pi}}$$

Then

$$r = \sqrt{\frac{785}{4 \times 3·14}}$$

Use logs for this calculation.

No.	Log	
4 3·14	0·6021 0·4969	Add to simplify denominator
	1·0990	
785	2·8949 1·0990	Subtract to simplify $\dfrac{\text{numerator}}{\text{denominator}}$
	1·7959	Divide by 2 to extract root.
7·905	0·8979	$\therefore$ Ans. $= 7·9$

Exercise 4

Use logs to find the value of the following. Give your answers correct
to 3 significant figures.

(1) If $W = I^2 R$ find W when $I = 0.59$ and $R = 198$.

(2) If $D = \dfrac{C}{\pi}$ find D when $C = 10.99$ and $\pi = 3.142$.

(3) $V = \pi r^2 h$. Find V when $\pi = 3.14$, $r = 2.75$ cm, and $h = 11.5$ cm.

(4) Express $\dfrac{A}{B}$ as a decimal when $A = 719$ and $B = 1124$.

(5) The area of a ring can be found by the formula $\pi(R^2 - r^2)$. Find
the area of a ring in which $R = 29.6$ cm, $r = 20.6$ cm, and $\pi = 3.14$.

(6) If $I = \dfrac{PRT}{100}$ find I when $P = 275$, $R = 1.25$, and $T = 1.3$.

(7) Given that $V = 8\sqrt{h}$ find V when $h = 75$.

(8) If $T = \dfrac{\pi}{4}\sqrt{2L}$ find T when $L = 1.125$ and $\pi = 3.14$.

(9) Find the value of $\sqrt{\dfrac{a^2 b^3 - b^2 c}{6}}$ when $a = 5.6$, $b = 0.41$, and $c = 5.8$.

(10) Find the value of A in the formula

$$A = \sqrt{s(s-a)(s-b)(s-c)}$$

when $s = \dfrac{a+b+c}{2}$ and $a = 4$, $b = 5$, $c = 6$.

34 Squares of Numbers from Tables

You will remember that to square a number is to multiply it by itself; thus 12 squared, written as 12^2, is $12 \times 12 = 144$. To square a number is to raise it to the power of 2 so that

$$2 \times \log \text{ of number} = \log \text{ of number squared}$$

However, it is possible to square a number even more quickly by making use of a Table of Squares. Here is an extract from a Table of Squares.

	0	1	2	3	4	5	6	7	8	9	Mean Differences 1 2 3 4	5 6 7 8 9
20	4000	4040	4080	4121	4162	4203	4244	4285	4326	4368	4 8 12 16	20 25 29 33 37
21	4410	4452	4494	4537	4580	4623	4666	4709	4752	4796	4 9 13 17	21 26 30 34 39
22	4840	4884	4928	4973	5018	5063	5108	5153	5198	5244	4 9 13 18	22 27 31 36 40
23	5290	5336	5382	5429	5476	5523	5570	5617	5664	5712	5 9 14 19	23 28 33 38 42
24	5760	5808	5856	5905	5954	6003	6052	6101	6150	6200	5 10 15 20	24 29 34 39 44
25	6250	6300	6350	6401	6452	6503	6554	6605	6656	6708	5 10 15 20	25 31 36 41 46
26	6760	6812	6864	6917	6970	7023	7076	7129	7182	7236	5 11 16 21	26 32 37 42 48
27	7290	7344	7398	7453	7508	7563	7618	7673	7728	7784	5 11 16 22	28 33 38 44 49
28	7840	7896	7952	8009	8066	8123	8180	8237	8294	8352	6 11 17 23	28 34 40 46 51
29	8410	8468	8526	8585	8644	8703	8762	8821	8880	8940	6 12 18 24	30 35 41 47 53

The tables are used in the following way:

Example 1. From the tables find the value of $(2 \cdot 67)^2$.

(i) Find 26 (first two figures of the original number) in the left-hand column of the extract from the tables.

(ii) Move to the right along the row to the column headed 7 (third figure of the original number). Note this number, i.e. 7129.

(iii) We know that $2^2 = 4$ and $3^2 = 9$, so that the value of $(2 \cdot 67)^2$ must lie between 4 and 9. The decimal point is placed by inspection thus, $7 \cdot 129$, since this is the only position that gives a result that lies between 4 and 9, so

$$(2 \cdot 67)^2 = 7 \cdot 129$$

Example 2. From the tables find the value of $(21 \cdot 52)^2$.

(i) Find 21 (first two figures of the original number) in the left-hand column of the extract from the tables (page 264).

(ii) Move to the right, along the row, to the column headed 5 (third figure of the original number). Note this number, i.e. 4623.

(iii) Continue, to the right, along the row to the second column headed 2 (fourth figure of the original number). Note this number, i.e. 9.

(iv) Add this 9 to 4623 (obtained in (ii)).

$$4623 + 9 = 4632$$

Place the decimal point by inspection. Since $(20)^2 = 400$ and $(30)^2 = 900$ then $(21 \cdot 52)^2$ must lie between 400 and 900, so that

$$(21 \cdot 52)^2 = 463 \cdot 2$$

since this position of the point is the only one that satisfies this condition.

Example 3. From the tables find the value of $(0 \cdot 028)^2$.

(i) Find 28 in the left-hand column of the extract from the tables (page 264).

(ii) Move to the right to the column headed 0. Note this number, i.e. 7840.

(iii) The decimal point is placed by inspection; since $(0 \cdot 02)^2 = 0 \cdot 0004$, then

$$(0 \cdot 028)^2 = 0 \cdot 000784$$

The positioning of the decimal point for the squares of numbers less than one needs a little care. The following table can be used to obtain the approximate size of the square of any number and thus give a guide in the positioning of the decimal point.

Number	Square	Number	Square	Number	Square	Number	Square
0·01	0·0001	0·1	0·01	1	1	10	100
0·02	0·0004	0·2	0·04	2	4	20	400
0·03	0·0009	0·3	0·09	3	9	30	900
0·04	0·0016	0·4	0·16	4	16	40	1,600
0·05	0·0025	0·5	0·25	5	25	50	2,500
0·06	0·0036	0·6	0·36	6	36	60	3,600
0·07	0·0049	0·7	0·49	7	49	70	4,900
0·08	0·0064	0·8	0·64	8	64	80	6,400
0·09	0·0081	0·9	0·81	9	81	90	8,100

Exercise 1

(1) Use the extract from the table of squares to find the value of:

    (*a*) $(21)^2$ (*d*) $(2·1)^2$ (*g*) $(0·21)^2$

    (*b*) $(24)^2$ (*e*) $(2·4)^2$ (*h*) $(0·24)^2$

    (*c*) $(28)^2$ (*f*) $(2·8)^2$ (*i*) $(0·28)^2$

(2) Use the extract from the table to find the value of:

    (*a*) $(22·5)^2$ (*d*) $(0·29)^2$ (*g*) $(0·0023)^2$

    (*b*) $(2·741)^2$ (*e*) $(0·254)^2$ (*h*) $(0·0261)^2$

    (*c*) $(20·73)^2$ (*f*) $(0·2675)^2$ (*i*) $(0·02378)^2$

Use the complete table of squares at the end of the book to work the following questions.

(3) Square these numbers:

    (*a*) 125   (*d*) 19·6   (*g*) 32·34

    (*b*) 17·5   (*e*) 14·9   (*h*) 1·4

    (*c*) 55·7   (*f*) 21·16   (*i*) 11·4

(4) Find the value of:

    (*a*) $(7·731)^2$ (*e*) $(0·0064)^2$ (*i*) $(0·0043)^2$

    (*b*) $(0·0631)^2$ (*f*) $(5·251)^2$ (*j*) $(0·175)^2$

    (*c*) $(0·04321)^2$ (*g*) $(22·54)^2$ (*k*) $(37·42)^2$

    (*d*) $(0·108)^2$ (*h*) $(9·63)^2$ (*l*) $(0·0574)^2$

35 Square Roots from Tables

Just as the squares of numbers can be obtained from the table of squares, square roots can be found from a table of square roots. Here is an extract from a table of square roots:

	0	1	2	3	4	5	6	7	8	9	Mean Differences								
											1	2	3	4	5	6	7	8	9
40	2000	2002	2005	2007	2010	2012	2015	2017	2020	2022	0	0	1	1	1	1	2	2	2
	6325	6332	6340	6348	6356	6364	6372	6380	6387	6395	1	2	2	3	4	5	6	6	7
41	2025	2027	2030	2032	2035	2037	2040	2042	2045	2047	0	0	1	1	1	1	2	2	2
	6403	6411	6419	6427	6434	6442	6450	6458	6465	6473	1	2	2	3	4	5	5	6	7
42	2049	2052	2054	2057	2059	2062	2064	2066	2069	2071	0	0	1	1	1	1	2	2	2
	6481	6488	6496	6504	6512	6519	6527	6535	6542	6550	1	2	2	3	4	5	5	6	7
43	2074	2076	2078	2081	2083	2086	2088	2090	2093	2095	0	0	1	1	1	1	2	2	2
	6557	6565	6573	6580	6588	6595	6603	6611	6618	6626	1	2	2	3	4	5	5	6	7
44	2098	2100	2102	2105	2107	2110	2112	2114	2117	2119	0	0	1	1	1	1	2	2	2
	6633	6641	6648	6656	6663	6671	6678	6686	6693	6701	1	2	2	3	4	4	5	6	7
45	2121	2124	2126	2128	2131	2133	2135	2138	2140	2142	0	0	1	1	1	1	2	2	2
	6708	6716	6723	6731	6738	6745	6753	6760	6768	6775	1	1	2	3	4	4	5	6	7
46	2145	2147	2149	2152	2154	2156	2159	2161	2163	2166	0	0	1	1	1	1	2	2	2
	6782	6790	6797	6804	6812	6819	6826	6834	6841	6848	1	1	2	3	4	4	5	6	7
47	2168	2170	2173	2175	2177	2179	2182	2184	2186	2189	0	0	1	1	1	1	2	2	2
	6856	6863	6870	6877	6885	6892	6899	6907	6914	6921	1	1	2	3	4	4	5	6	7
48	2191	2193	2195	2198	2200	2202	2205	2207	2209	2211	0	0	1	1	1	1	2	2	2
	6928	6935	6943	6950	6957	6964	6971	6979	6986	6993	1	1	2	3	4	4	5	6	6
49	2214	2216	2218	2220	2223	2225	2227	2229	2232	2234	0	0	1	1	1	1	2	2	2
	7000	7007	7014	7021	7029	7036	7043	7050	7057	7064	1	1	2	3	4	4	5	6	6

The tables are used in the following way:

Example 1. From the tables find the value of $\sqrt{4 \cdot 2}$.

(i) Find 42 in the left-hand column of the extract from the tables.

(ii) Move to the right along the row, to the column headed 0; you will find two numbers i.e. 2049 and 6481. Now $\sqrt{4} = 2$ so that $\sqrt{4 \cdot 2}$ is approximately 2, thus 2049 is the number we need since 6481 could not give us the value required.

(iii) Taking 2049, and bearing in mind that the approximate result is 2, the decimal point is placed by inspection, 2·049.

$$\text{Thus } \sqrt{4 \cdot 2} = 2 \cdot 049$$

Example 2. Use tables to find the value of $\sqrt{42}$.

 (i) Find 42 in the left-hand column of the extract from the tables.

 (ii) Move to the right, along the row, to the column headed 0. This time, of the two numbers 2049 and 6481, 6481 is selected because the square root of 42 must lie between 6 and 7 ($6 \times 6 = 36$ and $7 \times 7 = 49$).

 (iii) Taking 6481 the decimal point is placed by inspection, 6·481.

$$\text{Thus } \sqrt{42} = 6\cdot481$$

Example 3. From the tables find the value of $\sqrt{468\cdot3}$.

 (i) Find 46 (the first two figures of the number) in the left-hand column of the extract from the tables.

 (ii) Move to the right, along the row, to the column headed 8 (third figure of the number). Note these two numbers, i.e. 2163 and 6841.

 (iii) Now make an estimate of the square root of 468·3. From the table on page 265 we see that the $\sqrt{468\cdot3}$ lies between 20 and 30 so from the two numbers available we select 2163.

 (iv) Move further to the right along the row to the second column headed 3 and note this number, i.e. 1.

 (v) Add 2163 and 1, this gives 2164.

 (vi) Place the decimal point by inspection, 21·64. So

$$\sqrt{468\cdot3} = 21\cdot64$$

Example 4. Use the tables to find $\sqrt{0\cdot004368}$.

 (i) Find 43 in the left-hand column of the extract from the table.

 (ii) Move to the right, along the row, to the column headed 6. Note these two numbers, 2088 and 6603.

 (iii) Make an estimate of the square root of 0·004368. From the table on page 265 we can see that $(0\cdot06)^2 = 0\cdot0036$ and $(0\cdot07)^2 = 0\cdot0049$, thus $\sqrt{0\cdot004368}$ must lie between 0·06 and 0·07, so from the numbers in (ii), 2088 and 6603, we select 6603.

 (iv) Move further to the right along the row to the second column headed 8, note this number, i.e. 6.

 (v) $6603 + 6 = 6609$.

268

(vi) Place the decimal point by inspection (remember that $\sqrt{0.004368}$ lies between 0·06 and 0·07), 0·06609. So

$$\sqrt{0.004368} = 0.06609$$

Exercise 1

(1) Use the extract from the tables to find the value of:

(a) $\sqrt{49}$ (e) $\sqrt{0.44}$ (i) $\sqrt{0.435}$

(b) $\sqrt{4.9}$ (f) $\sqrt{0.0048}$ (j) $\sqrt{0.042}$

(c) $\sqrt{4.05}$ (g) $\sqrt{0.464}$ (k) $\sqrt{0.00416}$

(d) $\sqrt{405.1}$ (h) $\sqrt{4.832}$ (l) $\sqrt{0.004789}$

Use the complete table of square roots at the end of the book to work the following questions.

(2) Find the value of:

(a) $\sqrt{64}$ (d) $\sqrt{6.4}$ (g) $\sqrt{0.64}$

(b) $\sqrt{144}$ (e) $\sqrt{14.4}$ (h) $\sqrt{0.0144}$

(c) $\sqrt{625}$ (f) $\sqrt{6.25}$ (i) $\sqrt{0.00625}$

(3) Find from the tables, as accurately as you can, the square roots of the following numbers:

(a) 34·24   (e) 84·64   (i) 0·7396

(b) 56·74   (f) 9·574   (j) 0·000441

(c) 6·673   (g) 1,200   (k) 0·8281

(d) 7·756   (h) 0·2704   (l) 0·0529

(4) Find the value of:

(a) $\sqrt{5649}$ (e) $\sqrt{1.134}$ (i) $\sqrt{6.134}$

(b) $\sqrt{36.84}$ (f) $\sqrt{0.074}$ (j) $\sqrt{16.27}$

(c) $\sqrt{2.634}$ (g) $\sqrt{0.0842}$ (k) $\sqrt{0.3248}$

(d) $\sqrt{0.00691}$ (h) $\sqrt{2,340}$ (l) $\sqrt{249.6}$

36 Trigonometry

The basic principles of this branch of mathematics were known in earliest times. It combines all the skills of mathematics and its use in the solution of problems is an excellent illustration of the fact that mathematics is a 'whole' and not a collection of disconnected parts. The word trigonometry means 'triangle measurement', and the properties of triangles that you will learn in this section are the basis for calculations of heights and distances.

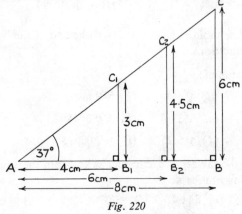

Fig. 220

In $\triangle ABC$ (Fig. 220), $\angle A = 37°$, $\angle B = 90°$, $AB = 8$ cm, $BC = 6$ cm; B_1C_1 and B_2C_2 are drawn perpendicular to AB to form $\triangle$'s AB_1C_1 and AB_2C_2.

From the diagram it can be seen that,

$$\frac{BC}{AB} = \frac{6 \text{ cm}}{8 \text{ cm}} = 0.75$$

$$\frac{B_1C_1}{AB_1} = \frac{3 \text{ cm}}{4 \text{ cm}} = 0.75$$

$$\frac{B_2C_2}{AB_2} = \frac{4.5 \text{ cm}}{6 \text{ cm}} = 0.75$$

Thus $$\frac{BC}{AB} = \frac{B_1C_1}{AB_1} = \frac{B_2C_2}{AB_2}$$

This is the result we would expect since $\triangle$s ABC, AB₁C₁, and AB₂C₂ are similar. Also the ratios $\frac{BC}{AB}$, $\frac{B_1C_1}{AB_1}$, $\frac{B_2C_2}{AB_2}$ can all be expressed as:

$$\text{the ratio of } \frac{\text{the side opposite } \angle A}{\text{the side adjacent to } \angle A}$$

Clearly the ratio of $\frac{\text{the side opp. } \angle A}{\text{the side adj. } \angle A}$ depends on the size of the angle and not on the length of the sides since the $\angle A$ is common to the three triangles, whereas the sides are of different lengths. The ratio of

$$\frac{\text{the side opposite an angle}}{\text{the side adjacent to the angle}}$$

then, is a rather special ratio that depends on the size of $\angle A$. It is called the **tangent of $\angle A$**.

The tangent of an angle is usually expressed as a decimal. As we have seen in $\triangle$ABC the tangent of $\angle A = \frac{BC}{AB} = \frac{6 \text{ cm}}{8 \text{ cm}} = 0.75$. Thus tangent 37° (written tan 37°) = 0·75.

In the same way, the tangent of any acute angle *in a right-angled triangle* can be found by drawing and measurement and by expressing the ratio $\frac{\text{side opp. the angle}}{\text{side adj. to the angle}}$ as a decimal. In practice it is much more convenient to use tangent tables, where the ratios are worked out to four places of decimals. A table giving the value of the tangents for all angles from 1° to 89° is included in the mathematical tables at the end of this book.

Example 1. In Fig. 221, calculate the length of the side ZY.

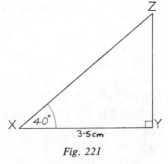

Fig. 221

In the $\triangle$XYZ, $\angle ZXY = 40°$, $\angle ZYX = 90°$, and XY = 3·5 cm

$$\therefore \tan \angle ZXY = \frac{ZY}{XY}$$

271

So that
$$\tan 40° = \frac{ZY}{3\cdot5}$$

From the tables we find that $\tan 40° = 0\cdot8391$, thus

$$0\cdot8391 = \frac{ZY}{3\cdot5}$$

Cross multiplying
$$ZY = 0\cdot8391 \times 3\cdot5$$
$$= 2\cdot9 \text{ cm}$$

Example 2. In Fig. 222, calculate the length of the side XY.

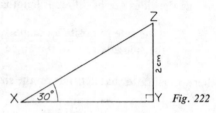

Fig. 222

In $\triangle$XYZ, $\angle ZXY = 30°$, $\angle XYZ = 90°$, and $ZY = 2$ cm

$$\therefore \tan \angle ZXY = \frac{ZY}{XY}$$

Thus
$$\tan 30° = \frac{2}{XY}$$

and
$$0\cdot5774 = \frac{2}{XY}$$

Cross multiplying

$$0\cdot5774 \times XY = 2$$

$$\therefore XY = \frac{2}{0\cdot5744}$$

$$= 3\cdot5 \text{ cm}$$

These results can be summarised as follows:

If ABC is any right-angled triangle (see Fig. 223), then

$$\tan \angle A = \frac{\text{opp.}}{\text{adj.}}$$

$$\text{side opposite} = \tan \angle A \times \text{side adj.}$$

$$\text{side adjacent} = \frac{\text{side opp.}}{\tan A}$$

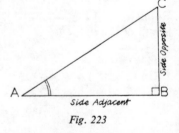

Fig. 223

Example 3. In Fig. 224, the angle A is the angle of elevation of the top of a vertical cliff measured by an observer 60 metres from the foot of the cliff. Use this information to calculate the height of the cliff. Since the cliff is vertical, $\angle B = 90°$ and we may use right-angled triangle ABC. So

$$\tan \angle A = \frac{\text{opp.}}{\text{adj.}}$$

$$\therefore \tan 32° = \frac{BC}{AB}$$

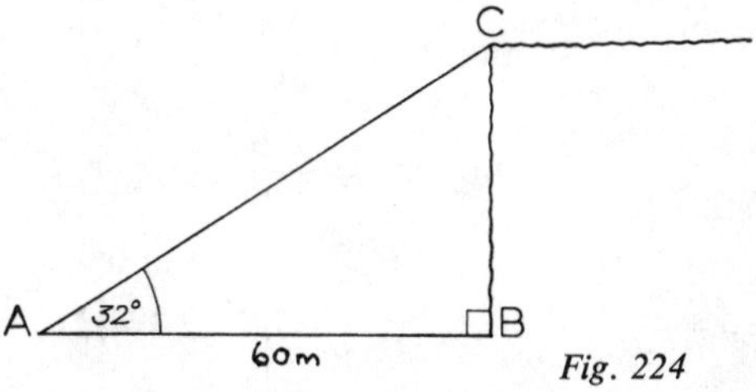

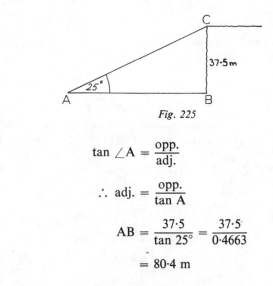

Fig. 224

Thus

$$0{\cdot}6249 = \frac{BC}{60}$$

$$BC = 0{\cdot}6249 \times 60$$

$$= 37{\cdot}49$$

$$BC = 37{\cdot}49 \text{ metres}$$

Example 4. If in the above example the angle of elevation had been 25°, and the height of the cliff is taken as 37·5 m, calculate the distance of the observer from the base of the cliff. (See Fig. 225.)

Fig. 225

$$\tan \angle A = \frac{\text{opp.}}{\text{adj.}}$$

$$\therefore \text{adj.} = \frac{\text{opp.}}{\tan A}$$

Thus

$$AB = \frac{37{\cdot}5}{\tan 25°} = \frac{37{\cdot}5}{0{\cdot}4663}$$

$$= 80{\cdot}4 \text{ m}$$

An alternative method that is easier in some ways is as follows:

In the $\triangle ABC$, $\angle A = 25°$, $\angle B = 90°$

$$\therefore \ \angle C = 65°$$

$$\tan \angle C = \frac{AB}{BC}$$

$$\therefore \ \tan 65° = \frac{AB}{37 \cdot 5}$$

$$\therefore \ AB = 37 \cdot 5 \times \tan 65°$$

$$= 37 \cdot 5 \times 2 \cdot 1445$$

$$= 80 \cdot 4 \text{ m}$$

No.	Log
37·5	1·5740
Tan 65°	0·3313
80·41	1·9053

Note

The calculation can be made easier if you work with the angle opposite the unknown side, as in this alternative method.

Often it is difficult or even impossible to obtain all the measurements needed for the calculation of a height or distance. In Figs. 223 and 224 we have assumed that the cliff presents a neat perpendicular face and that we are able to measure the distance AB to a point at the foot of the cliff so that BC is perpendicular to AB. In practice the cliff will probably be like the one represented by the diagram in Fig. 226.

BC is the height to be calculated, the distance AB cannot be measured. This difficulty can be overcome in the following way.

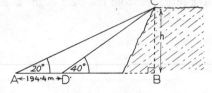

Fig. 226

Example 5. In Fig. 226 the angles of elevation of C from A and D are measured and found to be 20° and 40° respectively. AD is measured and found to be 194·4 m. Calculate the height of C (i.e. find the length of BC).

In $\triangle ABC$, $\angle ACB = 90° - \angle A = 70°$

$$\tan \angle ACB = \frac{AB}{h}$$

$$\therefore \ AB = h \times \tan 70°$$

$$= h \times 2 \cdot 7475$$

In $\triangle$DBC, $\angle$DCB $= 90° - \angle$D $= 50°$

$$\tan \angle DCB = \frac{DB}{h}$$

$$\therefore DB = h \times \tan 50°$$

$$= h \times 1·1918$$

But AB $-$ DB $=$ AD $=$ 194·4 m (given)

$$\therefore (h \times 2·7475) - (h \times 1·1918) = 194·4 \text{ m}$$

$$h(2·7475 - 1·1918) = 194·4 \text{ m}$$

$$1·5557h = 194·4 \text{ m}$$

No.	Log
194·4	2·2887
1·556	0·1920
124·9	2·0967

Then $\qquad h = \dfrac{194·4 \text{ m}}{1·5557}$

$$\therefore h = 124·9 \text{ m}$$

$$h = 125 \text{ m (to the nearest metre)}$$

The general method is as follows:

If $\angle$A is known, then $\angle$ACB $= 90° - $A ($\angle$CBA $=$ rt. angle).
If $\angle$B is known, then $\angle$DCB $= 90° - $D ($\angle$CBD $=$ rt. angle).

Let CB, the height to be found, be h.
In $\triangle$ABC,

$$\tan \angle ACB = \frac{AB}{h}$$

$$\therefore AB = h \times \tan \angle ACB$$

In $\triangle$DBC,

$$\tan \angle DCB = \frac{DB}{h}$$

$$\therefore DB = h \times \tan \angle DCB$$

But $\qquad$ AD $=$ AB $-$ DB

$$\therefore AD = (h \times \tan \angle ACB) - (h \times \tan \angle DCB)$$

$$AD = h(\tan \angle ACB - \tan \angle DCB)$$

$$\therefore h = \frac{AD}{\tan \angle ACB - \tan \angle DCB}$$

275

Exercise 1

(1) Find by drawing on squared paper the tangents of angles of 20°, 45°, 60°, 76°. Compare the results you obtain with the values given in the tables.

(2) From the tables find the angles whose tangents are 0·1763, 0·4663, 0·8391, 1·4281, 2·1445, 3·7321.

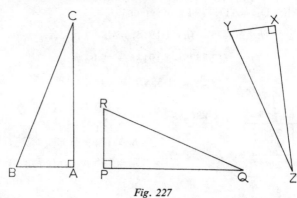

Fig. 227

Questions 3 to 10 refer to Fig. 227. The right angle in each triangle is marked.

(3) Tan $\angle B = \dfrac{AC}{BA}$ $\left(\text{i.e. } \dfrac{\text{opp.}}{\text{adj.}}\right)$. Write down an expression for:

(i) tan $\angle Q$. (ii) tan $\angle Z$.

(4) Complete the following:

(i) $\dfrac{AB}{AC} = \tan \angle\,?$ (ii) $\dfrac{PQ}{PR} = \tan \angle\,?$ (iii) $\dfrac{XZ}{XY} = \tan \angle\,?$

(5) In $\triangle ABC$, $AC = 125$ mm, $\angle C = 31°$. Find AB.

(6) In $\triangle PQR$, $PR = 8$ cm, $\angle R = 64°$. Find PQ.

(7) In $\triangle XYZ$, $XY = 3·5$ cm, $ZX = 14$ cm. Find $\angle Z$ to the nearest degree.

(8) In $\triangle XYZ$, $XY = 4$ cm, $\angle Z = 10°$. Find ZX.

(9) In $\triangle ABC$, $AB = 20$ cm, $\angle C = 35°$. Find AC.

(10) In $\triangle XYZ$, $XY = 0·75$ m, $XZ = 2·25$ m. Find $\angle Y$ to the nearest degree.

(11) The angle of elevation of the school water tower from a point 30 m from its base is 41°. Calculate the height of the tower.

(12) A wire stay is attached to the top of a flag pole, and to a point on the ground 2·5 m from the base of the pole. If the height of the pole is 10 m calculate the angle that the stay makes with the ground.

(13) When the sun's rays make an angle of 50° with the ground a chimney casts a shadow that is 63 m long. Calculate, to the nearest metre, the height of the chimney.

(14) A ladder reaches a window that is 10·5 m above ground level. If the ladder makes an angle of 65° with the ground, calculate the distance that the foot of the ladder will be from the wall of the building.

(15) Calculate the length of the shadow cast by a building 7·5 m high when the sun's rays make an angle of 55° with the ground.

(16) The sides of a rectangle are 20 cm and 12·5 cm. Calculate the size of the angles which the diagonal makes with the sides.

(17) In Fig. 228, $\angle DAB = 30°$, $\angle DBC = 60°$, $\angle DCB = 90°$, and $AB = 5·2$ cm. Calculate the length of the side CD.

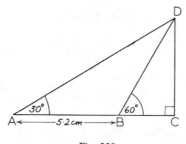

Fig. 228

(18) In Fig. 229, A and B are two boats anchored in line with a light-house. The distance between A and B is 400 m. The angle of elevation from A to the top of the lighthouse is 5° and from B 10°. Calculate (i) the height of the light-house above sea-level, (ii) the distance of boat B from the light-house.

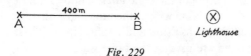

Fig. 229

277

(19) In Fig. 230, ABCD is a parallelogram with

AB = 3·5 cm, ∠ACD = 16°, ∠ACB = 21°.

Calculate the perpendicular height CE and hence find the area of the parallelogram.

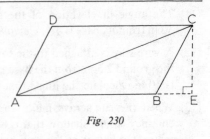

Fig. 230

The sine and cosine of an angle

You will remember that in any right-angled triangle the side opposite the right angle is called the **hypotenuse**. Just as the tangent ratio is a useful tool in mathematics, so the relationships of the other sides to the hypotenuse in a right-angled triangle are equally important ratios.

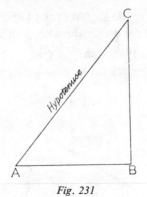

Fig. 231

In △ABC (Fig. 231), AC is the hypotenuse and the ratio

$$\frac{\text{side opposite } \angle A \text{ (i.e. BC)}}{\text{hypotenuse}}$$

is called the **sine** of A (written sin A); also the ratio

$$\frac{\text{side adjacent to } \angle A \text{ (i.e. AB)}}{\text{hypotenuse}}$$

is called the **cosine** of A (written cos A).

The sine and cosine of an acute angle can be found by drawing and measurements in the same way as the tangent of an angle. In practice it is more convenient to use sine and cosine tables. These are similar to tangent tables and are used in the same way.

278

Exercise 2

(1) On squared paper draw diagrams similar to Fig. 220 for values of ∠BAC=20°, 35°, 45°, and 65° respectively. In each case BC is any perpendicular drawn from AC to AB. Measure your diagrams and find sin ∠BAC (i.e. the ratio BC/AC) to two places of decimals. Compare your results with the sine table at the end of this book.

(2) Use the diagrams drawn for Question 1 to find the cos ∠BAC (i.e. the ratio AB/AC). Compare your results with the tables.

(3) Find from the tables (*a*) the sines, (*b*) the cosines of these angles: 8°, 15°, 30°, 39°, 45°, 75°, 83°.

(4) From the tables find the angles whose sines are 0·2079, 0·3907, 0·6428, 0·8192, 0·9903.

(5) From the tables find the angles whose cosines are 0·9848, 0·7193, 0·5000, 0·1736, 0·3420.

(6) From the diagrams in Fig. 232 write down an expression for (i) sin ∠B, (ii) cos ∠B, (iii) sin ∠Q, (iv) cos ∠Z, (v) cos ∠R, (vi) tan ∠C, (vii) sin ∠R, (viii) cos ∠Y, (ix) tan ∠Y, (x) sin ∠Z.

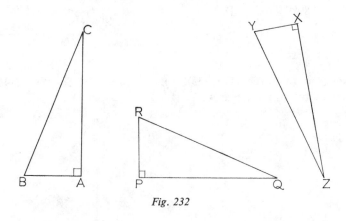

Fig. 232

Example 1. In △ABC (Fig. 233), ∠A=25°, ∠B=90°, AC=150 mm. Find AB and BC.

279

$$\sin \angle A = \frac{BC}{AC}$$

$$\therefore \ \sin 25° = \frac{BC}{150}$$

$$0·4226 = \frac{BC}{150} \text{ (cross multiply)}$$

$$BC = 63·39 \text{ mm}$$

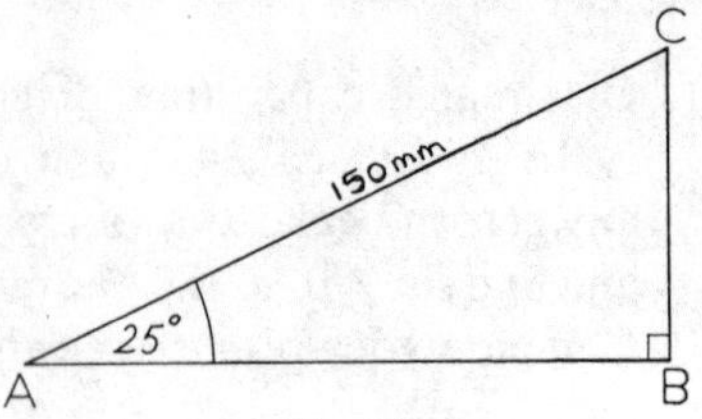

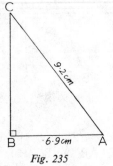

Fig. 233

Further

$$\cos \angle A = \frac{AB}{AC}$$

$$\therefore \ \cos 25° = \frac{AB}{150}$$

$$0·9063 = \frac{AB}{150}$$

$$AB = 135·9 \text{ mm}$$

Example 2. In $\triangle ABC$ (Fig. 234), $\angle A = 36°$, $\angle B = 90°$, $AB = 18$ m. Calculate the length of AC.

$$\cos \angle A = \frac{AB}{AC}$$

$$0·8090 = \frac{18}{AC} \text{ (cross multiply)}$$

$$\therefore \ 0·8090 \times AC = 18$$

$$AC = 22·2 \text{ m}$$

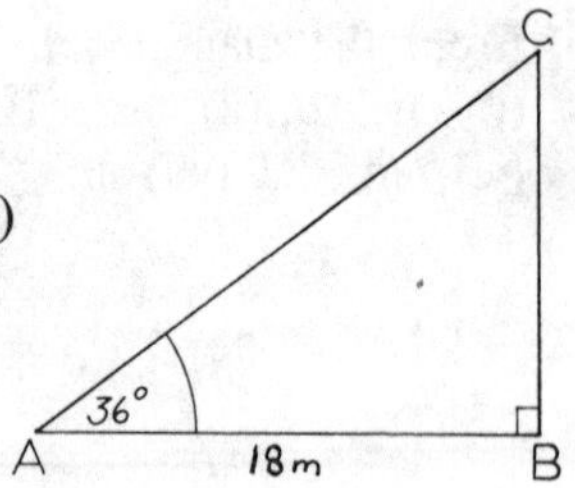

Fig. 234

Example 3. In $\triangle ABC$ (Fig. 235), $\angle B = 90°$, $AC = 9·2$ cm, $AB = 6·9$ cm. Calculate the size of angle A.

$$\cos \angle A = \frac{AB}{AC}$$

$$\cos \angle A = \frac{\overset{3}{\cancel{6·9}}}{\underset{4}{\cancel{9·2}}} = \frac{3}{4}$$

$$\cos \angle A = 0·75$$

From the tables cos 0·75 = 41° (to the nearest degree).

Fig. 235

280

Exercise 3

(1) In △ABC, ∠A = 35°, ∠B = 90°, and AC = 125 mm. Find the length of AB and the length of BC.

(2) In Fig. 236, if AC = 10·5 cm and BC = 6 cm, find the size of ∠C.

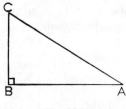

Fig. 236

(3) A ladder 7·5 m long rests against a wall and makes an angle of 23° with the wall. Calculate the distance from the foot of the ladder to the wall.

(4) A steep hill has a slope of 1 in 7, that is to say a vertical rise of 1 m for every 7 m of its length. Calculate the angle that the slope makes with the horizontal.

(5) A kite is flying on a string 165 m long that makes an angle with the ground of 40°. If we assume that the string is straight, at what height is the kite flying?

(6) In Fig. 237, ABCD is a rectangle with diagonal AC = 1·5 m and angle BAC = 24°. Calculate the area of the rectangle.

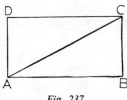

Fig. 237

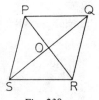

Fig. 238

(7) In Fig. 238, PQRS is a rhombus with side of 5 cm. Given that ∠QOR = 90° and ∠RQO = 33°, find the length of the diagonals.

(8) An observation post is situated 500 m from a straight stretch of road. If visibility is 1 kilometre, what length of road is under observation?

281

Area of a triangle

The area of △ABC (Fig. 239) can be found by using the sine.

The area of △ABC = ½bc sin ∠A = ½ac sin ∠B = ½ab sin ∠C

That is, the area of a triangle is half the product of any two sides and the sine of the angle between them.

This method of finding the area of a triangle is extremely useful since we do not have to obtain its perpendicular height.

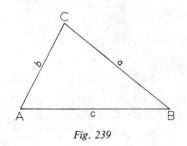

Fig. 239

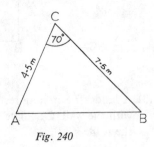

Fig. 240

Example. Calculate the area of △ABC, when AC = 4·5 m, BC = 7·5 m, and ∠ACB = 70° (Fig. 240).

Area of △ = ½(AC × BC) × sin ∠C
= ½(4·5 × 7·5) × 0·9397 m²
= 16·875 × 0·9397 m²
= 15·85 m²

No.	Log
16·87	1·2271
sin 70	1̄·9730
15·85	1·2001

The formula ½ab sin ∠C for the area of a triangle is found in the following way:

In the triangle ABC (Fig. 241) *h* is the perpendicular from A to BC.

So $\qquad \sin \angle C = \dfrac{h}{b}$

$\qquad \therefore h = b \sin \angle C$

$\qquad$ Area △ABC = ½*ht* × base

$\qquad\qquad\qquad = ½ah$

Since $\qquad\qquad h = b \sin \angle C$

Then $\qquad\qquad$ ½*ah* = ½*ab* sin ∠C

$\qquad\qquad\qquad = $ Area △ABC

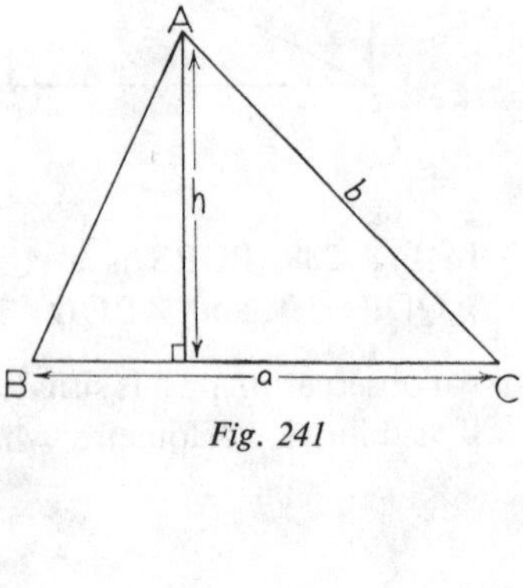

Fig. 241

Sine, Cosine, and Tangent of Obtuse angles

So far we have only been concerned with the sine, cosine, and tangent of acute angles ($<90°$). To make fuller use of these trigonometrical ratios we must extend their scope to include obtuse angles (between $90°$ and $180°$).

Imagine that Fig. 242a is a wheel with a single spoke laid on x, y axes so that the centre of the wheel is at O and OP_1 represents the spoke.

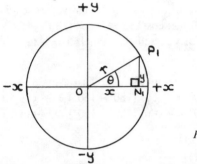

Fig. 242a

P_1N_1 is perpendicular to Ox and the angle P_1ON_1 is represented by the Greek letter θ (*theta*). Let r be the length of OP and x and y the lengths of ON_1 and P_1N_1 respectively, since they can be measured along the x and y axes. From the diagram it can be seen that

$$\sin \theta = \frac{y}{r}, \qquad \cos \theta = \frac{x}{r}, \qquad \tan \theta = \frac{y}{x}$$

If the wheel is now rotated in a counter-clockwise direction, as it turns the angle θ grows larger and becomes obtuse. Figure 242b shows the spoke in its new position, OP_2, where $OP_2 = r$, $P_2N_2 = y$, and $ON_2 = x$.

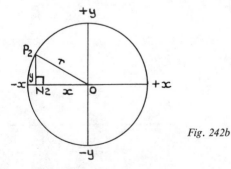

Fig. 242b

283

We have already decided that in Fig. 242a, $\sin \theta = \dfrac{y}{r}$, so this is also true for θ in Fig. 242b. Therefore the $\sin \angle P_2Ox = \dfrac{y}{r}$ and the $\sin \angle P_2ON_2 = \dfrac{y}{r}$ which means, in practice, that if $\angle P_2Ox = 150°$ then its sine is the same as $\sin(180° - 150°) = \sin 30°$. In the same way, from Fig. 242a, $\cos \theta = \dfrac{x}{r}$, but in Fig. 242b $\cos \theta = \dfrac{-x}{r}$, because x values in the second quadrant of the axes are negative, so $\cos \theta$ (when θ is obtuse) $= -\cos(180° - \theta)$, i.e. $\cos 150° = -\cos(180° - 150°) = -\cos 30°$.

Work out for yourself that $\tan 150° = -\tan 30°$.

To sum up:

$$\text{Sin } 150° = \sin(180° - 150°) = \sin 30° = 0·5.$$
$$\text{Cos } 150° = -\cos(180° - 150°) = -\cos 30° = -0·866.$$
$$\text{Tan } 150° = -\tan(180° - 150°) = -\tan 30° = -0·5774.$$

Exercise 4

Area of triangles

(1) Give the sines, cosines, and tangents of these angles: 145°, 180°, 85°, 160°, 98°.

(2) Find the area of triangle XYZ (Fig. 243) when XZ = 12·5 cm, YZ = 15 cm, and $\angle Z = 60°$.

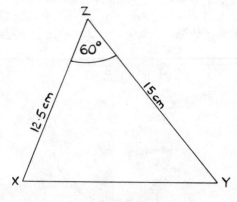

Fig. 243

(3) Calculate the area of triangle ABC, when AC=3·5 cm, BC=4·8 cm, and $\angle C=43°$.

(4) Calculate the area of triangle ABC, when AB=6 m, AC=9 m, and $\angle BAC=55°$.

(5) Calculate the area of triangle XYZ, when YZ=2·25 km, ZX= 1·85 km, and $\angle XZY=33°$.

(6) Find the area of $\triangle PQR$, when $\angle QPR=110°$, PQ=8 cm, PR= 17·7 cm.

(7) The triangle XYZ has XY=10·3 cm, YZ=5·7 cm, and $\angle XYZ=$ 120°. Find its area and draw a freehand sketch of the triangle using the side XY as the base. Calculate the perpendicular height of the triangle, i.e. the length of a perpendicular from Z to XY produced. Calculate the size of $\angle ZXY$ to the nearest degree.

(8) The triangle ABC has AB=5 cm, AC=2 cm, BC=4 cm, and the largest angle is an obtuse angle. Calculate the size of this angle to the nearest degree.

Example. Figure 244a represents the Earth with the parallels of latitude 30° N and 50° N, the lines of longitude 10° W and 25° W, and the Equator drawn on it. Four points are marked on it: A, 30° N, 25° W; B, 30° N, 10° W; C, 50° N, 10° W; and D, 50° N, 25° W. Given the radius of the Earth as 6,400 km, calculate the lengths AB, CD, AD, and BC.

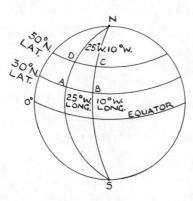

Fig. 244a

Before attempting any calculations it is as well to give some thought to the problem so that we are clear as to what is involved, and to work out a 'plan of attack'.

If we could cut right through the Earth at the line 10° W longitude, the cross-section we should obtain would be similar to Fig. 244b.

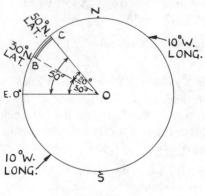

Fig. 244b

From this diagram it can be seen that $\angle BOC = 20°$, thus the arc BC that subtends $\angle BOC$ is $\frac{20°}{360°} = \frac{1}{18}$ of the circle NES i.e. $\frac{1}{18}$ of the circumference of the Earth. Given a radius of 6,400 km, then the length of BC can be calculated and also the length of AD, since BC = AD.

Next, imagine what our sphere in Fig. 244a will look like if viewed from some point above its north pole. Figure 244c is a diagrammatic impression of this view. The point N represents the north pole.

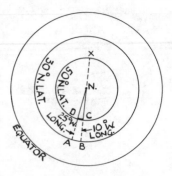

Fig. 244c

From this diagram we can see that, since NC is 10° W longitude and ND is 25° W longitude, angle CND = 15° and so the length of the arc CD is $\frac{15°}{360°} = \frac{1}{24}$ of the circumference of the 50° N circle of latitude.

However, this circle is not the full circumference of the Earth, and to calculate its circumference we must first find its radius.

Look again at a cross-section of the Earth through the 10° W longitude line (Fig. 244d). A line through the Earth passing through its axis and joining two points on the 50° N latitude circle will be a diameter of that circle, CX in Fig. 244c. A line from O, the centre of the Earth, perpendicular to this diameter CX, will bisect it.

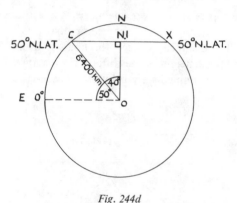

Fig. 244d

From Fig. 244d it is clear that OC is a radius of the Earth i.e. 6,400 km, and since ∠EOC = 50°, then ∠CON = 40°, thus, using the sine, CN can be calculated, and from this the circumference of the 50° N latitude circle and the length of CD. In a similar way, using 30° N latitude circle, the length of AB can be found.

Using this technique draw your own diagrams and do the complete calculation for yourself. The results, using $\pi = 3·14$, are AD = BC = 2,233 km, AB = 1,451 km, DC = 1,052 km.

Exercise 5

Miscellaneous

(1) Draw a triangle to find the angle whose tan is $\frac{3}{4}$. Check your result from the tables.

(2) Find by drawing the angle whose sine is 0·6. What is the cosine of this angle? (From tables.)

(3) In triangle ABC, $\angle A = 90°$, AB=0·04 m, AC=0·1 m. Find $\angle C$.

(4) In triangle DEF, $\angle D = 90°$, $\angle E = 30°$, EF=37·5 cm. Find DE and DF.

(5) In triangle XYZ, $\angle X = 90°$, YZ=25 cm, YX=15 cm. Find $\angle Y$ and $\angle Z$, also the length of XZ.

(6) The angle of elevation of the top of a television mast, from a point 45 m from its base, is 65°. Calculate the height of the mast.

(7) From the top of a cliff two boats are observed anchored in line. The angle of depression of the nearer boat is 55°, of the farther boat 38°, the distance between the boats is 27 m. (See Fig. 245.) Calculate (*a*) the height of the cliff, (*b*) the distance from the nearer boat to a point immediately below the observer.

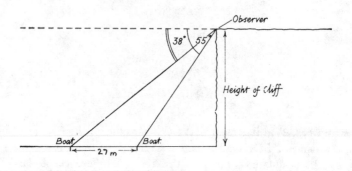

Fig. 245

(8) Calculate the height AB, of the spire in Fig. 246.

(9) A, B, C, D, are four points on the surface of the Earth. The latitude and longitude of A is 18° N, 2° W, of B 18° N, 16° E, of C 48° N, 16° E, and of D 48° N, 2° W. Draw a diagram to show the relative positions of the four points. Calculate the lengths of AB, CD, AD, and BC. (Take $\pi = 3\cdot14$, radius of the Earth = 6,400 km.)

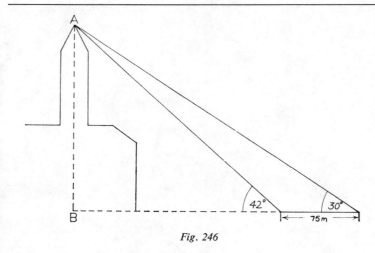

Fig. 246

(10) (*a*) The position of town T is 55° 45′ N and 2° W, the position of town P is 50° 45′ N and 2° W. How far north of P is T? (Ans. in km.)

(*b*) Both Madrid and Philadelphia lie near the 40° N parallel of latitude. The longitude of Madrid is approximately 3° 42′ W, and that of Philadelphia approximately 75° 18′ W. Working to the nearest degree, calculate the distance between the two cities. (Take $\pi = 3 \cdot 14$, radius of the Earth = 6,400 km.)

37 Miscellaneous Short Questions

(1) Divide £1·50 by 20.

(2) Fill in the missing numbers:

$$..) \overline{644}$$
$$28$$

(3) Use tables to find the value of $\sqrt{6·76}$.

(4) Divide £3·85 in the ratio of $4:7$.

(5) Factorise $15a^2 + 5a$.

(6) What is 30% of £165?

(7) Express $55\frac{1}{2}$ kg as a decimal fraction of 1 tonne.

(8) Express 81 as a power of 3.

(9) Divide 4·758 by 7·32. (Do not use tables.)

(10) Simplify: $\frac{7}{8} \times 3\frac{1}{7} \div 3\frac{2}{3}$

(11) Solve the equation:
$$3(x-4) - 3(x+6) = 6 - 2x$$

(12) Multiply $4a^2 - 3b$ by $2ab$.

(13) Factorise:

(i) $9x^2 - 25y^2$ (ii) $\pi R^2 - \pi r^2$

(14) Find the exact value of: $(63·7)^2 - (36·3)^2$

(15) If $2\frac{1}{2}$% commission is paid on sales, what will be the commission on sales valued at £650?

(16) Supply the missing figures in this set of numbers:
$$.., 5, 8, .., 14, 17, 20, .., ...$$

(17) Arrange these fractions in order of size starting with the largest.

$$\frac{7}{24} \quad \frac{5}{16} \quad \frac{3}{8} \quad \frac{9}{32} \quad \frac{1}{4}$$

(18) How many blocks of ice cream measuring 15 cm by 7·5 cm by 5 cm, can be packed into a box with inside measurements of 0·75 m by 0·45 m by 0·45 m?

(19) Use tables to find the value of: (*a*) $\sqrt{45\cdot6}$, (*b*) $\sqrt{0\cdot264}$.

(20) Given $S=\frac{1}{2}at^2$, find t when $a=3$ m/s², and $S=37\cdot5$ m. (*Note:* m/s² means metres per second per second.)

(21) In triangles ABC and XYZ, AB=YZ, AC=XZ, and $\angle$BAC= $\angle$XZY. Are these triangles congruent? If they are congruent which angle of triangle ABC is equal to $\angle$XYZ?

(22) An empty rectangular tank has a base 1·35 m long and 1·05 m wide. If 300 l of water are run into the tank what depth of water will there be in it?

(23) In Fig. 247, $\angle$BAC=25°, $\angle$ABC=100°, and AB is a tangent to the circle. Calculate the sizes of $\angle$BCD, $\angle$ABD, and $\angle$ADB.

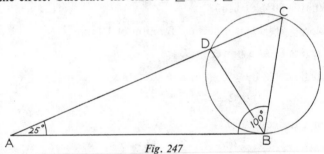

Fig. 247

(24) If tan $\angle a=0\cdot75$, without using tables find the value of sin $\angle a$.

(25) (*a*) Write 26·034 correct to 3 significant figures.
 (*b*) Write 26·034 correct to 2 decimal places.
 (*c*) Convert 473_8 to base 5.

(26) Solve: $x^2+x-2=0$.

(27) Find the compound interest on £150 for 2 years at 5% p.a.

(28) Change the binary number 1100111 to decimal.

(29) What is the value of: (i) $9^{1/2}$ (ii) 7^0 (iii) $27^{2/3}$?

(30) Solve: $\dfrac{x+3}{2}-\dfrac{3(x-4)}{4}=7\frac{1}{2}$.

38 Miscellaneous Problems

When you solve the problems in this section you must be prepared to use any of the techniques that you have learnt by working through this book. In fact you will find that several different techniques may have to be used on any particular problem. Before tackling a problem, then, it is as well to plan your campaign and then to use all the skills you have learnt to find its solution.

(1) Find the sum of three hundred and ninety-six, seven hundred and twenty-three, four thousand two hundred and forty-eight, and five hundred and sixty-six.

(2) A library contains 59,896 books. Of these, 33,249 are in the adult section, 19,738 are in the junior section, and the remainder are in the reference section. How many books are in the reference section of the library?

(3) A lorry weighs 3·5 tonnes when empty. It is loaded with 56 metal ingots each weighing 75 kg. What is the total weight of the lorry when loaded?

(4) Which is the greater and by how much, £8·70 per week or £455 per year?

(5) A man works from 8.05 a.m. to 12.55 p.m., has his lunch and then works from 2.10 p.m. to 5.50 p.m. What is the length of his working day? If he was paid at the rate of 27p per hour, what would he earn for his day's work?

(6) What is the total weight of coal carried in a train of 42 railway trucks if the average weight in 20 of the trucks is 19·5 tonnes per truck and in the remaining 22 trucks 14·5 tonnes per truck?

(7) The cost of a skiing holiday in Switzerland for each member of a school party is made up as follows:

	£
Fares	8·00
Hotel	15·00
Skiing Instruction	5·00
Hire of Equipment	1·25
Miscellaneous	0·75

Find: (i) the cost per child of the trip,

(ii) the total cost for a party of 40 children,

(iii) the fraction of the cost taken up by hotel expenses.

(8) Find the total length of timber needed to make the gate in Fig. 248, allowing an extra 1·50 m for joints and trimming. What is the cost of the timber at 39p per metre?

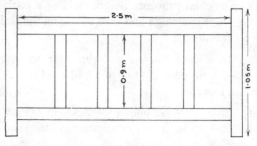

Fig. 248

(9) On a housing estate a two-bedroom bungalow costs £3,325 to build, and a three-bedroom house costs £3,975 to build. If 14 bungalows and 9 houses are built on the estate, calculate the total building cost.

(10) In a school there are 170 children in the first year, 165 in the second year, 161 in the third year, 157 in the fourth year, and 55 in the fifth year. How many pupils are there in the school? If $\frac{5}{12}$ of the pupils are girls, how many boys attend this school?

(11) In a by-election, candidate A polled 3,466 votes, candidate B, 9,742 votes, and candidate C, 7,276 votes. What is the total number of votes cast? Calculate the majority of candidate B over candidate A and over candidate C.

(12) The attendance figures at three football matches were

Arsenal	45,897
Chelsea	41,946
'Spurs	49,223

What was the total attendance at the three matches? How many more spectators were at the Arsenal match than at the Chelsea match?

(13) An electrician earns 27½p an hour. He works a 48-hour week, but this includes 6 hours overtime for which he is paid time-and-a-half. What are his total earnings for the week?

(14) A library issues 41,220 books in a period of 13 weeks. If the population of the town is 13,740, what is the average number of books issued per head of the population for this period?

(15) A man borrows £400 from his bank, to be repaid by regular monthly payments over a period of 3 years. The total amount to be repaid including bank charges, interest, etc. is £470·10. What will his monthly repayments be?

(16) A clock loses 6 min in every 24 h. If it is showing the correct time at mid-day on Monday, what is the correct time on Thursday when the clock shows 6 p.m.?

(17) A herd of 25 cows gives an average of 19·25 litres of milk per cow per day. Each cow is fed concentrates at the rate of 1·4 kg of concentrates for each 5 litres of milk given. Calculate the total weight of concentrates used per day.

(18) A school canteen serves an average of 728 lunches a day for 5 days a week. 250 grammes of potatoes are allowed for each lunch. Calculate (i) the total weight of potatoes used in a 12-week term, assuming that potatoes are served with every lunch, (ii) their cost if the average price paid is £9 per tonne.

(19) A Forestry Commission plantation with an area of 36·5 hectares is planted with trees at the rate of 1,500 trees per hectare. It is estimated that in 60 years, after thinning etc. there will be 310 trees to the hectare. From this information answer the following questions:

   (i) How many trees were originally planted?

   (ii) After 60 years, what is the estimated number of mature trees that will be produced?

   (iii) If the growth of the trees is reckoned to be the equivalent of 2·7 m^3 of timber per annum per hectare, estimate the volume of mature timber available if the trees are felled after 60 years.

(20) It takes 36 strips of wallpaper to decorate a room, each piece is 2·5 m long. What length of wallpaper is needed for the room? If a roll of wallpaper is 10 m long, how many rolls will be needed to decorate the room?

(21) A room is 2·7 m high and the distance around the walls is 14·3 m. How many strips of wallpaper 0·55 m wide will be needed to decorate the room? What is the total length of wallpaper needed? A roll of wallpaper is 10 m long so that only 3 strips can be cut from each roll. How many rolls will be needed to decorate the room?

(22) A cog wheel with 48 teeth is engaged with a smaller wheel which has 16 teeth. The smaller wheel is turning at the rate of 1,500 revolutions per minute. At how many revolutions per minute is the larger wheel turning?

(23) Simplify:

$$(2\tfrac{7}{8} - 1\tfrac{3}{4}) \times (1\tfrac{1}{6} - \tfrac{1}{2})$$

(24) Simplify:

$$\frac{3\tfrac{2}{9} - 1\tfrac{2}{3}}{1\tfrac{3}{4} \times \tfrac{2}{3}}$$

(25) What is the volume, in m^3, of a packing case 75 cm by 45 cm by 45 cm?

(26) A 125 g packet of tea is 125 mm by 37·5 mm by 37·5 mm. How many 125 g packets could be filled from a chest 0·75 m by 0·675 m by 0·675 m? What weight of tea would be contained in the chest?

(27) A shop assistant is paid a basic wage of £3·50 per week. In addition, she receives 3p in the £ commission on the value of the goods that she sells each week. What will be the total amount of money that she will be paid at the end of a week in which she sells goods to the value of £120?

(28) Find, to the nearest penny, the cost of 403 units of electricity at 0·7p per unit.

(29) A factory produces 330 gear-boxes per week. If output increases by $\tfrac{2}{15}$, how many gear-boxes will be produced?

(30) A hundred and twenty-five sheets of metal, all of the same thickness, are in a stack that is 37·5 cm high. What is the thickness of each sheet of metal?

(31) Which is greater, $\tfrac{9}{16}$ or 0·6875? Express the difference between the two amounts as a vulgar fraction in its lowest terms.

(32) Convert the following to vulgar fractions: 0·75, 3·125, 1·95, 2·625, 4·5625.

(33) A racing cyclist covers 200 metres in 12·5 sec. What is the average distance covered in 1 sec? Express this speed in km/h.

(34) Multiply £17·66 by (*a*) 10, (*b*), 100, (*c*) 1000.

(35) The cost of hiring ski equipment is 37·50 Swiss francs for a period of 10 days. How much is this in English money? (10·30 fc = £1)

(36) On his return from a holiday in Spain a man had 187 pesetas and 44·85 fc. If £1 = 165 pta and £1 = 13·40 fc, what amount of English money should he receive for this foreign money?

(37) Car 'A' does 13 km per litre of petrol, car 'B' goes 400 km on 32 litres. How far will each car travel on 45 litres of petrol?

(38) Evaluate to 3 significant figures

$$\frac{13\cdot8 \times 4\cdot25}{27\cdot5}$$

(39) The ratio of the pay of a sergeant to that of a private is 7 : 4. If the sergeant is paid £20·55 what will the private receive?

(40) In a sale there is a standard reduction on all articles. If a radio marked at £44 was sold for £33, what is the sale price of a record player marked at £30?

(41) The shadow cast by a flagpole is 12·6 m long when the shadow cast by a man 1·80 m tall is 1·20 m long. What is the height of the flagpole?

(42) The average weight of a rowing eight is 77 kg. If the average weight including the cox is 74 kg, what is the weight of the cox?

(43) Change to decimal: (*a*) 3423_5, (*b*) 766_8, (*c*) 11011_2

(44) How many kg in 0·0875 of a tonne?

(45) If $V = \frac{4}{3}\pi r^3$, find V when $r = 3$ and $\pi = 3\cdot14$.

(46) Find the area of $\triangle$ABC, when $\angle$A = 30°, AB = 2 cm, AC = 4 cm.

(47) Subtract $4x^2 - 6z$ from $14x^2 - 4z + 6y$ and add this result to $8x^2 - 24z$.

(48) Simplify:
    (i) $(2x-5)(x+6)$
    (ii) $2a+[3a-5(a+4)]$

(49) Find the missing dimension in each of the following:
    (i) Rectangle: area $=63$ cm²; length $=9$ cm; breadth $= ?$
    (ii) Trapezium: area $=80$ cm²; parallel sides 6·5 cm and 9·5 cm; height $= ?$
    (iii) Triangle: area $=3·75$ m²; base $=2·5$ m; height $= ?$

(50) A measuring cylinder full of water weighs 1·68 kg. If there are 875 ml of water in the cylinder what is the weight of the cylinder when empty? (Remember 1 ml of water weighs 1 g.)

(51) In an examination a girl obtains 588 marks out of a possible total of 980. Express the marks obtained as a percentage of the possible marks.

(52) ABC and XYZ are similar triangles with AB and XY corresponding sides. If AB $=3$ cm, BC $=5·4$ cm, XY $=5$ cm, and XZ $=7$ cm, find the lengths of CA and YZ.

(53) The sides of a triangle are in the ratio of 3:4:5. If the shortest side is 12 cm long, find the length of the other two sides. What is the size of the largest angle of the triangle?

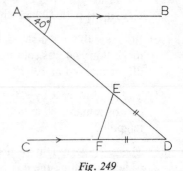

Fig. 249

(54) Solve: $2x+3y=5$, $3x-3y=15$.

(55) In Fig. 249, AB is parallel to CD, $\angle BAD=40°$, DE=DF. Calculate the size of $\angle CFE$.

(56) Solve:
    (i) $4x-3 = 9$ (ii) $\dfrac{3z}{4} = 6$ (iii) $\dfrac{3x}{4}-2\tfrac{3}{4} = 1\tfrac{1}{2}$

(57) The sum of three consecutive odd numbers is 27. Find the numbers.

(58) The three angles of a triangle are $x°$, $3x°$, and $6x°$. Find the size of each angle of the triangle.

(59) A greengrocer buys 150 kg of tomatoes for £24·75. The first 76 kg are sold at 26½p per kg, the next 65 kg at 18p per kg, the remainder is wasted. Calculate the profit made and express it as a percentage of the cost price of the tomatoes.

(60) In Fig. 250, O is the centre of the circle and $\angle OAB = 30°$. Find the size of $\angle AOB$, $\angle ACB$, $\angle ABO$.

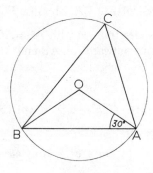

Fig. 250

(61) Each cylinder of a 6-cylinder car engine has a diameter of 6·4 cm and is 7·7 cm in length. Calculate the total volume of the cylinders. Why would this car be classed as 1½ litres?

(62) In Fig. 251, ABCD is a parallelogram, $\angle COD = 120°$, $\angle DAO = 80°$. Find the value of $\angle x$.

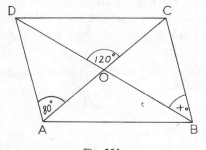

Fig. 251

(63) A rectangular water tank is 1·4 m long, 0·6 m wide, and 0·45 m deep. How much water does it contain when full?

(64) What area of sheet metal would be used to make a closed tin of diameter 10 cm and height 8 cm? Allow a further 10% for joints.

(65) Using ruler and compasses only, construct $\angle ABC = 45°$, with $BA = BC = 10$ cm. E is a point on BA so that $BE = 5$ cm, F is a point on BC so that $BF = 7·5$ cm. Draw EG perpendicular to BC and FH perpendicular to BA. Measure EG and FH.

(66) ABC is an isosceles triangle with $AB = AC$. ABEF and ACGH are squares drawn outwards on AB and AC. Show that triangles FBC and HCB are congruent.

(67) Simplify:

   (i) $3(a^2 + 2ab - b^2) - 4(2b^2 - 2a^2)$ (ii) $(2a - 3)(3a - 2)$

(68) Find the factors of:

   (i) $16a^2 - 25$ (ii) $9b^2 - c^2$ (iii) $4a^3 - 9a^5$

(69) Mother is three times as old as Ann. If their combined ages are 48 years, how old is Ann?

(70) A room is 4·5 m long and 3·6 m wide. The total surface area of the walls and the ceiling is 56·7 m. How high is the room?

(71) (i) Express 5 cm to 1 km as a Representative Fraction.
   (ii) Express 60 km/h in m/s.

(72) On a map with a scale of 5 cm : 1 km, a road is shown as a line 8 cm long. If a car travels this road in 1·5 minutes, at what speed is it travelling?

(73) A kite is being flown at the end of a string 60 m long. Assuming that the string is in a straight line and that it makes an angle of 60° with the ground, calculate the height of the kite above ground level.

(74) Draw circular or 'pie' diagrams to illustrate the composition of the following soils:

	Clay	Silt	Sand (fine)	Sand (coarse)
	%	%	%	%
Clay (Heavy)	48	21	29	2
Loam	6	22	52	20
Sandy (Light)	5	11	61	23

(75) (i) Find the Simple Interest on £175 at $3\frac{1}{2}\%$ per annum for 18 months.
   (ii) What sum of money will give £36 at 4% Simple Interest over a period of 2 years?

(76) On a plantation an estimated 5 m³ of timber is felled. If $7\frac{1}{2}\%$ is deducted for bark, etc. calculate the amount of useful timber felled.

(77) A cylindrical water tank has a radius of 0·5 m, and is 1·4 m high. Calculate the capacity of the tank in m³ and in litres.

(78) Curtains are to be made for a small stage, 9 m wide. The curtains are to be 3·5 m high and an extra 4 m is added to the width so that the curtains are full enough to hang correctly. They are to be made of velvet that is 1·4 m wide and lined with material also 1·4 m wide. The strips of material will run from top to bottom of the curtains so that the seams are vertical. Assume that an extra 15 cm must be added to the length of the curtains to allow for hems at top and bottom. If the velvet costs £1·56 per metre, the lining material is 45p per metre, and the cost of making up the curtains is £23, calculate the total cost.

(79) In Fig. 252 find the value of the letters in the diagrams.

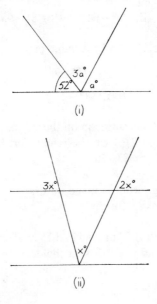

(i)

(ii)

Fig. 252

(80) (*a*) Multiply $3a^2 + 2a - 4$ by $a - 2$.

     (*b*) Divide $a^3 - 4a^2 + 5a - 2$ by $a - 2$.

(81) In triangle XYZ (Fig. 253), YP and ZR are altitudes. Prove that $\angle XYP = \angle XZR$.

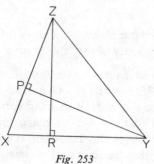

Fig. 253

(82) A car is travelling at V km/h. How many metres does it cover in t minutes?

(83) Factorise:

    (i) $c^2 - 25$ (ii) $4a^2 - 64$ (iii) $81 - 9x^2$

(84) Without using tables find the value of:

    (i) $(57^2 - 43^2)$ (iii) $(107^2 - 93^2)$

    (ii) $(68^2 - 32^2)$ (iv) $(48^2 - 28^2)$

(85) An estate agent's commission on the sale of a house is 5% on the the first £250 and $2\frac{1}{2}\%$ on the remainder. Find his commission on a house sold for £3,750.

(86) What percentage profit is made on oranges bought for $12\frac{1}{2}$p per dozen, and sold at 3 for 5p?

(87) A swimming bath is 50 m long and 15 m wide. The depths are 1 m at the shallow end and 2·5 m at the deep end; the bottom has a uniform slope. Calculate, to the nearest tonne, the weight of water in the bath.

(88) Fig. 254 is a graph showing the average monthly temperatures of Philbury.

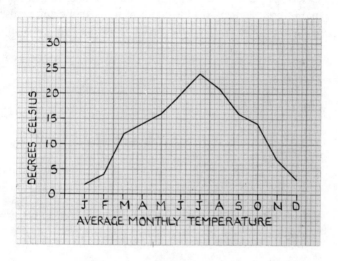

Fig. 254

(a) What is the average reading in (i) October, (ii) April?

(b) Use the figures recorded on the graph to find the average temperature for (i) the first three months of the year, (ii) the last three months of the year.

(c) By 'smoothing off' the graph estimate a temperature for May and June.

(89) A ship leaves point B and sails on a course of 050° for 64 km. It then sails due West for 56 km to point C. Find, by accurate drawing and measurement, the bearing and distance of B from C.

(90) Calculate (a) the exterior angle of a regular polygon of 8 sides, (b) the interior angle of a regular polygon of 10 sides.

11*

(91) If a regular polygon has an exterior angle of 18° find the number of its sides.

(92) During a heavy storm 6 mm of rain falls on a rectangular roof 4 m long by 3 m wide. Calculate: (i) the number of litres of water that fall on the roof, (ii) the depth of water in a cylindrical drum, of diameter 0·6 m, if all the water from the roof runs into the empty drum.

(93) Factorise:

    (i) $x^2 - 5x + 6$

    (ii) $1 + 2x - 3x^2$

    (iii) $2x^2 + 7x + 3$

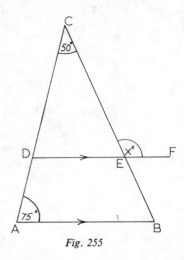

Fig. 255

(94) In triangle ABC (Fig. 255) the line DEF is parallel to AB. Calculate the size of the angle marked x.

(95) At 4% p.a. how long will be needed for £125 to earn £12·50 at simple interest?

(96) Draw triangle ABC with AB = 10 cm, BC = 8·5 cm, and ∠B = 55°. Use ruler and compasses to bisect each angle of the triangle so that the bisectors meet at point D. Measure AD, BD, and CD.

(97) In 10 years' time a man's age will be double what it was 20 years ago. Find his present age.

(98) Purchase tax is reduced from 30% to 20%. The price of an article with tax at the old rate was £1·95; find the price with tax at the new rate.

(99) A balk of timber is 22·5 cm by 22·5 cm by 5 m long. Find its weight if 0·025 m³ of the timber weighs 12 kg.

(100) Draw a graph that can be used to convert French francs into £s for amounts up to £5. Take 13·40 francs = £1.

(101) A man leaves home at 8.18 a.m. to catch a train at 8.48 a.m. He walks to the station at an average speed of 6 km/h. How far does he live from the station? At what time will he need to leave home if he cycles at an average speed of 20 km/h?

(102) Use logarithms to find the value of:

   (i) $1\cdot738 \times 4\cdot8$

   (ii) $62\cdot15 \div 11\cdot36$

   (iii) $\dfrac{17\cdot32 \times 6\cdot39}{7\cdot521}$

(103) In triangle ABC (Fig. 256), $\angle A=30°$, $\angle B=90°$, and AB = 12 cm. Find the length of BC.

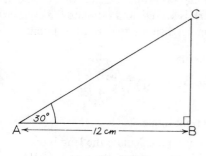

Fig. 256   Fig. 257

(104) The angles of elevation of the top of a building measured from two points in line with the building 50 m apart, are 25° and 55° respectively. Calculate the height of the building.

(105) Figure 257 is a dimensioned sketch of a steel plate. Calculate its area and the volume of metal if the plate is 18·75 mm thick.

(106) (a) Fertiliser is spread at the rate of 280 kg per hectare. How many kg are needed for a piece of ground 25 m by 10 m?

   (b) A man spends 19% of his income on rent and 6% on superannuation. If his rent was £177 find his superannuation payment.

(107) (*a*) If $y=10$, find the values of:

(i) $3y^2+2y+11$ (ii) $\dfrac{5}{y}+\dfrac{5}{y^2}$ (iii) $(y+2)(y-3)$

(*b*) When $a=3$, and $b=2$, find the value of:

(i) $5ab^2$ (ii) $(5ab)^2$

(108)

	No. of pupils	
Marks	*Maths.*	*Eng.*
20–29	3	5
30–39	5	9
40–49	6	7
50–59	8	7
60–69	7	4
70–79	4	3
80–89	2	0

These figures are the results of Mathematics and English examinations. Illustrate them by means of a block diagram, using only one diagram to plot both sets of marks. From your diagram decide in which subject the higher mark is scored, and estimate the average mark in Mathematics and in English for the group of pupils.

(109) Use logarithms to find the value of:

(*a*) $\sqrt{156\cdot2}$ (*b*) $\sqrt{0\cdot3969}$ (*c*) $\sqrt{\dfrac{61\cdot7\times7\cdot24}{4\cdot932}}$

(110) In $\triangle ABC$ (Fig. 258), $\angle A=$ right angle.

(*a*) If $BA=12$ mm and $AC=9$ mm, calculate the length of BC.
(*b*) If $BC=13$ cm and $AC=5$ cm, calculate the length of BA.
(*c*) If $BC=3\cdot5$ m and $BA=1\cdot4$ m, calculate the length of AC.

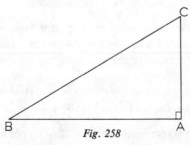

Fig. 258

(111) Solve the following equations for *x* and *y*.

(*a*) $3x+2y = 8$; $2x-2y = 6$
(*b*) $4x-3y = 7$; $x-y = 1$

(112) What is the volume of the largest sphere that will fit into a cylinder whose internal measurements are diameter 15 cm, height 15 cm? Working to the nearest cm³ find the ratio of the volume of the sphere to the volume of the cylinder. (Take $\pi = 3 \cdot 14$.)

(113) Revise the properties of a rhombus and then calculate the perimeter of a rhombus with diagonals of 12 cm and 5 cm.

(114) When the angle that the sun's rays makes with the ground is 61° the shadow cast by a pole is 3 m long. Calculate the height of the pole. What angle would the sun's rays make with the ground if the shadow was 4·8 m long? (Work to the nearest degree.)

(115) (a) A roller is 0·75 m in diameter and is 2·4 m wide. Calculate the area it rolls (i) in 1 revolution, (ii) after 30 revoultions.

(b) A square has an area of 42·25 cm². What is the length of its side?

(116) Look up the S-rule for finding the area of a triangle and then calculate the area of a triangle with sides of 4 cm, 7 cm, and 9 cm.

(117) Calculate the compound interest on £180 for 2 years at $2\frac{1}{2}\%$ p.a. (Work to the nearest penny.)

(118) Solve the equations:

(a) $\dfrac{a}{6} - \dfrac{a-2}{3} = 1$ (b) $\dfrac{x-1}{4} = 2 + \dfrac{x-2}{6}$

(119) A man sets out from A at 10.30 a.m. to cycle to B. At midday he stops for 30 min to have lunch and then continues his journey reaching B at 2.30 p.m. While cycling his average speed is 16 km/h. At 1 p.m. another man leaves B by car and drive directly to A at an average speed of 48 km/h.

Illustrate both journeys on the same graph. Use your graph to find the distance from A and the time at which the two travellers pass each other.

(120) The formula $s = ut + \frac{1}{2}at^2$ can be used to find the net distance covered by a body moving with constant acceleration; u is the initial velocity of the body in m/s, t is the time in seconds and a is the constant acceleration expressed in m/s². Find the distance moved by a body that has an initial velocity of 12 m/s, a constant acceleration of 1·2 m/s² in a time of 6 seconds.

(121) In Fig. 259, A and B are two pulley wheels with centres 75 cm apart. Wheel A has a radius = 16 cm and wheel B a radius = 20 cm. Calculate the length of a belt that goes around both wheels.

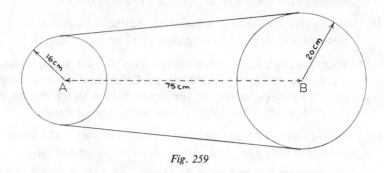

Fig. 259

(122) In Fig. 260, O is the centre of the circle and ABC a tangent. ∠CBE = 60°. Calculate the size of ∠BDE and ∠BOE.

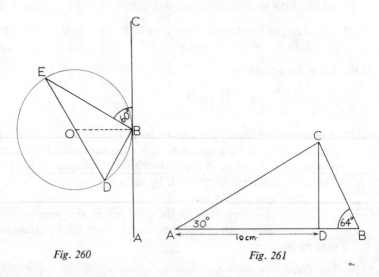

Fig. 260   *Fig. 261*

(123) In triangle ABC (Fig. 261), CD is perpendicular to AB. AD = 10 cm, ∠A = 30°, ∠B = 64°. Calculate the lengths of CD and DB and then find the area of the triangle ABC.

(124) Find the volume of metal in a cylindrical pipe of internal diameter 150 mm, external diameter 175 mm, and length 4·2 m.

(125) (a) The angles of a triangle are $3.5x°$, $4.5x°$, and $4x°$. Find the value of x.

     (b) If the width of a piece of wood is reduced by 10% and becomes 150 mm, what was the original width?

(126) (a) Use logarithms to find: (i) $74.25 \div 8.89$, (ii) $\sqrt[3]{26\frac{3}{4}}$

     (b) Change to standard form: (i) 96 000 000, (ii) 0.00054

(127) At what time will a train which leaves London for Crewe at 10.00 hours and averages 80 km/h, pass a train which leaves Crewe for London at 10.30 hours and averages 72 km/h? The distance from London to Crewe is 256 km.

(128) The length L mm of a helical spring when supporting a weight of W kg is as follows:

W (kg)	0.9	1.6	4.5	7
L (mm)	145	160	225	280

Draw a graph with L measured vertically, to illustrate these figures, and find the length of the spring when there is no weight attached to it.

(129) From the top of a cliff 96 m high, it is found that the angles of depression of two boats lying in line due east of the cliff are 21° and 17°. Calculate the distance between the two boats.

(130) Make L the subject of $P = 2(L + W)$, and find the value of L when $P = 20$ cm and $W = 2$ cm.

(131) The shadow of the Eiffel Tower is found to be 49.2 m long at the same time as the shadow of a man 1.65 m tall is 27.5 cm long. From this information calculate the height of the Eiffel Tower.

(132) The floor of a room 5.8 m long and 4 m wide is covered with carpet 0.7 m wide.

     (a) What area of carpet is wasted if the strips are laid parallel to the length?

     (b) What area of carpet is wasted if the strips are laid parallel to the width?

(133) (a) If tan $\angle A = \frac{3}{4}$, what is the value of sin $\angle A$ as a vulgar fraction?

(b) A ship due south of a lighthouse takes a bearing of a factory chimney. This bearing is 030°. The factory is 6·4 km due east of the lighthouse. Draw a sketch to illustrate these facts. Find by calculation the distance south of the lighthouse that the ship lies.

(134) Of his working week in school a boy spends $\frac{2}{3}$ of his time on classroom subjects, and $\frac{3}{5}$ of his remaining time in the workshops. He then has 2 h left for games. Calculate the length of his working week in hours. Express the time spent on games as a percentage of the time he spends on classroom subjects.

(135) 48 metal spheres of 37·5 mm diameter are packed inside a cylinder 350 mm high and 175 mm internal diameter. The cylinder is then filled with oil. What volume of oil will be needed to fill the cylinder?

(136) In a right-angled triangle the two sides that contain the right angle are 16 cm and 10 cm long. Calculate, to the nearest degree, the size of the smallest angle of the triangle.

(137) Find to the nearest penny the amount at compound interest of £400 after 3 years at 4% p.a.

(138) Solve, by factorizing, the following equations:

    (i) $x^2 - 7x + 10 = 0$

    (ii) $a^2 + 10a + 21 = 0$

    (iii) $x^2 + 3x = 0$

(139) In Fig. 262, PQ=4 cm, QR= 5 cm, RS=8 cm, ST=7 cm, and angles Q, R, S are right angles. Calculate the lengths of PR and TP (to two decimal places).

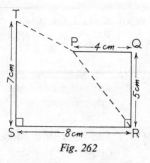

Fig. 262

(140) Using ruler and compasses only, draw a triangle XYZ with XY = 10 cm, XZ=8·75 cm, and $\angle ZXY = 45°$. Find a point W equidistant from XZ and YZ and at the same time equidistant from X and Y.

(141) A satellite orbits the earth in a circle at a height of 2,000 km.
  (a) If the radius of the earth is approximately 6,400 km, calculate the distance the satellite travels in making one circuit of the earth.
  (b) If the satellite takes 108 min to make one orbit, calculate its speed in km/h ($\pi = 3.14$).

(142) The sketch (Fig. 263) represents a sheet-metal water trough. Calculate the area of sheet metal needed to make it and also its capacity in litres.

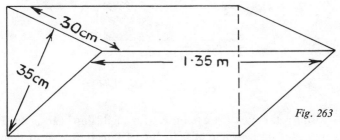

Fig. 263

(143) The formula $d = 4.9t^2$ can be used to find the depth of a well where d is the depth in metres, and t is the time in seconds that it takes a stone to hit the surface of the water. Use this formula to find the depth of a well where (i) $t = 5$ seconds, and (ii) $t = 2.5$ seconds. What would be the value of t when a well is 100 m deep?

(144) Draw graphs to solve the following pair of equations:

$$x - y = 3$$
$$x + 2y = 9$$

(145) An article for sale at a cash price of £41·60 is offered on hire purchase terms of 25% deposit and 12 monthly payments of £2·92½.

  (a) Calculate the extra amount paid under the hire purchase agreement.
  (b) Calculate as a percentage, the interest that will be paid on the money outstanding after the deposit has been paid.

(146) The profits from a business are divided in the same ratio as the capital invested. 'A' invested £1,500, 'B' invested £2,000, and 'C' invested £2,500. If the profit to be distributed is £1,450 what amount will each receive?

(147) Figure 264 is a dimensioned sketch of a section cut out of a ring. Calculate the area of the shaded section.

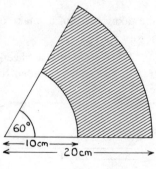

Fig. 264

(148) A ship sets course from point A with a lightship bearing due East, and sails on a course of 030° for 64 km. It is then at point B, exactly north of the lightship. Calculate the distance of point B from the lightship.

(149) (a) $\ldots, \dfrac{2}{5}, \dfrac{x}{y}, \dfrac{1}{2}, \ldots$ are three members of a Farey sequence. Find $\dfrac{x}{y}$.

    (b) Find the number of members of the Farey sequence order 4 and order 6.

    (c) Use the Lattice Point method to rewrite these fractions in ascending order: $\dfrac{3}{4}, \dfrac{2}{7}, \dfrac{1}{5}, \dfrac{5}{6}, \dfrac{6}{7}, \dfrac{2}{3}, \dfrac{2}{5}$.

(150) (a) Add: $5347_8 + 334_5 + 7859_{10} + 1100101_2$. Give your answer as a duodecimal.

    (b) Multiply 725_8 by 346_8

    (c) Divide 1110110111_2 by 1011_2

(151) (a) Add: $27p + 96\frac{1}{2}p + 48p + 10\frac{1}{2}p + 76p + 37\frac{1}{2}p$. Give your answer in £s and pence.

    (b) Multiply £17·86 by 52.

    (c) Divide £64·38 by 12.

(152) Two towns, A and B, have the same longitude. A is 5,024 km north of B. If the latitude of B is 15° 30′ S and the radius of the Earth is taken as 6,400 km, find the latitude of town A.

TABLE OF LOGARITHMS

	0	1	2	3	4	5	6	7	8	9	Mean Differences 1	2	3	4	5	6	7	8	9
10	0000	0043	0086	0128	0170	0212	0253	0294	0334	0374	4	8	12	17	21	25	29	33	3
11	0414	0453	0492	0531	0569	0607	0645	0682	0719	0755	4	8	11	15	19	23	26	30	3
12	0792	0828	0864	0899	0934	0969	1004	1038	1072	1106	3	7	10	14	17	21	24	28	3
13	1139	1173	1206	1239	1271	1303	1335	1367	1399	1430	3	6	10	13	16	19	23	26	2
14	1461	1492	1523	1553	1584	1614	1644	1673	1703	1732	3	6	9	12	15	18	21	24	2
15	1761	1790	1818	1847	1875	1903	1931	1959	1987	2014	3	6	8	11	14	17	20	22	2
16	2041	2068	2095	2122	2148	2175	2201	2227	2253	2279	3	5	8	11	13	16	18	21	2
17	2304	2330	2355	2380	2405	2430	2455	2480	2504	2529	2	5	7	10	12	15	17	20	2
18	2553	2577	2601	2625	2648	2672	2695	2718	2742	2765	2	5	7	9	12	14	16	19	2
19	2788	2810	2833	2856	2878	2900	2923	2945	2967	2989	2	4	7	9	11	13	16	18	2
20	3010	3032	3054	3075	3096	3118	3139	3160	3181	3201	2	4	6	8	11	13	15	17	1
21	3222	3243	3263	3284	3304	3324	3345	3365	3385	3404	2	4	6	8	10	12	14	16	1
22	3424	3444	3464	3483	3502	3522	3541	3560	3579	3598	2	4	6	8	10	12	14	15	1
23	3617	3636	3655	3674	3692	3711	3729	3747	3766	3784	2	4	6	7	9	11	13	15	1
24	3802	3820	3838	3856	3874	3892	3909	3927	3945	3962	2	4	5	7	9	11	12	14	1
25	3979	3997	4014	4031	4048	4065	4082	4099	4116	4133	2	3	5	7	9	10	12	14	1
26	4150	4166	4183	4200	4216	4232	4249	4265	4281	4298	2	3	5	7	8	10	11	13	1
27	4314	4330	4346	4362	4378	4393	4409	4425	4440	4456	2	3	5	6	8	9	11	13	1
28	4472	4487	4502	4518	4533	4548	4564	4579	4594	4609	2	3	5	6	8	9	11	12	1
29	4624	4639	4654	4669	4683	4698	4713	4728	4742	4757	1	3	4	6	7	9	10	12	1
30	4771	4786	4800	4814	4829	4843	4857	4871	4886	4900	1	3	4	6	7	9	10	11	1
31	4914	4928	4942	4955	4969	4983	4997	5011	5024	5038	1	3	4	6	7	8	10	11	1
32	5051	5065	5079	5092	5105	5119	5132	5145	5159	5172	1	3	4	5	7	8	9	11	1
33	5185	5198	5211	5224	5237	5250	5263	5276	5289	5302	1	3	4	5	6	8	9	10	1
34	5315	5328	5340	5353	5366	5378	5391	5403	5416	5428	1	3	4	5	6	8	9	10	1
35	5441	5453	5465	5478	5490	5502	5514	5527	5539	5551	1	2	4	5	6	7	9	10	1
36	5563	5575	5587	5599	5611	5623	5635	5647	5658	5670	1	2	4	5	6	7	8	10	1
37	5682	5694	5705	5717	5729	5740	5752	5763	5775	5786	1	2	3	5	6	7	8	9	1
38	5798	5809	5821	5832	5843	5855	5866	5877	5888	5899	1	2	3	5	6	7	8	9	1
39	5911	5922	5933	5944	5955	5966	5977	5988	5999	6010	1	2	3	4	5	7	8	9	1
40	6021	6031	6042	6053	6064	6075	6085	6096	6107	6117	1	2	3	4	5	6	8	9	1
41	6128	6138	6149	6160	6170	6180	6191	6201	6212	6222	1	2	3	4	5	6	7	8	
42	6232	6243	6253	6263	6274	6284	6294	6304	6314	6325	1	2	3	4	5	6	7	8	
43	6335	6345	6355	6365	6375	6385	6395	6405	6415	6425	1	2	3	4	5	6	7	8	
44	6435	6444	6454	6464	6474	6484	6493	6503	6513	6522	1	2	3	4	5	6	7	8	
45	6532	6542	6551	6561	6571	6580	6590	6599	6609	6618	1	2	3	4	5	6	7	8	
46	6628	6637	6646	6656	6665	6675	6684	6693	6702	6712	1	2	3	4	5	6	7	7	
47	6721	6730	6739	6749	6758	6767	6776	6785	6794	6803	1	2	3	4	5	5	6	7	
48	6812	6821	6830	6839	6848	6857	6866	6875	6884	6893	1	2	3	4	4	5	6	7	
49	6902	6911	6920	6928	6937	6946	6955	6964	6972	6981	1	2	3	4	4	5	6	7	
50	6990	6998	7007	7016	7024	7033	7042	7050	7059	7067	1	2	3	3	4	5	6	7	
51	7076	7084	7093	7101	7110	7118	7126	7135	7143	7152	1	2	3	3	4	5	6	7	
52	7160	7168	7177	7185	7193	7202	7210	7218	7226	7235	1	2	2	3	4	5	6	7	
53	7243	7251	7259	7267	7275	7284	7292	7300	7308	7316	1	2	2	3	4	5	6	6	
54	7324	7332	7340	7348	7356	7364	7372	7380	7388	7396	1	2	2	3	4	5	6	6	
	0	1	2	3	4	5	6	7	8	9	1	2	3	4	5	6	7	8	

TABLE OF LOGARITHMS

	0	1	2	3	4	5	6	7	8	9	Mean Differences 1	2	3	4	5	6	7	8	9
55	7404	7412	7419	7427	7435	7443	7451	7459	7466	7474	1	2	2	3	4	5	5	6	7
56	7482	7490	7497	7505	7513	7520	7528	7536	7543	7551	1	2	2	3	4	5	5	6	7
57	7559	7566	7574	7582	7589	7597	7604	7612	7619	7627	1	2	2	3	4	5	5	6	7
58	7634	7642	7649	7657	7664	7672	7679	7686	7694	7701	1	1	2	3	4	4	5	6	7
59	7709	7716	7723	7731	7738	7745	7752	7760	7767	7774	1	1	2	3	4	4	5	6	7
60	7782	7789	7796	7803	7810	7818	7825	7832	7839	7846	1	1	2	3	4	4	5	6	6
61	7853	7860	7868	7875	7882	7889	7896	7903	7910	7917	1	1	2	3	4	4	5	6	6
62	7924	7931	7938	7945	7952	7959	7966	7973	7980	7987	1	1	2	3	3	4	5	6	6
63	7993	8000	8007	8014	8021	8028	8035	8041	8048	8055	1	1	2	3	3	4	5	5	6
64	8062	8069	8075	8082	8089	8096	8102	8109	8116	8122	1	1	2	3	3	4	5	5	6
65	8129	8136	8142	8149	8156	8162	8169	8176	8182	8189	1	1	2	3	3	4	5	5	6
66	8195	8202	8209	8215	8222	8228	8235	8241	8248	8254	1	1	2	3	3	4	5	5	6
67	8261	8267	8274	8280	8287	8293	8299	8306	8312	8319	1	1	2	3	3	4	5	5	6
68	8325	8331	8338	8344	8351	8357	8363	8370	8376	8382	1	1	2	3	3	4	4	5	6
69	8388	8395	8401	8407	8414	8420	8426	8432	8439	8445	1	1	2	2	3	4	4	5	6
70	8451	8457	8463	8470	8476	8482	8488	8494	8500	8506	1	1	2	2	3	4	4	5	6
71	8513	8519	8525	8531	8537	8543	8549	8555	8561	8567	1	1	2	2	3	4	4	5	5
72	8573	8579	8585	8591	8597	8603	8609	8615	8621	8627	1	1	2	2	3	4	4	5	5
73	8633	8639	8645	8651	8657	8663	8669	8675	8681	8686	1	1	2	2	3	4	4	5	5
74	8692	8698	8704	8710	8716	8722	8727	8733	8739	8745	1	1	2	2	3	4	4	5	5
75	8751	8756	8762	8768	8774	8779	8785	8791	8797	8802	1	1	2	2	3	3	4	5	5
76	8808	8814	8820	8825	8831	8837	8842	8848	8854	8859	1	1	2	2	3	3	4	5	5
77	8865	8871	8876	8882	8887	8893	8899	8904	8910	8915	1	1	2	2	3	3	4	4	5
78	8921	8927	8932	8938	8943	8949	8954	8960	8965	8971	1	1	2	2	3	3	4	4	5
79	8976	8982	8987	8993	8998	9004	9009	9015	9020	9025	1	1	2	2	3	3	4	4	5
80	9031	9036	9042	9047	9053	9058	9063	9069	9074	9079	1	1	2	2	3	3	4	4	5
81	9085	9090	9096	9101	9106	9112	9117	9122	9128	9133	1	1	2	2	3	3	4	4	5
82	9138	9143	9149	9154	9159	9165	9170	9175	9180	9186	1	1	2	2	3	3	4	4	5
83	9191	9196	9201	9206	9212	9217	9222	9227	9232	9238	1	1	2	2	3	3	4	4	5
84	9243	9248	9253	9258	9263	9269	9274	9279	9284	9289	1	1	2	2	3	3	4	4	5
85	9294	9299	9304	9309	9315	9320	9325	9330	9335	9340	1	1	2	2	3	3	4	4	5
86	9345	9350	9355	9360	9365	9370	9375	9380	9385	9390	1	1	2	2	3	3	4	4	4
87	9395	9400	9405	9410	9415	9420	9425	9430	9435	9440	0	1	1	2	2	3	3	4	4
88	9445	9450	9455	9460	9465	9469	9474	9479	9484	9489	0	1	1	2	2	3	3	4	4
89	9494	9499	9504	9509	9513	9518	9523	9528	9533	9538	0	1	1	2	2	3	3	4	4
90	9542	9547	9552	9557	9562	9566	9571	9576	9581	9586	0	1	1	2	2	3	3	4	4
91	9590	9595	9600	9605	9609	9614	9619	9624	9628	9633	0	1	1	2	2	3	3	4	4
92	9638	9643	9647	9652	9657	9661	9666	9671	9675	9680	0	1	1	2	2	3	3	4	4
93	9685	9689	9694	9699	9703	9708	9713	9717	9722	9727	0	1	1	2	2	3	3	4	4
94	9731	9736	9741	9745	9750	9754	9759	9763	9768	9773	0	1	1	2	2	3	3	4	4
95	9777	9782	9786	9791	9795	9800	9805	9809	9814	9818	0	1	1	2	2	3	3	4	4
96	9823	9827	9832	9836	9841	9845	9850	9854	9859	9863	0	1	1	2	2	3	3	4	4
97	9868	9872	9877	9881	9886	9890	9894	9899	9903	9908	0	1	1	2	2	3	3	4	4
98	9912	9917	9921	9926	9930	9934	9939	9943	9948	9952	0	1	1	2	2	3	3	4	4
99	9956	9961	9965	9969	9974	9978	9983	9987	9991	9996	0	1	1	2	2	3	3	3	4
	0	1	2	3	4	5	6	7	8	9	1 2 3 4				5 6 7 8 9				

TABLE OF ANTILOGARITHMS

	0	1	2	3	4	5	6	7	8	9	Mean Differences 1	2	3	4	5	6	7	8
·00	1000	1002	1005	1007	1009	1012	1014	1016	1019	1021	0	0	1	1	1	1	2	2
·01	1023	1026	1028	1030	1033	1035	1038	1040	1042	1045	0	0	1	1	1	1	2	2
·02	1047	1050	1052	1054	1057	1059	1062	1064	1067	1069	0	0	1	1	1	1	2	2
·03	1072	1074	1076	1079	1081	1084	1086	1089	1091	1094	0	0	1	1	1	1	2	2
·04	1096	1099	1102	1104	1107	1109	1112	1114	1117	1119	0	1	1	1	1	2	2	2
·05	1122	1125	1127	1130	1132	1135	1138	1140	1143	1146	0	1	1	1	1	2	2	2
·06	1148	1151	1153	1156	1159	1161	1164	1167	1169	1172	0	1	1	1	1	2	2	2
·07	1175	1178	1180	1183	1186	1189	1191	1194	1197	1199	0	1	1	1	1	2	2	2
·08	1202	1205	1208	1211	1213	1216	1219	1222	1225	1227	0	1	1	1	1	2	2	2
·09	1230	1233	1236	1239	1242	1245	1247	1250	1253	1256	0	1	1	1	1	2	2	2
·10	1259	1262	1265	1268	1271	1274	1276	1279	1282	1285	0	1	1	1	1	2	2	2
·11	1288	1291	1294	1297	1300	1303	1306	1309	1312	1315	0	1	1	1	2	2	2	2
·12	1318	1321	1324	1327	1330	1334	1337	1340	1343	1346	0	1	1	1	2	2	2	2
·13	1349	1352	1355	1358	1361	1365	1368	1371	1374	1377	0	1	1	1	2	2	2	3
·14	1380	1384	1387	1390	1393	1396	1400	1403	1406	1409	0	1	1	1	2	2	2	3
·15	1413	1416	1419	1422	1426	1429	1432	1435	1439	1442	0	1	1	1	2	2	2	3
·16	1445	1449	1452	1455	1459	1462	1466	1469	1472	1476	0	1	1	1	2	2	2	3
·17	1479	1483	1486	1489	1493	1496	1500	1503	1507	1510	0	1	1	1	2	2	2	3
·18	1514	1517	1521	1524	1528	1531	1535	1538	1542	1545	0	1	1	1	2	2	3	3
·19	1549	1552	1556	1560	1563	1567	1570	1574	1578	1581	0	1	1	1	2	2	3	3
·20	1585	1589	1592	1596	1600	1603	1607	1611	1614	1618	0	1	1	1	2	2	3	3
·21	1622	1626	1629	1633	1637	1641	1644	1648	1652	1656	0	1	1	2	2	2	3	3
·22	1660	1663	1667	1671	1675	1679	1683	1687	1690	1694	0	1	1	2	2	2	3	3
·23	1698	1702	1706	1710	1714	1718	1722	1726	1730	1734	0	1	1	2	2	2	3	3
·24	1738	1742	1746	1750	1754	1758	1762	1766	1770	1774	0	1	1	2	2	2	3	3
·25	1778	1782	1786	1791	1795	1799	1803	1807	1811	1816	0	1	1	2	2	2	3	3
·26	1820	1824	1828	1832	1837	1841	1845	1849	1854	1858	0	1	1	2	2	3	3	3
·27	1862	1866	1871	1875	1879	1884	1888	1892	1897	1901	0	1	1	2	2	3	3	3
·28	1905	1910	1914	1919	1923	1928	1932	1936	1941	1945	0	1	1	2	2	3	3	4
·29	1950	1954	1959	1963	1968	1972	1977	1982	1986	1991	0	1	1	2	2	3	3	4
·30	1995	2000	2004	2009	2014	2018	2023	2028	2032	2037	0	1	1	2	2	3	3	4
·31	2042	2046	2051	2056	2061	2065	2070	2075	2080	2084	0	1	1	2	2	3	3	4
·32	2089	2094	2099	2104	2109	2113	2118	2123	2128	2133	0	1	1	2	2	3	3	4
·33	2138	2143	2148	2153	2158	2163	2168	2173	2178	2183	0	1	1	2	2	3	3	4
·34	2188	2193	2198	2203	2208	2213	2218	2223	2228	2234	1	1	2	2	3	3	4	4
·35	2239	2244	2249	2254	2259	2265	2270	2275	2280	2286	1	1	2	2	3	3	4	4
·36	2291	2296	2301	2307	2312	2317	2323	2328	2333	2339	1	1	2	2	3	3	4	4
·37	2344	2350	2355	2360	2366	2371	2377	2382	2388	2393	1	1	2	2	3	3	4	4
·38	2399	2404	2410	2415	2421	2427	2432	2438	2443	2449	1	1	2	2	3	3	4	4
·39	2455	2460	2466	2472	2477	2483	2489	2495	2500	2506	1	1	2	2	3	3	4	5
·40	2512	2518	2523	2529	2535	2541	2547	2553	2559	2564	1	1	2	2	3	4	4	5
·41	2570	2576	2582	2588	2594	2600	2606	2612	2618	2624	1	1	2	2	3	4	4	5
·42	2630	2636	2642	2649	2655	2661	2667	2673	2679	2685	1	1	2	2	3	4	4	5
·43	2692	2698	2704	2710	2716	2723	2729	2735	2742	2748	1	1	2	3	3	4	4	5
·44	2754	2761	2767	2773	2780	2786	2793	2799	2805	2812	1	1	2	3	3	4	4	5
·45	2818	2825	2831	2838	2844	2851	2858	2864	2871	2877	1	1	2	3	3	4	5	5
·46	2884	2891	2897	2904	2911	2917	2924	2931	2938	2944	1	1	2	3	3	4	5	5
·47	2951	2958	2965	2972	2979	2985	2992	2999	3006	3013	1	1	2	3	3	4	5	5
·48	3020	3027	3034	3041	3048	3055	3062	3069	3076	3083	1	1	2	3	4	4	5	6
·49	3090	3097	3105	3112	3119	3126	3133	3141	3148	3155	1	1	2	3	4	4	5	6

TABLE OF ANTILOGARITHMS

	0	1	2	3	4	5	6	7	8	9	Mean Differences								
											1	2	3	4	5	6	7	8	9
50	3162	3170	3177	3184	3192	3199	3206	3214	3221	3228	1	1	2	3	4	4	5	6	7
51	3236	3243	3251	3258	3266	3273	3281	3289	3296	3304	1	2	2	3	4	5	5	6	7
52	3311	3319	3327	3334	3342	3350	3357	3365	3373	3381	1	2	2	3	4	5	5	6	7
53	3388	3396	3404	3412	3420	3428	3436	3443	3451	3459	1	2	2	3	4	5	6	6	7
54	3467	3475	3483	3491	3499	3508	3516	3524	3532	3540	1	2	2	3	4	5	6	6	7
55	3548	3556	3565	3573	3581	3589	3597	3606	3614	3622	1	2	2	3	4	5	6	7	7
56	3631	3639	3648	3656	3664	3673	3681	3690	3698	3707	1	2	3	3	4	5	6	7	8
57	3715	3724	3733	3741	3750	3758	3767	3776	3784	3793	1	2	3	3	4	5	6	7	8
58	3802	3811	3819	3828	3837	3846	3855	3864	3873	3882	1	2	3	4	4	5	6	7	8
59	3890	3899	3908	3917	3926	3936	3945	3954	3963	3972	1	2	3	4	5	5	6	7	8
60	3981	3990	3999	4009	4018	4027	4036	4046	4055	4064	1	2	3	4	5	6	6	7	8
61	4074	4083	4093	4102	4111	4121	4130	4140	4150	4159	1	2	3	4	5	6	7	8	9
62	4169	4178	4188	4198	4207	4217	4227	4236	4246	4256	1	2	3	4	5	6	7	8	9
63	4266	4276	4285	4295	4305	4315	4325	4335	4345	4355	1	2	3	4	5	6	7	8	9
64	4365	4375	4385	4395	4406	4416	4426	4436	4446	4457	1	2	3	4	5	6	7	8	9
65	4467	4477	4487	4498	4508	4519	4529	4539	4550	4560	1	2	3	4	5	6	7	8	9
66	4571	4581	4592	4603	4613	4624	4634	4645	4656	4667	1	2	3	4	5	6	7	9	10
67	4677	4688	4699	4710	4721	4732	4742	4753	4764	4775	1	2	3	4	5	7	8	9	10
68	4786	4797	4808	4819	4831	4842	4853	4864	4875	4887	1	2	3	4	6	7	8	9	10
69	4898	4909	4920	4932	4943	4955	4966	4977	4989	5000	1	2	3	5	6	7	8	9	10
70	5012	5023	5035	5047	5058	5070	5082	5093	5105	5117	1	2	4	5	6	7	8	9	11
71	5129	5140	5152	5164	5176	5188	5200	5212	5224	5236	1	2	4	5	6	7	8	10	11
72	5248	5260	5272	5284	5297	5309	5321	5333	5346	5358	1	2	4	5	6	7	9	10	11
73	5370	5383	5395	5408	5420	5433	5445	5458	5470	5483	1	3	4	5	6	8	9	10	11
74	5495	5508	5521	5534	5546	5559	5572	5585	5598	5610	1	3	4	5	6	8	9	10	12
75	5623	5636	5649	5662	5675	5689	5702	5715	5728	5741	1	3	4	5	7	8	9	10	12
76	5754	5768	5781	5794	5808	5821	5834	5848	5861	5875	1	3	4	5	7	8	9	11	12
77	5888	5902	5916	5929	5943	5957	5970	5984	5998	6012	1	3	4	5	7	8	10	11	12
78	6026	6039	6053	6067	6081	6095	6109	6124	6138	6152	1	3	4	6	7	8	10	11	13
79	6166	6180	6194	6209	6223	6237	6252	6266	6281	6295	1	3	4	6	7	9	10	11	13
80	6310	6324	6339	6353	6368	6383	6397	6412	6427	6442	1	3	4	6	7	9	10	12	13
81	6457	6471	6486	6501	6516	6531	6546	6561	6577	6592	2	3	5	6	8	9	11	12	14
82	6607	6622	6637	6653	6668	6683	6699	6714	6730	6745	2	3	5	6	8	9	11	12	14
83	6761	6776	6792	6808	6823	6839	6855	6871	6887	6902	2	3	5	6	8	9	11	13	14
84	6918	6934	6950	6966	6982	6998	7015	7031	7047	7063	2	3	5	6	8	10	11	13	15
85	7079	7096	7112	7129	7145	7161	7178	7194	7211	7228	2	3	5	7	8	10	12	13	15
86	7244	7261	7278	7295	7311	7328	7345	7362	7379	7396	2	3	5	7	8	10	12	13	15
87	7413	7430	7447	7464	7482	7499	7516	7534	7551	7568	2	3	5	7	9	10	12	14	16
88	7586	7603	7621	7638	7656	7674	7691	7709	7727	7745	2	4	5	7	9	11	12	14	16
89	7762	7780	7798	7816	7834	7852	7870	7889	7907	7925	2	4	5	7	9	11	13	14	16
90	7943	7962	7980	7998	8017	8035	8054	8072	8091	8110	2	4	6	7	9	11	13	15	17
91	8128	8147	8166	8185	8204	8222	8241	8260	8279	8299	2	4	6	8	9	11	13	15	17
92	8318	8337	8356	8375	8395	8414	8433	8453	8472	8492	2	4	6	8	10	12	14	15	17
93	8511	8531	8551	8570	8590	8610	8630	8650	8670	8690	2	4	6	8	10	12	14	16	18
94	8710	8730	8750	8770	8790	8810	8831	8851	8872	8892	2	4	6	8	10	12	14	16	18
95	8913	8933	8954	8974	8995	9016	9036	9057	9078	9099	2	4	6	8	10	12	15	17	19
96	9120	9141	9162	9183	9204	9226	9247	9268	9290	9311	2	4	6	8	11	13	15	17	19
97	9333	9354	9376	9397	9419	9441	9462	9484	9506	9528	2	4	7	9	11	13	15	17	20
98	9550	9572	9594	9616	9638	9661	9683	9705	9727	9750	2	4	7	9	11	13	16	18	20
99	9772	9795	9817	9840	9863	9886	9908	9931	9954	9977	2	5	7	9	11	14	16	18	20

SQUARES

	0	1	2	3	4	5	6	7	8	9	1	2	3	4	5	6	7	8	9
10	1000	1020	1040	1061	1082	1103	1124	1145	1166	1188	2	4	6	8	10	13	15	17	19
11	1210	1232	1254	1277	1300	1323	1346	1369	1392	1416	2	5	7	9	11	14	16	18	21
12	1440	1464	1488	1513	1538	1563	1588	1613	1638	1664	2	5	7	10	12	15	17	20	22
13	1690	1716	1742	1769	1796	1823	1850	1877	1904	1932	3	5	8	11	13	16	19	22	24
14	1960	1988	2016	2045	2074	2103	2132	2161	2190	2220	3	6	9	12	14	17	20	23	26
15	2250	2280	2310	2341	2372	2403	2434	2465	2496	2528	3	6	9	12	15	19	22	25	28
16	2560	2592	2624	2657	2690	2723	2756	2789	2822	2856	3	7	10	13	16	20	23	26	30
17	2890	2924	2958	2993	3028	3063	3098	3133	3168	3204	3	7	10	14	17	21	24	28	31
18	3240	3276	3312	3349	3386	3423	3460	3497	3534	3572	4	7	11	15	18	22	26	30	33
19	3610	3648	3686	3725	3764	3803	3842	3881	3920	3960	4	8	12	16	19	23	27	31	35
20	4000	4040	4080	4121	4162	4203	4244	4285	4326	4368	4	8	12	16	20	25	29	33	37
21	4410	4452	4494	4537	4580	4623	4666	4709	4752	4796	4	9	13	17	21	26	30	34	39
22	4840	4884	4928	4973	5018	5063	5108	5153	5198	5244	4	9	13	18	22	27	31	36	40
23	5290	5336	5382	5429	5476	5523	5570	5617	5664	5712	5	9	14	19	23	28	33	38	42
24	5760	5808	5856	5905	5954	6003	6052	6101	6150	6200	5	10	15	20	24	29	34	39	44
25	6250	6300	6350	6401	6452	6503	6554	6605	6656	6708	5	10	15	20	25	31	36	41	46
26	6760	6812	6864	6917	6970	7023	7076	7129	7182	7236	5	11	16	21	26	32	37	42	48
27	7290	7344	7398	7453	7508	7563	7618	7673	7728	7784	5	11	16	22	28	33	38	44	49
28	7840	7896	7952	8009	8066	8123	8180	8237	8294	8352	6	11	17	23	28	34	40	46	51
29	8410	8468	8526	8585	8644	8703	8762	8821	8880	8940	6	12	18	24	30	35	41	47	53
30	9000	9060	9120	9181	9242	9303	9364	9425	9486	9548	6	12	18	24	31	37	43	49	55
31	9610	9672	9734	9797	9860	9923	9986	1005	1011	1018	1	1	2	3	3	4	5	5	6
32	1024	1030	1037	1043	1050	1056	1063	1069	1076	1082	1	1	2	3	3	4	5	5	6
33	1089	1096	1102	1109	1116	1122	1129	1136	1142	1149	1	1	2	3	3	4	5	6	6
34	1156	1163	1170	1176	1183	1190	1197	1204	1211	1218	1	1	2	3	3	4	5	6	6
35	1225	1232	1239	1246	1253	1260	1267	1274	1282	1289	1	1	2	3	4	4	5	6	6
36	1296	1303	1310	1318	1325	1332	1340	1347	1354	1362	1	1	2	3	4	4	5	6	7
37	1369	1376	1384	1391	1399	1406	1414	1421	1429	1436	1	2	2	3	4	5	5	6	7
38	1444	1452	1459	1467	1475	1482	1490	1498	1505	1513	1	2	2	3	4	5	5	6	7
39	1521	1529	1537	1544	1552	1560	1568	1576	1584	1592	1	2	2	3	4	5	6	6	7
40	1600	1608	1616	1624	1632	1640	1648	1656	1665	1673	1	2	2	3	4	5	6	6	7
41	1681	1689	1697	1706	1714	1722	1731	1739	1747	1756	1	2	2	3	4	5	6	7	7
42	1764	1772	1781	1789	1798	1806	1815	1823	1832	1840	1	2	3	3	4	5	6	7	8
43	1849	1858	1866	1875	1884	1892	1901	1910	1918	1927	1	2	3	3	4	5	6	7	8
44	1936	1945	1954	1962	1971	1980	1989	1998	2007	2016	1	2	3	4	5	5	6	7	8
45	2025	2034	2043	2052	2061	2070	2079	2088	2098	2107	1	2	3	4	5	5	6	7	8
46	2116	2125	2134	2144	2153	2162	2172	2181	2190	2200	1	2	3	4	5	6	7	7	8
47	2209	2218	2228	2237	2247	2256	2266	2275	2285	2294	1	2	3	4	5	6	7	8	9
48	2304	2314	2323	2333	2343	2352	2362	2372	2381	2391	1	2	3	4	5	6	7	8	9
49	2401	2411	2421	2430	2440	2450	2460	2470	2480	2490	1	2	3	4	5	6	7	8	9
50	2500	2510	2520	2530	2540	2550	2560	2570	2581	2591	1	2	3	4	5	6	7	8	9
51	2601	2611	2621	2632	2642	2652	2663	2673	2683	2694	1	2	3	4	5	6	7	8	9
52	2704	2714	2725	2735	2746	2756	2767	2777	2788	2798	1	2	3	4	5	6	7	8	9
53	2809	2820	2830	2841	2852	2862	2873	2884	2894	2905	1	2	3	4	5	6	7	9	10
54	2916	2927	2938	2948	2959	2970	2981	2992	3003	3014	1	2	3	4	6	7	8	9	10
	0	1	2	3	4	5	6	7	8	9	1	2	3	4	5	6	7	8	9

The position of the decimal point must be determined by inspection.

SQUARES

	0	1	2	3	4	5	6	7	8	9	1	2	3	4	5	6	7	8	9
55	3025	3036	3047	3058	3069	3080	3091	3102	3114	3125	1	2	3	4	6	7	8	9	10
56	3136	3147	3158	3170	3181	3192	3204	3215	3226	3238	1	2	3	5	6	7	8	9	10
57	3249	3260	3272	3283	3295	3306	3318	3329	3341	3352	1	2	3	5	6	7	8	9	10
58	3364	3376	3387	3399	3411	3422	3434	3446	3457	3469	1	2	4	5	6	7	8	9	11
59	3481	3493	3505	3516	3528	3540	3552	3564	3576	3588	1	2	4	5	6	7	8	10	11
60	3600	3612	3624	3636	3648	3660	3672	3684	3697	3709	1	2	4	5	6	7	8	10	11
61	3721	3733	3745	3758	3770	3782	3795	3807	3819	3832	1	2	4	5	6	7	9	10	11
62	3844	3856	3869	3881	3894	3906	3919	3931	3944	3956	1	3	4	5	6	8	9	10	11
63	3969	3982	3994	4007	4020	4032	4045	4058	4070	4083	1	3	4	5	6	8	9	10	11
64	4096	4109	4122	4134	4147	4160	4173	4186	4199	4212	1	3	4	5	6	8	9	10	12
65	4225	4238	4251	4264	4277	4290	4303	4316	4330	4343	1	3	4	5	7	8	9	10	12
66	4356	4369	4382	4396	4409	4422	4436	4449	4462	4476	1	3	4	5	7	8	9	11	12
67	4489	4502	4516	4529	4543	4556	4570	4583	4597	4610	1	3	4	5	7	8	9	11	12
68	4624	4638	4651	4665	4679	4692	4706	4720	4733	4747	1	3	4	5	7	8	10	11	12
69	4761	4775	4789	4802	4816	4830	4844	4858	4872	4886	1	3	4	6	7	8	10	11	13
70	4900	4914	4928	4942	4956	4970	4984	4998	5013	5027	1	3	4	6	7	8	10	11	13
71	5041	5055	5069	5084	5098	5112	5127	5141	5155	5170	1	3	4	6	7	9	10	11	13
72	5184	5198	5213	5227	5242	5256	5271	5285	5300	5314	1	3	4	6	7	9	10	11	13
73	5329	5344	5358	5373	5388	5402	5417	5432	5446	5461	1	3	4	6	7	9	10	12	13
74	5476	5491	5506	5520	5535	5550	5565	5580	5595	5610	1	3	4	6	7	9	10	12	13
75	5625	5640	5655	5670	5685	5700	5715	5730	5746	5761	2	3	5	6	8	9	11	12	14
76	5776	5791	5806	5822	5837	5852	5868	5883	5898	5914	2	3	5	6	8	9	11	12	14
77	5929	5944	5960	5975	5991	6006	6022	6037	6053	6068	2	3	5	6	8	9	11	12	14
78	6084	6100	6115	6131	6147	6162	6178	6194	6209	6225	2	3	5	6	8	9	11	13	14
79	6241	6257	6273	6288	6304	6320	6336	6352	6368	6384	2	3	5	6	8	10	11	13	14
80	6400	6416	6432	6448	6464	6480	6496	6512	6529	6545	2	3	5	6	8	10	11	13	14
81	6561	6577	6593	6610	6626	6642	6659	6675	6691	6708	2	3	5	7	8	10	11	13	15
82	6724	6740	6757	6773	6790	6806	6823	6839	6856	6872	2	3	5	7	8	10	12	13	15
83	6889	6906	6922	6939	6956	6972	6989	7006	7022	7039	2	3	5	7	8	10	12	13	15
84	7056	7073	7090	7106	7123	7140	7157	7174	7191	7208	2	3	5	7	8	10	12	14	15
85	7225	7242	7259	7276	7293	7310	7327	7344	7362	7379	2	3	5	7	9	10	12	14	15
86	7396	7413	7430	7448	7465	7482	7500	7517	7534	7552	2	3	5	7	9	10	12	14	16
87	7569	7586	7604	7621	7639	7656	7674	7691	7709	7726	2	4	5	7	9	11	12	14	16
88	7744	7762	7779	7797	7815	7832	7850	7868	7885	7903	2	4	5	7	9	11	12	14	16
89	7921	7939	7957	7974	7992	8010	8028	8046	8064	8082	2	4	5	7	9	11	13	14	16
90	8100	8118	8136	8154	8172	8190	8208	8226	8245	8263	2	4	5	7	9	11	13	14	16
91	8281	8299	8317	8336	8354	8372	8391	8409	8427	8446	2	4	5	7	9	11	13	15	16
92	8464	8482	8501	8519	8538	8556	8575	8593	8612	8630	2	4	6	7	9	11	13	15	17
93	8649	8668	8686	8705	8724	8742	8761	8780	8798	8817	2	4	6	7	9	11	13	15	17
94	8836	8855	8874	8892	8911	8930	8949	8968	8987	9006	2	4	6	8	9	11	13	15	17
95	9025	9044	9063	9082	9101	9120	9139	9158	9178	9197	2	4	6	8	10	11	13	15	17
96	9216	9235	9254	9274	9293	9312	9332	9351	9370	9390	2	4	6	8	10	12	14	15	17
97	9409	9428	9448	9467	9487	9506	9526	9545	9565	9584	2	4	6	8	10	12	14	16	18
98	9604	9624	9643	9663	9683	9702	9722	9742	9761	9781	2	4	6	8	10	12	14	16	18
99	9801	9821	9841	9860	9880	9900	9920	9940	9960	9980	2	4	6	8	10	12	14	16	18
	0	1	2	3	4	5	6	7	8	9	1	2	3	4	5	6	7	8	9

The position of the decimal point must be determined by inspection.

SQUARE ROOTS

	0	1	2	3	4	5	6	7	8	9	1	2	3	4	5	6	7	8
10	1000	1005	1010	1015	1020	1025	1030	1034	1039	1044	0	1	1	2	2	3	3	4
	3162	3178	3194	3209	3225	3240	3256	3271	3286	3302	2	3	5	6	8	9	11	12
11	1049	1054	1058	1063	1068	1072	1077	1082	1086	1091	0	1	1	2	2	3	3	4
	3317	3332	3347	3362	3376	3391	3406	3421	3435	3450	1	3	4	6	7	9	10	12
12	1095	1100	1105	1109	1114	1118	1122	1127	1131	1136	0	1	1	2	2	3	3	4
	3464	3479	3493	3507	3521	3536	3550	3564	3578	3592	1	3	4	6	7	8	10	11
13	1140	1145	1149	1153	1158	1162	1166	1170	1175	1179	0	1	1	2	2	3	3	3
	3606	3619	3633	3647	3661	3674	3688	3701	3715	3728	1	3	4	5-	7	8	10	11
14	1183	1187	1192	1196	1200	1204	1208	1212	1217	1221	0	1	1	2	2	3	3	3
	3742	3755	3768	3782	3795	3808	3821	3834	3847	3860	1	3	4	5	7	8	9	11
15	1225	1229	1233	1237	1241	1245	1249	1253	1257	1261	0	1	1	2	2	3	3	3
	3873	3886	3899	3912	3924	3937	3950	3962	3975	3987	1	3	4	5	6	8	9	10
16	1265	1269	1273	1277	1281	1285	1288	1292	1296	1300	0	1	1	2	2	3	3	3
	4000	4012	4025	4037	4050	4062	4074	4087	4099	4111	1	2	4	5	6	7	9	10
17	1304	1308	1311	1315	1319	1323	1327	1330	1334	1338	0	1	1	2	2	2	3	3
	4123	4135	4147	4159	4171	4183	4195	4207	4219	4231	1	2	4	5	6	7	8	10
18	1342	1345	1349	1353	1356	1360	1364	1367	1371	1375	0	1	1	1	2	2	3	3
	4243	4254	4266	4278	4290	4301	4313	4324	4336	4347	1	2	3	5	6	7	8	9
19	1378	1382	1386	1389	1393	1396	1400	1404	1407	1411	0	1	1	1	2	2	3	3
	4359	4370	4382	4393	4405	4416	4427	4438	4450	4461	1	2	3	5	6	7	8	9
20	1414	1418	1421	1425	1428	1432	1435	1439	1442	1446	0	1	1	1	2	2	2	3
	4472	4483	4494	4506	4517	4528	4539	4550	4561	4572	1	2	3	4	5	7	8	9
21	1449	1453	1456	1459	1463	1466	1470	1473	1476	1480	0	1	1	1	2	2	2	3
	4583	4593	4604	4615	4626	4637	4648	4658	4669	4680	1	2	3	4	5	6	8	9
22	1483	1487	1490	1493	1497	1500	1503	1507	1510	1513	0	1	1	1	2	2	2	3
	4690	4701	4712	4722	4733	4743	4754	4764	4775	4785	1	2	3	4	5	6	7	8
23	1517	1520	1523	1526	1530	1533	1536	1539	1543	1546	0	1	1	1	2	2	2	3
	4796	4806	4817	4827	4837	4848	4858	4868	4879	4889	1	2	3	4	5	6	7	8
24	1549	1552	1556	1559	1562	1565	1568	1572	1575	1578	0	1	1	1	2	2	2	3
	4899	4909	4919	4930	4940	4950	4960	4970	4980	4990	1	2	3	4	5	6	7	8
25	1581	1584	1587	1591	1594	1597	1600	1603	1606	1609	0	1	1	1	2	2	2	3
	5000	5010	5020	5030	5040	5050	5060	5070	5079	5089	1	2	3	4	5	6	7	8
26	1612	1616	1619	1622	1625	1628	1631	1634	1637	1640	0	1	1	1	2	2	2	2
	5099	5109	5119	5128	5138	5148	5158	5167	5177	5187	1	2	3	4	5	6	7	8
27	1643	1646	1649	1652	1655	1658	1661	1664	1667	1670	0	1	1	1	2	2	2	2
	5196	5206	5215	5225	5235	5244	5254	5263	5273	5282	1	2	3	4	5	6	7	8
28	1673	1676	1679	1682	1685	1688	1691	1694	1697	1700	0	1	1	1	1	2	2	2
	5292	5301	5310	5320	5329	5339	5348	5357	5367	5376	1	2	3	4	5	6	7	7
29	1703	1706	1709	1712	1715	1718	1720	1723	1726	1729	0	1	1	1	1	2	2	2
	5385	5394	5404	5413	5422	5431	5441	5450	5459	5468	1	2	3	4	5	5	6	7
30	1732	1735	1738	1741	1744	1746	1749	1752	1755	1758	0	1	1	1	1	2	2	2
	5477	5486	5495	5505	5514	5523	5532	5541	5550	5559	1	2	3	4	4	5	6	7
31	1761	1764	1766	1769	1772	1775	1778	1780	1783	1786	0	1	1	1	1	2	2	2
	5568	5577	5586	5595	5604	5612	5621	5630	5639	5648	1	2	3	3	4	5	6	7
32	1789	1792	1794	1797	1800	1803	1806	1808	1811	1814	0	1	1	1	1	2	2	2
	5657	5666	5675	5683	5692	5701	5710	5718	5727	5736	1	2	3	3	4	5	6	7
	0	1	2	3	4	5	6	7	8	9	1	2	3	4	5	6	7	8

The first significant figure and the position of the decimal point must be determined by inspection.

SQUARE ROOTS

	0	1	2	3	4	5	6	7	8	9	1	2	3	4	5	6	7	8	9
3	1817	1819	1822	1825	1828	1830	1833	1836	1838	1841	0	1	1	1	1	2	2	2	2
	5745	5753	5762	5771	5779	5788	5797	5805	5814	5822	1	2	3	3	4	5	6	7	8
4	1844	1847	1849	1852	1855	1857	1860	1863	1865	1868	0	1	1	1	1	2	2	2	2
	5831	5840	5848	5857	5865	5874	5882	5891	5899	5908	1	2	3	3	4	5	6	7	8
5	1871	1873	1876	1879	1881	1884	1887	1889	1892	1895	0	1	1	1	1	2	2	2	2
	5916	5925	5933	5941	5950	5958	5967	5975	5983	5992	1	2	2	3	4	5	6	7	8
6	1897	1900	1903	1905	1908	1910	1913	1916	1918	1921	0	1	1	1	1	2	2	2	2
	6000	6008	6017	6025	6033	6042	6050	6058	6066	6075	1	2	2	3	4	5	6	7	7
7	1924	1926	1929	1931	1934	1936	1939	1942	1944	1947	0	1	1	1	1	2	2	2	2
	6083	6091	6099	6107	6116	6124	6132	6140	6148	6156	1	2	2	3	4	5	6	7	7
8	1949	1952	1954	1957	1960	1962	1965	1967	1970	1972	0	1	1	1	1	2	2	2	2
	6164	6173	6181	6189	6197	6205	6213	6221	6229	6237	1	2	2	3	4	5	6	6	7
9	1975	1977	1980	1982	1985	1987	1990	1992	1995	1997	0	1	1	1	1	2	2	2	2
	6245	6253	6261	6269	6277	6285	6293	6301	6309	6317	1	2	2	3	4	5	6	6	7
0	2000	2002	2005	2007	2010	2012	2015	2017	2020	2022	0	0	1	1	1	1	2	2	2
	6325	6332	6340	6348	6356	6364	6372	6380	6387	6395	1	2	2	3	4	5	6	6	7
1	2025	2027	2030	2032	2035	2037	2040	2042	2045	2047	0	0	1	1	1	1	2	2	2
	6403	6411	6419	6427	6434	6442	6450	6458	6465	6473	1	2	2	3	4	5	5	6	7
2	2049	2052	2054	2057	2059	2062	2064	2066	2069	2071	0	0	1	1	1	1	2	2	2
	6481	6488	6496	6504	6512	6519	6527	6535	6542	6550	1	2	2	3	4	5	5	6	7
3	2074	2076	2078	2081	2083	2086	2088	2090	2093	2095	0	0	1	1	1	1	2	2	2
	6557	6565	6573	6580	6588	6595	6603	6611	6618	6626	1	2	2	3	4	5	5	6	7
4	2098	2100	2102	2105	2107	2110	2112	2114	2117	2119	0	0	1	1	1	1	2	2	2
	6633	6641	6648	6656	6663	6671	6678	6686	6693	6701	1	2	2	3	4	4	5	6	7
5	2121	2124	2126	2128	2131	2133	2135	2138	2140	2142	0	0	1	1	1	1	2	2	2
	6708	6716	6723	6731	6738	6745	6753	6760	6768	6775	1	1	2	3	4	4	5	6	7
6	2145	2147	2149	2152	2154	2156	2159	2161	2163	2166	0	0	1	1	1	1	2	2	2
	6782	6790	6797	6804	6812	6819	6826	6834	6841	6848	1	1	2	3	4	4	5	6	7
7	2168	2170	2173	2175	2177	2179	2182	2184	2186	2189	0	0	1	1	1	1	2	2	2
	6856	6863	6870	6877	6885	6892	6899	6907	6914	6921	1	1	2	3	4	4	5	6	7
8	2191	2193	2195	2198	2200	2202	2205	2207	2209	2211	0	0	1	1	1	1	2	2	2
	6928	6935	6943	6950	6957	6964	6971	6979	6986	6993	1	1	2	3	4	4	5	6	6
9	2214	2216	2218	2220	2223	2225	2227	2229	2232	2234	0	0	1	1	1	1	2	2	2
	7000	7007	7014	7021	7029	7036	7043	7050	7057	7064	1	1	2	3	4	4	5	6	6
0	2236	2238	2241	2243	2245	2247	2249	2252	2254	2256	0	0	1	1	1	1	2	2	2
	7071	7078	7085	7092	7099	7106	7113	7120	7127	7134	1	1	2	3	4	4	5	6	6
1	2258	2261	2263	2265	2267	2269	2272	2274	2276	2278	0	0	1	1	1	1	2	2	2
	7141	7148	7155	7162	7169	7176	7183	7190	7197	7204	1	1	2	3	4	4	5	6	6
2	2280	2283	2285	2287	2289	2291	2293	2296	2298	2300	0	0	1	1	1	1	2	2	2
	7211	7218	7225	7232	7239	7246	7253	7259	7266	7273	1	1	2	3	3	4	5	6	6
3	2302	2304	2307	2309	2311	2313	2315	2317	2319	2322	0	0	1	1	1	1	2	2	2
	7280	7287	7294	7301	7308	7314	7321	7328	7335	7342	1	1	2	3	3	4	5	5	6
4	2324	2326	2328	2330	2332	2335	2337	2339	2341	2343	0	0	1	1	1	1	1	2	2
	7348	7355	7362	7369	7376	7382	7389	7396	7403	7409	1	1	2	3	3	4	5	5	6
	0	1	2	3	4	5	6	7	8	9	1	2	3	4	5	6	7	8	9

The first significant figure and the position of the decimal point must
be determined by inspection.

SQUARE ROOTS

	0	1	2	3	4	5	6	7	8	9	1	2	3	4	5	6	7	8
55	2345	2347	2349	2352	2354	2356	2358	2360	2362	2364	0	0	1	1	1	1	1	2
	7416	7423	7430	7436	7443	7450	7457	7463	7470	7477	1	1	2	3	3	4	5	5
56	2366	2369	2371	2373	2375	2377	2379	2381	2383	2385	0	0	1	1	1	1	1	2
	7483	7490	7497	7503	7510	7517	7523	7530	7537	7543	1	1	2	3	3	4	5	5
57	2387	2390	2392	2394	2396	2398	2400	2402	2404	2406	0	0	1	1	1	1	1	2
	7550	7556	7563	7570	7576	7583	7589	7596	7603	7609	1	1	2	3	3	4	5	5
58	2408	2410	2412	2415	2417	2419	2421	2423	2425	2427	0	0	1	1	1	1	1	2
	7616	7622	7629	7635	7642	7649	7655	7662	7668	7675	1	1	2	3	3	4	5	5
59	2429	2431	2433	2435	2437	2439	2441	2443	2445	2447	0	0	1	1	1	1	1	2
	7681	7688	7694	7701	7707	7714	7720	7727	7733	7740	1	1	2	3	3	4	5	5
60	2449	2452	2454	2456	2458	2460	2462	2464	2466	2468	0	0	1	1	1	1	1	2
	7746	7752	7759	7765	7772	7778	7785	7791	7797	7804	1	1	2	3	3	4	4	5
61	2470	2472	2474	2476	2478	2480	2482	2484	2486	2488	0	0	1	1	1	1	1	2
	7810	7817	7823	7829	7836	7842	7849	7855	7861	7868	1	1	2	3	3	4	4	5
62	2490	2492	2494	2496	2498	2500	2502	2504	2506	2508	0	0	1	1	1	1	1	2
	7874	7880	7887	7893	7899	7906	7912	7918	7925	7931	1	1	2	3	3	4	4	5
63	2510	2512	2514	2516	2518	2520	2522	2524	2526	2528	0	0	1	1	1	1	1	2
	7937	7944	7950	7956	7962	7969	7975	7981	7987	7994	1	1	2	3	3	4	4	5
64	2530	2532	2534	2536	2538	2540	2542	2544	2546	2548	0	0	1	1	1	1	1	2
	8000	8006	8012	8019	8025	8031	8037	8044	8050	8056	1	1	2	2	3	4	4	5
65	2550	2551	2553	2555	2557	2559	2561	2563	2565	2567	0	0	1	1	1	1	1	2
	8062	8068	8075	8081	8087	8093	8099	8106	8112	8118	1	1	2	2	3	4	4	5
66	2569	2571	2573	2575	2577	2579	2581	2583	2585	2587	0	0	1	1	1	1	1	2
	8124	8130	8136	8142	8149	8155	8161	8167	8173	8179	1	1	2	2	3	4	4	5
67	2588	2590	2592	2594	2596	2598	2600	2602	2604	2606	0	0	1	1	1	1	1	2
	8185	8191	8198	8204	8210	8216	8222	8228	8234	8240	1	1	2	2	3	4	4	5
68	2608	2610	2612	2613	2615	2617	2619	2621	2623	2625	0	0	1	1	1	1	1	2
	8246	8252	8258	8264	8270	8276	8283	8289	8295	8301	1	1	2	2	3	4	4	5
69	2627	2629	2631	2632	2634	2636	2638	2640	2642	2644	0	0	1	1	1	1	1	2
	8307	8313	8319	8325	8331	8337	8343	8349	8355	8361	1	1	2	2	3	4	4	5
70	2646	2648	2650	2651	2653	2655	2657	2659	2661	2663	0	0	1	1	1	1	1	2
	8367	8373	8379	8385	8390	8396	8402	8408	8414	8420	1	1	2	2	3	4	4	5
71	2665	2666	2668	2670	2672	2674	2676	2678	2680	2681	0	0	1	1	1	1	1	1
	8426	8432	8438	8444	8450	8456	8462	8468	8473	8479	1	1	2	2	3	3	4	5
72	2683	2685	2687	2689	2691	2693	2694	2696	2698	2700	0	0	1	1	1	1	1	1
	8485	8491	8497	8503	8509	8515	8521	8526	8532	8538	1	1	2	2	3	3	4	5
73	2702	2704	2706	2707	2709	2711	2713	2715	2717	2718	0	0	1	1	1	1	1	1
	8544	8550	8556	8562	8567	8573	8579	8585	8591	8597	1	1	2	2	3	3	4	5
74	2720	2722	2724	2726	2728	2729	2731	2733	2735	2737	0	0	1	1	1	1	1	1
	8602	8608	8614	8620	8626	8631	8637	8643	8649	8654	1	1	2	2	3	3	4	5
75	2739	2740	2742	2744	2746	2748	2750	2751	2753	2755	0	0	1	1	1	1	1	1
	8660	8666	8672	8678	8683	8689	8695	8701	8706	8712	1	1	2	2	3	3	4	5
76	2757	2759	2760	2762	2764	2766	2768	2769	2771	2773	0	0	1	1	1	1	1	1
	8718	8724	8729	8735	8741	8746	8752	8758	8764	8769	1	1	2	2	3	3	4	5
77	2775	2777	2778	2780	2782	2784	2786	2787	2789	2791	0	0	1	1	1	1	1	1
	8775	8781	8786	8792	8798	8803	8809	8815	8820	8826	1	1	2	2	3	3	4	4
	0	1	2	3	4	5	6	7	8	9	1	2	3	4	5	6	7	8

The first significant figure and the position of the decimal point must be determined by inspection.

SQUARE ROOTS

	0	1	2	3	4	5	6	7	8	9	1	2	3	4	5	6	7	8	9
8	2793	2795	2796	2798	2800	2802	2804	2805	2807	2809	0	0	1	1	1	1	1	1	2
	8832	8837	8843	8849	8854	8860	8866	8871	8877	8883	1	1	2	2	3	3	4	4	5
9	2811	2812	2814	2816	2818	2820	2821	2823	2825	2827	0	0	1	1	1	1	1	1	2
	8888	8894	8899	8905	8911	8916	8922	8927	8933	8939	1	1	2	2	3	3	4	4	5
0	2828	2830	2832	2834	2835	2837	2839	2841	2843	2844	0	0	1	1	1	1	1	1	2
	8944	8950	8955	8961	8967	8972	8978	8983	8989	8994	1	1	2	2	3	3	4	4	5
1	2846	2848	2850	2851	2853	2855	2857	2858	2860	2862	0	0	1	1	1	1	1	1	2
	9000	9006	9011	9017	9022	9028	9033	9039	9044	9050	1	1	2	2	3	3	4	4	5
2	2864	2865	2867	2869	2871	2872	2874	2876	2877	2879	0	0	1	1	1	1	1	1	2
	9055	9061	9066	9072	9077	9083	9088	9094	9099	9105	1	1	2	2	3	3	4	4	5
3	2881	2883	2884	2886	2888	2890	2891	2893	2895	2897	0	0	1	1	1	1	1	1	2
	9110	9116	9121	9127	9132	9138	9143	9149	9154	9160	1	1	2	2	3	3	4	4	5
4	2898	2900	2902	2903	2905	2907	2909	2910	2912	2914	0	0	1	1	1	1	1	1	2
	9165	9171	9176	9182	9187	9192	9198	9203	9209	9214	1	1	2	2	3	3	4	4	5
5	2915	2917	2919	2921	2922	2924	2926	2927	2929	2931	0	0	1	1	1	1	1	1	2
	9220	9225	9230	9236	9241	9247	9252	9257	9263	9268	1	1	2	2	3	3	4	4	5
6	2933	2934	2936	2938	2939	2941	2943	2944	2946	2948	0	0	1	1	1	1	1	1	2
	9274	9279	9284	9290	9295	9301	9306	9311	9317	9322	1	1	2	2	3	3	4	4	5
7	2950	2951	2953	2955	2956	2958	2960	2961	2963	2965	0	0	1	1	1	1	1	1	2
	9327	9333	9338	9343	9349	9354	9359	9365	9370	9375	1	1	2	2	3	3	4	4	5
8	2966	2968	2970	2972	2973	2975	2977	2978	2980	2982	0	0	1	1	1	1	1	1	2
	9381	9386	9391	9397	9402	9407	9413	9418	9423	9429	1	1	2	2	3	3	4	4	5
9	2983	2985	2987	2988	2990	2992	2993	2995	2997	2998	0	0	1	1	1	1	1	1	2
	9434	9439	9445	9450	9455	9460	9466	9471	9476	9482	1	1	2	2	3	3	4	4	5
0	3000	3002	3003	3005	3007	3008	3010	3012	3013	3015	0	0	0	1	1	1	1	1	1
	9487	9492	9497	9503	9508	9513	9518	9524	9529	9534	1	1	2	2	3	3	4	4	5
1	3017	3018	3020	3022	3023	3025	3027	3028	3030	3032	0	0	0	1	1	1	1	1	1
	9539	9545	9550	9555	9560	9566	9571	9576	9581	9586	1	1	2	2	3	3	4	4	5
2	3033	3035	3036	3038	3040	3041	3043	3045	3046	3048	0	0	0	1	1	1	1	1	1
	9592	9597	9602	9607	9612	9618	9623	9628	9633	9638	1	1	2	2	3	3	4	4	5
3	3050	3051	3053	3055	3056	3058	3059	3061	3063	3064	0	0	0	1	1	1	1	1	1
	9644	9649	9654	9659	9664	9670	9675	9680	9685	9690	1	1	2	2	3	3	4	4	5
4	3066	3068	3069	3071	3072	3074	3076	3077	3079	3081	0	0	0	1	1	1	1	1	1
	9695	9701	9706	9711	9716	9721	9726	9731	9737	9742	1	1	2	2	3	3	4	4	5
5	3082	3084	3085	3087	3089	3090	3092	3094	3095	3097	0	0	0	1	1	1	1	1	1
	9747	9752	9757	9762	9767	9772	9778	9783	9788	9793	1	1	2	2	3	3	4	4	5
6	3098	3100	3102	3103	3105	3106	3108	3110	3111	3113	0	0	0	1	1	1	1	1	1
	9798	9803	9808	9813	9818	9823	9829	9834	9839	9844	1	1	2	2	3	3	4	4	5
7	3114	3116	3118	3119	3121	3122	3124	3126	3127	3129	0	0	0	1	1	1	1	1	1
	9849	9854	9859	9864	9869	9874	9879	9884	9889	9894	1	1	2	2	3	3	4	4	5
8	3130	3132	3134	3135	3137	3138	3140	3142	3143	3145	0	0	0	1	1	1	1	1	1
	9899	9905	9910	9915	9920	9925	9930	9935	9940	9945	0	1	1	2	2	3	3	4	4
9	3146	3148	3150	3151	3153	3154	3156	3158	3159	3161	0	0	0	1	1	1	1	1	1
	9950	9955	9960	9965	9970	9975	9980	9985	9990	9995	0	1	1	2	2	3	3	4	4
	0	1	2	3	4	5	6	7	8	9	1	2	3	4	5	6	7	8	9

The first significant figure and the position of the decimal point must be determined by inspection.

TRIGONOMETRICAL RATIOS

DEGREE	SINES	COSINES	TANGENTS	DEGREE	SINES	COSINES	TANGEN
0	·0000	1·000	·0000	45	·7071	·7071	1·000
1	·0175	·9998	·0175	46	·7193	·6947	1·035
2	·0349	·9994	·0349	47	·7314	·6820	1·072
3	·0523	·9986	·0524	48	·7431	·6691	1·110
4	·0698	·9976	·0699	49	·7547	·6561	1·150
5	·0872	·9962	·0875	50	·7660	·6428	1·191
6	·1045	·9945	·1051	51	·7771	·6293	1·234
7	·1219	·9925	·1228	52	·7880	·6157	1·27
8	·1392	·9903	·1405	53	·7986	·6018	1·32
9	·1564	·9877	·1584	54	·8090	·5878	1·376
10	·1736	·9848	·1763	55	·8192	·5736	1·42
11	·1908	·9816	·1944	56	·8290	·5592	1·48
12	·2079	·9781	·2126	57	·8387	·5446	1·53
13	·2250	·9744	·2309	58	·8480	·5299	1·600
14	·2419	·9703	·2493	59	·8572	·5150	1·664
15	·2588	·9659	·2679	60	·8660	·5000	1·73
16	·2756	·9613	·2867	61	·8746	·4848	1·804
17	·2924	·9563	·3057	62	·8829	·4695	1·88
18	·3090	·9511	·3249	63	·8910	·4540	1·962
19	·3256	·9455	·3443	64	·8988	·4384	2·05
20	·3420	·9397	·3640	65	·9063	·4226	2·14
21	·3584	·9336	·3839	66	·9135	·4067	2·24
22	·3746	·9272	·4040	67	·9205	·3907	2·35
23	·3907	·9205	·4245	68	·9272	·3746	2·47
24	·4067	·9135	·4452	69	·9336	·3584	2·60
25	·4226	·9063	·4663	70	·9397	·3420	2·74
26	·4384	·8988	·4877	71	·9455	·3256	2·90
27	·4540	·8910	·5095	72	·9511	·3090	3·07
28	·4695	·8829	·5317	73	·9563	·2924	3·27
29	·4848	·8746	·5543	74	·9613	·2756	3·48
30	·5000	·8660	·5774	75	·9659	·2588	3·73
31	·5150	·8572	·6009	76	·9703	·2419	4·01
32	·5299	·8480	·6249	77	·9744	·2250	4·33
33	·5446	·8387	·6494	78	·9781	·2079	4·70
34	·5592	·8290	·6745	79	·9816	·1908	5·14
35	·5736	·8192	·7002	80	·9848	·1736	5·67
36	·5878	·8090	·7265	81	·9877	·1564	6·31
37	·6018	·7986	·7536	82	·9903	·1392	7·11
38	·6157	·7880	·7813	83	·9925	·1219	8·14
39	·6293	·7771	·8098	84	·9945	·1045	9·51
40	·6428	·7660	·8391	85	·9962	·0872	11·43
41	·6561	·7547	·8693	86	·9976	·0698	14·30
42	·6691	·7431	·9004	87	·9986	·0523	19·08
43	·6820	·7314	·9325	88	·9994	·0349	28·64
44	·6947	·7193	·9657	89	·9998	·0175	57·29
				90	1·0000	·0000	Infin